PETER DRANSFIELD

Associate Professor, Weapons Department
United States Naval Academy

Engineering systems
and
automatic control

Prentice-Hall, Inc.   **Englewood Cliffs, N. J.**

Current printing (last digit):
10 9 8 7 6 5 4 3 2 1

Library of Congress Catalog Card Number: 68-18247

Printed in the United States of America

PRENTICE-HALL INTERNATIONAL, INC., *London*
PRENTICE-HALL OF AUSTRALIA, PTY. LTD., *Sydney*
PRENTICE-HALL OF CANADA, LTD., *Toronto*
PRENTICE-HALL OF INDIA PRIVATE LTD., *New Delhi*
PRENTICE-HALL OF JAPAN, INC., *Tokyo*

Preface

This text is intended for engineering students who are undertaking first courses in automatic control theory. A basic treatment of the linear analysis of engineering systems in general provides the necessary background (or review) for the control systems chapters. Chapters 6 through 9 extend the general approach to a basic treatment of the linear analysis of automatic control systems. Chapter 10 introduces engineering non-linearities and the methods with which they can be included in analysis. Chapter 11 introduces the increasingly popular use of matrices and state variables to describe and analyze engineering systems having multiple input and response variables. Chapters 6 through 11 provide the material for a course in automatic control theory at the junior or senior level.

As with most undergraduate texts, there is little in the concepts presented that is original to the author. My objective was to produce a text solely for the *teaching* of undergraduate engineering students. A number of texts in the field of automatic control theory exist which are excellent for graduate level courses and for reference. It has been my experience that undergraduates have difficulty separating the basic ideas from the detailed extensions described in these texts. Thus, the originality in the present work lies in its selection, organization, and emphasis. Abstract notions are kept to a minimum, and stress is placed on connecting ideas and theory with physical engineering reality. In some cases, only the primary qualifications associated with concepts and ideas are presented, so that initial understanding will not be impaired. Unnecessary mathematical transformations are avoided for the same reason. Thus, most of the material presented is maintained in the time domain, the real domain in which engineering systems operate, by using operators $D = d/dt$ and $1/D = \int dt$ in equations and transfer functions. Equations are transformed to the Laplace Transform domain only when actual solutions are required. With the increasing use of computers by students, the Laplace Transform method of solving differential equations is becoming of secondary importance. The automatic Laplace transformation of equations and transfer functions, universally used throughout earlier texts, is unnecessary to most areas of engineering systems analysis. My experience is that most undergraduates readily accept time-operator D, but find a detailed study and use of the Laplace Transform in the early stages of a systems analysis course a barrier to understanding. In this text, the Laplace Transform technique is treated only as an excellent hand method for solving linear differential equations.

Most students using this text will have some familiarity with basic mathematical concepts such as linear differential equations and their solution, complex numbers and their manipulation, etc. Hence, such fundamentals are reviewed briefly in the text, with a more extensive review in the Appendices. (Use of these Appendices permits the text to remain uncluttered by material familiar to most students.)

All sections of the text are heavily illustrated with worked examples, with the objective of positively relating ideas and theory to practical reality. Because of the level of the text and because of their basic importance even to complicated systems, first- and second-order systems are treated in detail. It is believed that a student having a genuine understanding of the nature of first- and second-order systems will find it only a short step to mastery of more complex systems. Chapter 9 is intended to consolidate and reinforce the ideas and techniques introduced in earlier chapters.

Understanding of the material of the text can be enhanced by laboratory work. Teachers wishing to implement or improve laboratory courses in this area are directed to the report *A Manual of Control Systems Laboratory Experiments* by D. J. Lomont and A. F. D'Souza (School of Mechanical Engineering, Illinois Institute of Technology).

The present text is intended as a *teaching medium* for engineering students in general. The idea of programmed learning has been kept in mind in its formation, and it has been planned so that a teacher using the text may assign substantial private reading from it.

Many people have contributed to the evolution of this text. My work has been influenced by several former colleagues: Edward Hind, University of New South Wales, Australia; Leslie Eaton, University of Salford, England; Ernest C. Fitch and Karl N. Reid, Oklahoma State University. Betty Stewart at Oklahoma State, Ellen Lonergan at the U.S. Naval Academy, and Nevillie Dransfield typed the manuscript. Key personnel of Prentice-Hall, Inc. were James Campbell, James P. Levy, Walter R. Welch, Bert N. Zelman, and several helpful reviewers. I gratefully recognize the contribution of each.

Peter Dransfield

Contents

1 Introduction, 1

1.1 CLASSIFICATION OF CONTROL SYSTEMS, 1
1.2 CONTINUOUS AUTOMATIC CONTROL SYSTEMS, 4
1.3 THE PERFORMANCE OF AUTOMATIC CONTROL SYSTEMS, 6
1.4 MATHEMATICAL REPRESENTATION OF COMPONENTS AND SYSTEMS, 7
1.5 LINEAR ANALYSIS, 11
1.6 SUMMARY, 14
1.7 EXAMPLES OF AUTOMATIC CONTROL SYSTEMS, 15

2 Basic laws, relationships, components, and analogies, 18

2.1 INTRODUCTION, 18
2.2 MECHANICAL RELATIONSHIPS, 18
2.3 ELECTRICAL RELATIONSHIPS, 24
2.4 THERMAL RELATIONSHIPS, 26
2.5 FLUID PRESSURE RELATIONSHIPS, 28
2.6 SUMMARY OF DIRECT ANALOGIES, 38
2.7 SUMMARY, 39

3 The derivation of system equations, 40

3.1 *INTRODUCTION*, 40
3.2 *THE SIMULTANEOUS EQUATION METHOD*, 45
3.3 *THE BLOCK DIAGRAM METHOD*, 60
3.4 *THE LAPLACE TRANSFORM APPROACH*, 76
3.5 *SUMMARY*, 76
3.6 *EXAMPLES WITH OUTLINE SOLUTIONS*, 77
PROBLEMS, 84

4 The response characteristics of components and systems, 89

4.1 *INTRODUCTION*, 89
4.2 *CLASSICAL SOLUTION OF SYSTEM EQUATIONS*, 90
4.3 *LAPLACE TRANSFORM SOLUTION OF SYSTEM EQUATIONS*, 113
4.4 *RESPONSE BY ANALOGUE COMPUTER*, 129
4.5 *GENERAL SUMMARY*, 147
PROBLEMS, 148

5 Frequency response analysis, 150

5.1 *INTRODUCTION*, 150
5.2 *THE FREQUENCY RESPONSE CHARACTERISTIC*, 151
5.3 *THE FREQUENCY RESPONSE OF SECOND-ORDER SYSTEMS*, 158
5.4 *THE EFFECT OF NUMERATOR FACTORS*, 165
5.5 *THE EFFECT OF ZERO FACTORS IN A TRANSFER FUNCTION*, 169
5.6 *LOGARITHMIC REPRESENTATION — THE BODE DIAGRAM*, 172
5.7 *EXPERIMENTAL FREQUENCY RESPONSE ANALYSIS*, 187
5.8 *SUMMARY*, 192
PROBLEMS, 193

6 The stability of components and systems, 195

6.1 *INTRODUCTION*, 195
6.2 *ROOTS OF THE CHARACTERISTIC EQUATION*, 197
6.3 *STABILITY FROM TIME RESPONSE*, 197
6.4 *THE ROUTH CRITERION OF STABILITY*, 201
6.5 *THE NYQUIST CRITERION OF STABILITY*, 207
6.6 *SUMMARY*, 234
PROBLEMS, 235

7 The root locus method of analysis, 237

7.1 *INTRODUCTION*, 237
7.2 *THE NATURE OF A ROOT LOCUS PLOT*, 238
7.3 *THE OPEN LOOP TRANSFER FUNCTION*, 241
7.4 *THE POLE-ZERO CONCEPT*, 243
7.5 *CRITERIA USED FOR RAPID PLOTTING OF ROOT LOCUS*, 246
7.6 *EXAMPLES WITH SOLUTIONS*, 267

7.7 USE OF THE SPIRULE, 277
7.8 FREQUENCY RESPONSE DATA FROM ROOT LOCUS, 279
7.9 SUMMARY, 280
     PROBLEMS, 282

8 System characteristics from open loop data, 285

8.1 INTRODUCTION, 285
8.2 THE RELATIONSHIP BETWEEN OPEN LOOP AND
     SYSTEM TRANSFER FUNCTIONS, 286
8.3 CONSTANT CONTOURS OF SYSTEM MAGNITUDE RATIO
     AND PHASE ON THE NYQUIST PLANE, 289
8.4 CONSTANT CONTOURS ON THE INVERSE NYQUIST PLANE, 293
8.5 CONSTANT CONTOURS ON LOGARITHMIC
     PLANES — THE NICHOLS CHART, 295
8.6 STABILITY FROM THE NICHOLS PLOT, 299
8.7 SUMMARY, 301
     PROBLEMS, 303

9 Improving system performance, 305

9.1 INTRODUCTION, 305
9.2 COMPENSATION, 307
9.3 CONTROLLER ACTIONS, 309
9.4 LAG AND LEAD ACTIONS, 328
9.5 USING FREQUENCY RESPONSE TECHNIQUES IN
     COMPENSATION, 332
9.6 USING ROOT LOCUS TECHNIQUES IN COMPENSATION, 346
9.7 FEEDBACK COMPENSATION, 358
9.8 SUMMARY, 358
     PROBLEMS, 359

10 Introduction to nonlinear analysis, 362

10.1 INTRODUCTION, 362
10.2 SOME TYPES AND CLASSIFICATIONS OF
      ENGINEERING NONLINEARITIES, 365
10.3 SOME TYPICAL BEHAVIOR PATTERNS, 369
10.4 SOME TECHNIQUES OF ANALYSIS, 371
10.5 SUMMARY, 375
      BIBLIOGRAPHY, 375

11 Introduction to the state-variable method of analysis, 377

11.1 INTRODUCTION, 377
11.2 OUTLINE OF THE STATE-VARIABLE METHOD, 378
11.3 THE STATE VARIABLES OF A SIMPLE SYSTEM, 379
11.4 THE STATE VARIABLES OF A SYSTEM — GENERAL, 381
11.5 THE STATE VECTOR, 383

11.6 *THE STATE MODEL*, 386
11.7 *DERIVING STATE MODELS*, 392
11.8 *SUMMARY*, 401
     PROBLEMS, 402
     BIBLIOGRAPHY, 405

appendices

A   *Classification of differential equations,* **406**

B   *Complex numbers,* **411**

C   *Conversion tables,* **416**
     DECIBEL CONVERSION TABLE, 416
     TABLE: G AND ϕ FOR $1 + j\omega T$, 417

D   *Matrices: some matrix operations,* **419**

     Index, **425**

*Engineering systems
and
automatic control*

1 *Introduction*

1.1 CLASSIFICATION OF CONTROL SYSTEMS

A machine or process is restrained to operate in a predetermined manner —
that is, it is controlled. Restraint is usually achieved by controlling a
selected physical variable vital to the performance of the particular machine
or process.

Example (a): The driver controls the speed of a locomotive by controlling the
flow rate of fuel.

Example (b): The speed of an electricity generating set must be held constant;
this is achieved by regulating the energy supply (steam or fuel oil) to the prime
mover (turbine or engine).

Example (c): The temperature inside a refrigerator cabinet is held within a predetermined narrow range by controlling the rate of flow of refrigerant in the system.

These examples illustrate an important division in the following classification of control systems.

(a) *Manual control*

Example (a) involves a human operator, who must judge the speed of the locomotive (by eye or by reading a speed meter) and then adjust the throttle accordingly to maintain his desired speed. The driver's assessments and adjustments are made intermittently. Manual control is adequate for many situations, particularly where close control is not essential and operating conditions are relatively steady and predictable from experience. For example, central heating for a large building can be achieved economically with a manually controlled basement boiler setup. The human operator provides the **feedback** of information by mentally comparing the **desired condition** of the physical variable being controlled with the **actual condition** of this variable. If any discrepancy exists between desired and actual conditions, the operator makes adjustments in the system so as to reduce or eliminate the discrepancy.

(b) *Continuous automatic control*

The generating set of Example (b) includes an engine speed governor which is sensitive to changes in speed and which is linked to the engine's energy supply. The unit is set to run at a predetermined constant speed, known as the **desired value** of the speed. If any cause (such as a load change on the generator) acts to change the speed of the unit, the governor acts to increase or decrease the rate of flow of energy to the engine so as to restore its speed to the desired value. The governor action is continuous in time, involves no human operator, and is fully automatic. See Example 1.1 for details of the action of a typical engine governor.

The characteristic feature of a continuous automatic control system is the continuous comparison between the instantaneous **actual value** of the variable chosen to be controlled (the **controlled variable**) and the **desired value** of this variable. Any discrepancy existing between the desired and actual values of the controlled variable is called the **error.** An automatic control system acts to eliminate error by making suitable adjustments within the system. Continuous monitoring of the actual value of the controlled variable and comparison with the desired value is called **feedback.** A system containing feedback is called a **closed loop system** or a feedback system. A system not having automatic feedback is called an **open loop system.** Systems involving human operators are classified as open loop systems, even though the purpose of the operator is to provide feedback of operating information.

In its simplest form, a continuous automatic control system can be represented graphically as in Fig. 1.1.

Control action is taken only when error is finite. No action is necessary if the desired and actual values of the controlled variable are equal. Thus

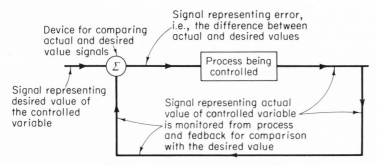

Fig. 1.1 Basic automatic control setup.

an automatic control system is **error-actuated:** the error acts to adjust the system so as to eliminate itself, and so restore the controlled variable to its desired value.

(c) Discontinuous automatic control

It is often adequate to maintain the value of the selected controlled variable within a certain range, rather than at a single value. The refrigerating system of Example (c) is of this type. The temperature inside the cabinet is held within a predetermined narrow range. If the temperature in the cabinet rises above the upper limit of this range, the refrigerating system cuts in automatically; refrigerant flows at a constant rate until the cabinet temperature has fallen to the lower limit, and then cuts out automatically. Control action is automatic but intermittent. Such control is referred to as **discontinuous automatic control** or **on-off control.** The quantity used to effect the control (the flow rate of refrigerant, in the present example) is either full on or full off. Discontinuous automatic control is considerably simpler and less expensive than continuous automatic control, and is widely used where a discrete range of the controlled variable is acceptable. Examples 1.3 and 1.4 represent typical on-off control situations.

Another type of discontinuous automatic control exists where the actual condition of a controlled variable is monitored intermittently. The monitoring can be carried out at discrete intervals of time, either on a timed program basis or in a random manner. The intermittent output signal is fed back for comparison with a desired condition, and corrective action is automatically initiated if any error exists. In this case, the degree of corrective action can depend on the size and nature of the error as distinct from on-off control, where corrective action is either full on or full off.

1.2 CONTINUOUS AUTOMATIC CONTROL SYSTEMS

The present text is primarily concerned with continuous automatic control, and hence with continuous feedback or closed loop systems. An automatic control system consists of a series of components linked together so as to perform the desired control function. Information signals flow continuously between the components in closed loops. The signals represent the instantaneous values of system variables such as pressure, temperature, displacement, velocity, voltage, and so on.

Figure 1.2 shows the basic elements of a typical automatic control system in block diagram form. Each block represents a physical component, each of which receives an incoming signal (an **input**) and generates a corresponding outgoing signal (an **output** or **response**). For example, the amplifier unit receives the error signal θ as its input and generates the signal θ_c which goes on to the next component, the **regulator.**

The controller unit (comparator plus amplifier in Fig. 1.2) is the action

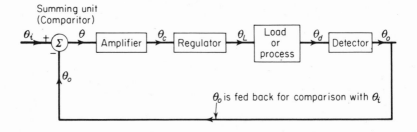

θ_i − signal representing desired value of controlled variable

θ_o − signal representing actual value of controlled variable

$\theta = \theta_i - \theta_o$, is the error

Fig. 1.2   Block diagram of basic automatic control system.

motivator. If there is an error (i.e., if $\theta_i - \theta_o \neq 0$ and θ is finite), action is taken and will continue until the error is eliminated (i.e., until $\theta_i - \theta_o = 0$ and $\theta = 0$).* With sensitive systems, control action is required for very small errors. To be able to actuate the regulator, the error signal must be amplified. The amplifier is usually a high gain device which multiplies the magnitude of the error many times.

The regulator unit receives the signal θ_c from the controller, and adjusts

---

*It will be seen later that it is not always possible to eliminate error completely. In this case, error is minimized by feedback action.

itself accordingly. For a steam turbine, the regulator is the steam control valve. Thus the amplified error signal θ_c would act to close or open the steam supply to the turbine, depending on whether the error was positive or negative. The regulator adjusts the quantity which activates the load or process (signal θ_L) according to the signal θ_c which it receives.

The load or process being controlled receives its activating quantity from the regulator (steam, fuel oil, refrigerant, and so on). It is common for the load or process to be subjected to external disturbances which affect its operation. For example, the load on an electricity generating set can increase or decrease; the door of a refrigerator can be opened to admit warm air to the cabinet; and so forth. The whole purpose of the control system is to counter these effects automatically.

A signal representing the condition of the load or process (θ_d) is monitored continuously. The detecting unit receives this signal and generates a signal representing the process condition (θ_o). This signal is fed back for comparison with the signal representing the desired value (θ_i).

Typical comparing, amplifying, regulating, and detecting components used in control systems are introduced in Chapters 2 and 3.

Figure 1.3 shows a simple tank the head of which is controlled by connecting the float by a lever to the inflow regulating valve. When in a

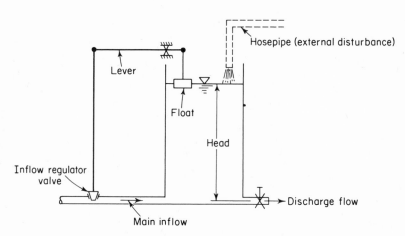

Fig. 1.3   Automatic control of a tank system.

steady operating condition, the head in the tank is constant and the inflow rate and discharge rate are equal. The steady head in the tank is the desired value of head. If an external disturbance is introduced by applying a hose discharge into the tank, the head in the tank will start to rise. The float will sense the rise, the rise in the tank becoming the error between the desired value and actual value of the head. The float movement (i.e., the error) will act to close the inflow regulating valve, reducing the inflow rate. The action will continue until the sum of the inflow rate plus the hose discharge rate equals the discharge rate, in which case the head in the tank is again constant. The float can be identified as a combination detecting and comparing unit, which compares the desired and actual values of head. Float movement is the error. The lever is the amplifier, which amplifies small float movements to sizes sufficient to activate the regulating valve. The regulating valve adjusts the rate of the flow of liquid to the tank. The tank unit itself is the process being controlled, and is controlled by controlling the head in the tank. This example illustrates a vital factor of control systems — that it takes *time* for the system to adjust itself following a disturbance.

Continuous automatic control systems can be broadly classified as:

(*a*) *Regulator Systems* — the object is to maintain the controlled variable at a constant value in the face of disturbances to the system. The desired value of the controlled variable is held constant, although there is usually provision for it to be adjusted somewhat if required. The constant speed electricity generating set already discussed is an example. The tank system of Fig. 1.3 is another example. Constant temperature refrigeration and space heating plants are further examples of regulating systems.

(*b*) *Follow-up Systems* — the object is for the actual value of the controlled variable to change in a manner dictated by deliberate changes made in its desired value. With a machine tool copying device, for example, the position of the cutting tool relative to the job blank is made to correspond with the position of a stylus following a suitable cam or profile template. Figure 3.14 shows a simplified version of this situation. The desired value is represented by the position of the stylus, which changes as the cam rotates.

(*c*) *Servomechanisms* — the controlled variable is mechanical position or displacement, and there is significant power amplification present. Thus a machine tool copying system requiring large thrust forces for very small stylus forces is a servomechanism.

1.3 THE PERFORMANCE OF AUTOMATIC CONTROL SYSTEMS

The quality of an automatic control system depends on its ability to make adjustments to offset the effects of predicted or unpredicted disturbances (such as load changes). As indicated with the example employing Figure 1.3, it takes time for a physical system to respond to a disturbance. The important requirements of a good system are:

(a) it should be stable during operation;
(b) it should be able to attain and maintain the desired value of the controlled variable with acceptable accuracy;
(c) it should have an acceptable transient behavior between the time a disturbance is introduced and until the system has regained a steady operating condition.

The performance of a component or system can be assessed by examining its response to deliberately introduced disturbances. Analysis can be attempted mathematically or experimentally. To be most useful for analysis, a disturbance should be simple to describe mathematically and readily generated experimentally. It is often most useful and convenient to introduce the disturbance as a change in the desired value of the controlled variable, and then to study the corresponding change-in-time of the actual value of the controlled variable as it seeks to attain the new desired value.

Some commonly used disturbances (inputs, or forcing functions), denoted by θ_i', are shown in Fig. 1.4.

1.4 MATHEMATICAL REPRESENTATION OF COMPONENTS AND SYSTEMS

All physical actions take time to be accomplished. Thus if a spring is acted upon by a force, it takes a finite time for the spring to be deflected. Depending upon the context in which it takes place, a rapid action may sometimes be regarded as being instantaneous.

Each component of a system provides a time relationship between any disturbance experienced by it and its response to this disturbance. The manner in which a component behaves in going from one condition to another is as important as the static change in condition finally achieved. For example, if a force acts on a mass and causes it to move from position A to position B, we are as vitally interested in how the mass behaves in moving from A to B as we are in the final total movement achieved. In other words, we are concerned with the **dynamic response** of components and systems.

An initial object of analytical work is to establish the dynamic equation(s) relating response to input. These equations will normally be differential equations in time involving the operators d/dt and $\int dt$.

For example, Fig. 1.5 shows a mass (M slugs) being disturbed by an applied force (F lb). Ignoring all loss effects, we know that the mass will accelerate according to Newton's law,

$$F = Ma$$

$$= M\frac{d^2x}{dt^2}, \quad \text{as} \quad \frac{d^2x}{dt^2} = a \quad \text{(acceleration)}$$

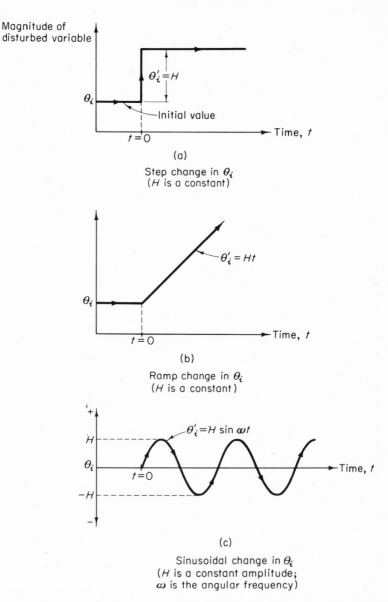

Magnitude of disturbed variable

$\theta'_i = H$

Initial value

θ_i

$t = 0$

Time, t

(a)

Step change in θ_i
(H is a constant)

θ_i

$\theta'_i = Ht$

$t = 0$

Time, t

(b)

Ramp change in θ_i
(H is a constant)

$\theta'_i = H \sin \omega t$

H

θ_i

$t = 0$

$-H$

Time, t

(c)

Sinusoidal change in θ_i
(H is a constant amplitude;
ω is the angular frequency)

Fig. 1.4 Some common forms of input disturbance: θ_i represents the initial value of the disturbed variable; $z'\theta'_i$ represents the change in θ_i introduced at time $t = 0$.

which is the differential equation in time relating x and F. The equation can be written

$$F = M \, D^2 x$$

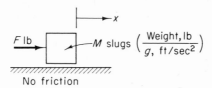

Fig. 1.5   Mass disturbed by force.

where D is the operator d/dt, and represents time in an operational form. This dynamic equation can be written in the form

$$\frac{x}{F} = \frac{1}{M\,D^2}$$

where x is identifiable as the response of the body, and F is identifiable as the input disturbance applied to the body. The expression $x/F = 1/M\,D^2$ is known as the **transfer function** of the body. In systems analysis, it is common to express dynamic equations in transfer function form, rather than as ordinary differential equations.

Similarly, a full system comprised of a series of components can be described by the **system transfer function,**

$$\frac{\text{system output (response)}}{\text{system input (disturbance)}} = \frac{\theta_o}{\theta_i} = f(D)$$

where θ_i is the variable to which the input disturbance θ_i' is applied; θ_o is the variable whose response θ_o' to the input θ_i' is being studied; $f(D)$ is the function of D relating θ_o' to θ_i', and consequently θ_o to θ_i.

Table 1.1 shows the several forms of notation used for expressing differential operations and equations in time, including the transfer function forms where applicable. It should be appreciated that the transfer function is only an operational method of expressing a conventional linear differential equation with constant coefficients. For example, the transfer function (Table 1.1),

$$\frac{\theta_o}{\theta_i} = \frac{1}{1 + K\,D}$$

can be cross-multiplied to give

$$(K\,D + 1)\theta_o = \theta_i \quad \text{or} \quad K\,D\theta_o + \theta_o = \theta_i \quad \text{or} \quad K\frac{d\theta_o}{dt} + \theta_o = \theta_i$$

The transfer function of a component or system is its mathematical model. If the transfer function for a particular case is known, the response

TABLE 1.1: *Several Ways to Represent Time-Differential Operations and Equations*

Conventional notation	Simplified notation	Operational notation	Transfer function notation
θ	θ	θ	not applicable
$\dfrac{d\theta}{dt}$	$\dot{\theta}$	$D\theta$	not applicable
$\dfrac{d^2\theta}{dt^2}$	$\ddot{\theta}$	$D^2\theta$	not applicable
$\int \theta \, dt$		$\dfrac{\theta}{D}$	not applicable
$\int\int \theta \, dt \, dt$		$\dfrac{\theta}{D^2}$	not applicable
$K\dfrac{d\theta_o}{dt} + \theta_o = \theta_i$	$K\dot{\theta}_o + \theta_o = \theta_i$	$K\,D\theta_o + \theta_o = \theta_i$	$\dfrac{\theta_o}{\theta_i} = \dfrac{1}{1 + K\,D}$
$K_1\dfrac{d^2\theta_o}{dt^2} + K_2\dfrac{d\theta_o}{dt} + K_3\theta_o = \theta_i$	$K_1\ddot{\theta}_o + K_2\dot{\theta}_o + K_3\theta_o = \theta_i$	$K_1\,D^2\,\theta_o + K_2\,D\,\theta_o + K_3\theta_o = \theta_i$	$\dfrac{\theta_o}{\theta_i} = \dfrac{1}{K_1\,D^2 + K_2\,D + K_3}$

can be studied for various forms of disturbance (step, ramp, sinusoid, and so on) with a view toward understanding the nature of the component or system. If the transfer function of a particular system is unknown, it may be established experimentally by introducing known disturbances and studying the measured response of the system. Once established, a transfer function gives a full description of the nature of the component or system,* as distinct from its physical description. As will be demonstrated in Chapter 3, the transfer function of a linear system is completely independent of the size or nature of an input disturbance and of the initial condition of all of the system variables. The transfer function is a characteristic only of the system itself.

It is common, but not necessary, for the transfer function of an automatic control system to relate the actual and desired values of the controlled variable. It is possible to relate the response of any system variable to a disturbance introduced at any point in the system.

1.5 LINEAR ANALYSIS

By using transfer functions to describe both system components and full systems, a single theory has been developed to cover the various types of physical hardware — electrical, mechanical, pneumatic, thermal, hydraulic, etc. The basic theory of automatic control covers components and systems which have linear transfer functions, i.e., which can be described by linear algebraic or differential equations having constant coefficients. For example:

(a) $3(d^2x/dt^2) + 4(dx/dt) + 2x = 2f(t)$ is a linear differential equation with constant coefficients, i.e., the terms of the equation are all of first degree — although the equation is of second order — and coefficients 3, 4, 2, and 2 are constants. The equation can be written in transfer function form as

$$\frac{x}{f(t)} = \frac{2}{3D^2 + 4D + 2} = \frac{1}{1.5D^2 + 2D + 1}$$

where $D = d/dt$. Check by cross multiplying.

(b) $t^3(d^2x/dt^2) + t(dx/dt) + 3 = 8f(t)$ is a linear differential equation with variable coefficients, i.e., the terms are all of first degree — although the equation is of second order — but coefficients t^3 and t are variable in time.

(c) $6(d^2x/dt^2)^2 + 3x = 4$ is a nonlinear differential equation with constant coefficients. The nonlinearity is due to the term $(d^2x/dt^2)^2$ being of second degree.

*This is strictly true only for linear components and systems, as will be discussed in Section 1.5.

Only in case (a) is the concept of a transfer function fully meaningful.

Note that the term on the right side of these equations is the forcing function, known also as the driving function or the input. In control work, $f(t)$ is likely to be a step, ramp, or sinusoid, as discussed previously.

Two of the main properties of linear equations are:

(1) The transfer function form of the equation is independent of the type or size of input used in an analysis.
(2) The principle of superposition holds. That is, independent solutions of the equation for several independent inputs can be added together to give the total solution for the total disturbance.

A linear system is composed of linear components. Many engineering components are linear or quasi-linear. Often, essentially nonlinear components can be linearized by restricting the operation of the component to a narrow range. It is common that automatic control system components are required to operate over narrow ranges only. For example, the automatic speed controller (i.e., the governor) on the engine of an electricity generating set designed to run at 3000 rpm would be useful for only a narrow range of speed — say, within 2900–3100 rpm.

Examples of Linearization:

(a) With a flyweight engine speed governor, changes in speed are sensed as changes in the centripetal action on two or more weights driven in a circular path by the engine. Figure 1.7 (p. 15) shows the operation of a flyweight governor. Its action is described in Example 1.1. The well-known relationship between speed of rotation and the centripetal force experienced by each weight is

$$F_c = \frac{W}{g}\omega^2\, r = \frac{1}{g}\left(\frac{2\pi}{60}\right)^2 WrN^2$$

where F_c is the centripetal force experienced by a mass rotating in a circular path; W is the weight of the mass: r is the radius of the path of rotation; ω and N are respectively the angular velocity and rpm of rotation. With the present governor, the centripetal force acting to keep the masses on their circular path is provided by the spring lever system. For a particular governor operating at a particular mean path radius,

$$F_c \propto N^2$$

which is a nonlinear relationship (second degree), as represented graphically in Fig. 1.6(a). Figure 1.6(a) includes the desired value of engine speed (N_i) and the range over which the governor is to be effective (N_1 to N_2). As long as $N_2 - N_1$ is small relative to N_i, the $F_c - N$ relationship is close to linear, i.e., $\Delta F_c/\Delta N \approx$ constant in the speed range N_1 to N_2. Thus the nonlinear relationship $F_c = (1/g)$ $(2\pi/60)^2\, W\, r\, N^2$ can be linearized in the working range of the governor.

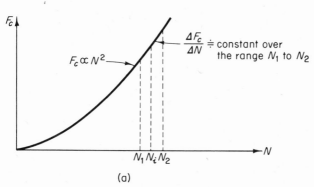

(a)

Centripetal force–speed relationship
for mass rotating in fixed circular path

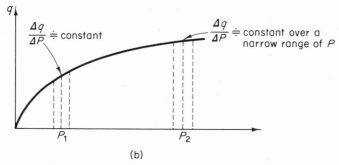

(b)

Flow rate–pressure drop relationship
for a fluid restriction

Fig. 1.6 Linearizing typical nonlinear relationships.

(b) Flow of liquid under pressure through a restriction such as an orifice, valve, or venturi is commonly expressed as

$$q = C_d A \left(\frac{2g \cdot \Delta P}{W}\right)^{1/2} = C_d A \left(\frac{2g}{W}\right)^{1/2} \cdot \Delta P^{1/2}$$

where q is the flow rate of liquid; C_d is the flow coefficient associated with the restriction; A is the flow area of the restriction; w is the specific weight of the liquid; ΔP is the pressure drop across the restriction, which causes flow.

Hence, for a particular restriction and liquid, $q \propto \Delta P^{1/2}$ whose nonlinear form is shown plotted in Fig. 1.6(b).

Using the notion that relatively small changes of the variables are involved with automatic control practice, the curve of Fig. 1.6(b) can be linearized over narrow ranges of pressure drop, i.e.,

$$\frac{\Delta P}{\Delta q} \approx \text{constant in a narrow range about } P_1$$

It is important to realize that for the situations of Fig. 1.6 the linearity constant varies for different sections of the curves, i.e., in Fig. 1.6(b),

$$\frac{\Delta P}{\Delta q} = K_1 \text{ about the mean pressure } P_1$$

and

$$\frac{\Delta P}{\Delta q} = K_2 \text{ about the mean pressure } P_2$$

It should not be inferred that linearity is an essential, or even a desirable requirement, of all control systems components. Nonlinear characteristics can be used to improve the performance of real systems. Also, numerous techniques exist whereby nonlinear analysis can be performed.

1.6 SUMMARY

The main feature of automatic control systems is the automatic comparison of the actual value of the variable being controlled to the desired value of that variable. Any difference between these two values causes action to be taken in such a manner as to eliminate the difference.

The present text is principally concerned with continuous feedback systems in which the process of comparison between actual and desired values, and any subsequent action, is continuous in time.

The present text is principally concerned with linear theory. Many engineering components are linear, quasi-linear, or can be linearized in defined narrow operating ranges.

Linear analysis is essentially a study of the response of a component or system to well-defined input disturbances (i.e., the disturbance is applied and the response to it, as a function of time, is studied). This text is generally confined to analysis of the relationship between a single input and single output variable. An approach for multiple input-multiple output analysis is introduced in Chapter 11.

A first essential to analysis is to establish the mathematical models (i.e., the dynamic equations) of the various components which form a system. The component models can then be combined to yield the mathematical model of the system. In general, the mathematical models are differential equations in time relating the response and the input disturbance. It is normal to express the mathematical model in the transfer function form:

$$\frac{\text{response of system}}{\text{input to system}} = \frac{\theta_o}{\theta_i} = f(D)$$

where θ_o and θ_i are the response and the input disturbance respectively; D is the operator d/dt.

System response can be examined analytically by solving the system's equation(s) for specified input disturbances.

System response can be examined experimentally by measuring its response when a suitable disturbance is generated in the system.

Special techniques have been developed (i.e., the frequency response method of Chapter 5 and the root locus method of Chapter 7) to circumvent the necessity of making full solutions of system equations, and to give means of synthesizing control systems.

1.7 EXAMPLES OF AUTOMATIC CONTROL SYSTEMS

The following examples should be interpreted as simplified versions of the sophisticated control systems often used in practice.

Example 1.1 — The Engine Speed Governor: Figure 1.7 shows diagrammatically a simple centripetal governor, as used to automatically maintain the speed of a turbine, engine, or motor in the face of disturbances to the driven load. The engine output shaft is direct-connected via gearing to drive the rotating parts of the governor. The two hinged bell crank levers with their attached masses are driven in a circular path about the governor axis. The inner ends of the bell crank

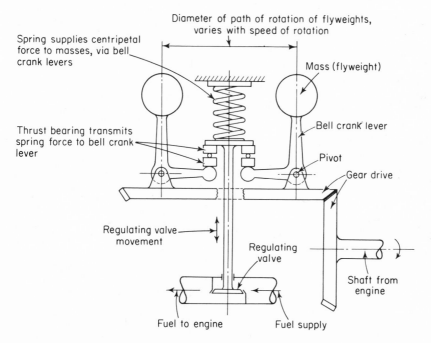

Fig. 1.7 Simple centripetal governor.

levers react against a thrust bearing, whose upper half is restrained from vertical (axial) motion by a spring. The spring acts through the bell crank levers to provide the centripetal action necessary to keep the masses on a circular path. The thrust bearing is connected to the governor spindle so that any vertical deflection of the spring is also experienced by the spindle. The lower end of the spindle is connected to the fuel supply valve of the engine. When the engine is running at a constant speed against a fixed load, the masses will rotate in a circular path at a particular path radius, as governed by the balance between the spring force acting on one end of each bell crank lever and the centripetal force required to force the masses to maintain their circular path. If the load on the engine is increased, the engine will tend to slow down; the governor masses will move toward a new, smaller, path radius, and the spring will tend to extend, causing the governor spindle to move downward. The fuel valve opening is thereby increased, allowing more fuel to go to the engine. The extra fuel supply acts to increase engine speed toward its former value. Similarly, if engine speed tends to increase, the governor masses seek a larger path radius with subsequent reduction of the fuel supply to the engine.

Example 1.2 — The Automatic Pilot in an Aircraft: To avoid pilot tedium on long flights, modern aircraft are fitted with automatic flight controllers. When steady flight conditions have been achieved, a desired direction and a desired altitude are set on the device. Actual direction and altitude are monitored continually with a compass and altimeter respectively, and automatically compared with their desired values. Any discrepancies will, by actuating the appropriate flight controls, promote the action necessary to restore the desired flight conditions. Discrepancies could occur due to external disturbances such as crosswinds or updraft currents.

Example 1.3 — A Domestic Refrigerator Cycle: A thermostat is preset to a desired operating temperature. The actual temperature in the refrigerator cabinet is monitored and compared with the desired value. When the actual temperature rises a predetermined amount above the desired value, a switch closes to cause refrigerant to flow in the coils. Heat is taken from the cabinet, causing its temperature to fall. When the temperature falls a predetermined amount below the desired value, the thermostat switch opens to cut off refrigerant flow. Because the system is not operated continuously, but only when the error between desired and actual values of temperature exceeds an acceptable tolerance, the system is discontinuous. External disturbances to the system include opening of the door to admit warm air, placing warm food in the refrigerator, etc.

Example 1.4 — An On-Off Tank Level Control: Figure 1.8 shows a tank the head of which is sensed by a float. The float contains an electrical contactor, which is positioned between two separated fixed contactors. The inflow regulating valve to the tank is electrically operated. Its electrical circuit is open unless the float contactor touches one of the fixed contactors. If the level in the tank rises, the rising float will eventually close the electrical circuit of the regulating valve, causing the valve to close and reduce flow to the tank. If the electrical circuit is

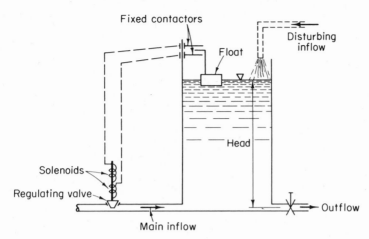

Fig. 1.8   Simple on-off tank level control.

completed through the lower fixed contactor — i.e., if the head in the tank falls — the regulating valve opens to increase flow to the tank. Note that the regulating valve has only three operating positions:

(a) to give a predetermined steady flow when the electrical control circuit is open;
(b) to give a reduced (or zero) flow when the float contact makes the circuit with the upper fixed contact
(c) to give an increased (or full open) flow when the float contact makes the circuit with the lower fixed contact.

Example 1.5 — Radar Controlled Antiaircraft and Naval Guns: Radar is used to assess the position of the target, and generates a signal representing the desired direction of aim. The actual position of the gun is automatically compared with this desired value, and any error causes action to reaim the gun. When error is eliminated, the aim is correct and the gun is fixed. Control allowances can be made to accommodate a moving target, and to allow for the time required to perform the positioning operations.

2 Basic laws, relationships, components, and analogies

2.1 INTRODUCTION

This chapter is intended as a brief review of the simple basic laws associated with mechanical, electrical, thermal, and fluid pressure dynamics. These laws, and their associated relationships, must be understood in order that mathematical models of engineering systems can be derived. Simple engineering components which behave according to the basic dynamic relationships, and which commonly appear in control systems, will be introduced. Direct dynamic analogies among electrical, thermal, and fluid pressure relationships will be discussed. The whole art of analyzing dynamic engineering systems depends on the ability to form good mathematical models (equations) of the systems. In general, such models will be differential equations, with time as the independent variable.

2.2 MECHANICAL RELATIONSHIPS

2.2.1 Mass

The plane linear motion of a physical body due to the action of a system of forces is governed by Newton's second law,

$$\sum \bar{F} = \frac{d}{dt}(m\bar{v}) \tag{2.1}$$

where $\sum \bar{F}$ is the vector sum of the force system, lb; m is the mass of the body, lb sec²/ft or slug; $\bar{v}$ is the velocity (vector) of the body, ft/sec.

For common engineering situations, mass is a constant and Eq. 2.1 can be written

$$\sum \bar{F} = m\frac{d\bar{v}}{dt} = m\bar{a} \tag{2.1a}$$

where $\bar{a}$ is the acceleration (a vector) of the body, ft/sec².

Recognizing that velocity is the first derivative of displacement, and that acceleration is the second derivative of displacement,

$$\sum \bar{F} = m\bar{a} = m\frac{d\bar{v}}{dt} = m\frac{d^2\bar{x}}{dt^2} \tag{2.1b}$$

$$\text{or} \qquad = m\, D\bar{v} = m\, D^2\bar{x}$$

where $\bar{x}$ is the displacement (a vector) of the mass. Also, using the relationship mass = weight/g,

$$\sum \bar{F} = \frac{W}{g}\bar{a} = \frac{W}{g}D^2\bar{x} \tag{2.1c}$$

where W is the weight of the body, lb; g is acceleration due to gravity (32.2 ft/sec² at sea level). While W and g are both vectors, the ratio W/g is a scalar.

Equation 2.1(c) is a linear ordinary differential equation in time, which can be solved for $x(t)$ for any given force system $\sum \bar{F}$ and a particular mass.

For the common engineering situation where the direction of motion of the body is linear and is obvious by inspection, Newton's law is written

$$F = \frac{W}{g}a = \frac{W}{g}Dv = \frac{W}{g}D^2x \tag{2.1d}$$

For the plane rotation of a body about a fixed axis, Eq. 2.1 reduces to

$$\bar{L} = I\bar{\alpha} = I\, D\bar{\omega} = I\, D^2\bar{\theta} \tag{2.1e}$$

where $\bar{L}$ is the net driving torque (a vector) on the body, lb ft; I is the moment of inertia of the body about the axis of rotation, lb ft sec²; $\bar{\alpha}$ radian/sec² is the angular acceleration (a vector) of the body due to $\bar{L}$; θ radian is the angular displacement (a vector) of the body due to $\bar{L}$. Equation 2.1(e) is the rotational equivalent of the linear motion Eq. 2.1(b).

Newton's law is readily extended to encompass combined linear and rotational plane motion, and also space motion. It can be developed into several other convenient forms, such as the work-energy equation and the impulse-momentum equation, which are convenient for solution of particular types of mechanical motion problems. However, the forms of Eqs. 2.1(d) and 2.1(e) are sufficient for the purposes of the present text.

The import of the dynamic Eq. 2.1(d) (and of Eq. 2.1e) is that if the net force on the body is zero, then acceleration of the body is zero and it is in equilibrium (either stationary or at constant velocity). Note that equilibrium does not imply that the position of the body — i.e., its displacement $x(t)$ — is necessarily zero or constant.

2.2.2 Linear Spring

A spring is linear if its equilibrium condition satisfies the relationship

$$F_s = kx \qquad \text{(Fig. 2.1a)} \tag{2.2}$$

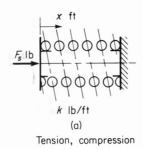

(a)

Tension, compression

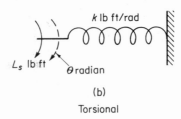

(b)

Torsional

Fig. 2.1 Linear springs.

where F is the axial force applied to the spring, lb; k is the constant characteristic of the spring, lb/ft; x ft is the displacement of the free end of the spring due to F. Linear springs are widely used in control systems components.

No physical action can take place in zero time. If the axial force on a spring changes by F_s', it takes a finite time for the spring to deflect an additional amount x'. The inertia of the spring has to be overcome. Commonly, the inertia of a coil spring is taken as one-third of its mass. However, for most common engineering situations, the inertia effect of the spring's reaction to a change of force is so small that the spring is assumed to deflect instantaneously. In effect, the spring reacts to a change in force much more rapidly than do the other components with which the spring is associated. Thus the static Eq. 2.2 is usually assumed also to be the dynamic relationship describing the action of the spring. Equation 2.2 is commonly used in the form

$$F_s' = kx' \tag{2.2a}$$

where F_s' and x' are changes in F_s and x respectively.

Torsional springs can also have a linear characteristic, described by the relationship

$$L_s = k\theta \quad \text{(Fig. 2.1b)} \tag{2.2b}$$

where L_s is the torque applied to the spring, lb ft; θ radian is the angular displacement of the spring due to L_s; k is the constant characteristic of the spring, lb ft/radian.

2.2.3 Viscous Friction

Friction is always present when there is relative motion between components, and it induces a force which opposes the motion. Coulomb (dry) friction is nonlinear in nature, and cannot be directly handled with linear theory. Friction is not always an undesirable feature, and is often deliberately induced to provide a damping or restraining effect on moving masses. Physical devices exist which can provide a friction force which is proportional to the velocity of a body. This condition is called viscous friction, and is described by

$$F_f \propto \dot{x}, \qquad F_f = c\dot{x} \tag{2.3}$$

where F_f is the viscous friction force opposing motion, lb; $\dot{x} = Dx$ is the velocity of the body to which F_f is applied, ft/sec; c is the viscous damping coefficient, lb sec/ft.

The friction in well-lubricated motions which operate without dwell can often be approximated with viscous friction for an approximate linear analysis. This is commonly the case with air or oil pressure servomechanisms.

The dashpot, Fig. 2.2, is a widely used device for providing the damping effect of viscous friction. The piston is a relatively loose fit in the cylinder, which is filled with fluid. If the cylinder is fixed and a force is applied to the piston (or vice versa), a pressure builds up on one side of the piston to resist the force. The resulting pressure drop across the piston causes

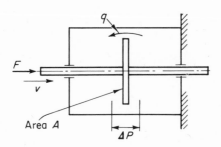

Fig. 2.2 Viscous friction dashpot.

fluid to flow past the piston, and the piston moves in the cylinder. If the piston-cylinder clearance is relatively small, flow past the piston is laminar and flow rate q is proportional to the pressure drop ΔP. That is,

$$q \propto \Delta P, \qquad q = K \cdot \Delta P \tag{2.3a}$$

If the mass of the moving part of the dashpot is negligible, then $\sum F = ma$ applied to the piston yields

$$F - \Delta P \cdot A = 0 \qquad \text{or} \qquad F = A \cdot \Delta P \tag{2.3b}$$

where A is the piston area.

If the dashpot fluid is incompressible, the flow rate from one end of the cylinder to the other equals the volumetric displacement of the piston in the cylinder. That is,

$$q = Av \tag{2.3c}$$

where v is the velocity of the piston in the cylinder. Combining Eqs. (a), (b), and (c),

$$F = A \cdot \Delta P = A\frac{q}{K} = \frac{A^2 v}{K} = cv \tag{2.3d}$$

where $c = A^2 K$.

Equations (d) and 2.3 are identical, showing that the dashpot operated under the conditions layed down provides a viscous frictional resistance to motion.

Many types of linear and rotary viscous dampers exist. The value of the coefficient c dictates the degree of damping offered.

2.2.4 Lever Systems

Levers are used to provide ratios between displacements, force, velocities, and accelerations. Figure 2.3(a) shows a simple lever, from which it can be seen that

$$\frac{x_o}{x_i} = \frac{\dot{x}_o}{\dot{x}_i} = \frac{\ddot{x}_o}{\ddot{x}_i} = \frac{a}{a+b} \quad \text{(a constant)} \tag{2.4}$$

and

$$\frac{F_o}{F_i} = \frac{a+b}{a} = \left(\frac{x_o}{x_i}\right)^{-1} \tag{2.5}$$

where x_o and x_i are displacements; F_o and F_i are forces.

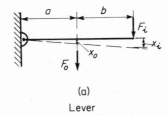

(a)

Lever

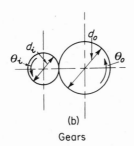

(b)

Gears

Fig. 2.3 Mechanical ratio systems.

Rotational displacement, velocity and acceleration, and torque can be similarly multiplied by constants by the use of gearing, belt drives, etc. Figure 2.3(b) shows a simple gear pair, for which

$$\frac{\theta_o}{\theta_i} = \frac{\dot{\theta}_o}{\dot{\theta}_i} = \frac{\ddot{\theta}_o}{\ddot{\theta}_i} = -\frac{d_i}{d_o} \quad \text{(a constant)} \tag{2.4a}$$

and

$$\frac{L_o}{L_i} = -\frac{d_o}{d_i} = \left(\frac{\theta_o}{\theta_i}\right)^{-1} \tag{2.5a}$$

where θ_o and θ_i are angular displacements; L_o and L_i are torques; and d_o and d_i are the pitch circle diameters of the driven and driving gears respectively. The negative sign indicates a reversal of the direction of rotation. Inclusion of an idler gear of any size between the driven and driving gears restores the sense of rotation.

Both lever and gear systems can be compounded to give wide ranges of motion amplification or reduction.

2.3 ELECTRICAL RELATIONSHIPS

2.3.1 Resistance

Potential difference (voltage drop) across an electrical resistor causes flow rate of electricity through the resistor according to Ohm's law (Fig. 2.4a),

$$\Delta E = iR \qquad (2.6)$$

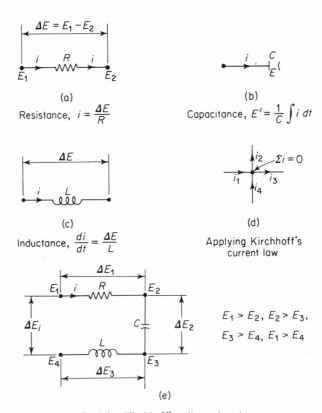

(a)

Resistance, $i = \dfrac{\Delta E}{R}$

(b)

Capacitance, $E' = \dfrac{1}{C}\int i\, dt$

(c)

Inductance, $\dfrac{di}{dt} = \dfrac{\Delta E}{L}$

(d)

Applying Kirchhoff's current law

$E_1 > E_2,\ E_2 > E_3,$
$E_3 > E_4,\ E_1 > E_4$

(e)

Applying Kirchhoff's voltage drop law

Fig. 2.4 The basic laws of electrical circuits.

where ΔE is the potential difference, volts; i is the flow rate of electricity (current), coulombs/sec or amperes; R is the resistance of the resistor, volt sec/coulomb, volt/amp, or ohm.
Thus

$$i = \frac{\Delta E}{R} \tag{2.6a}$$

describes the rate of flow of electricity.

The concept of a resistor is that it restricts flow.

2.3.2 Capacitance

The voltage (potential) within an electrical capacitor is related to the flow rate of electricity (current) into the capacitor by Faraday's law (Fig. 2.4b),

$$E' = \frac{1}{C}\int_{t_1}^{t_2} i\, dt \tag{2.7}$$

where $(t_2 - t_1)$ describes the time during which flow occurs; E' is the change in voltage in time $(t_2 - t_1)$; C is the capacitance of the capacitor, coulomb/volt or farad.

Equation 2.7 can be written in the operational form

$$E' = \frac{i}{C\,D} \tag{2.7a}$$

where $1/D$ denotes $\int dt$ of the associated parameters.

Noting that $\int_{t_1}^{t_2} i\, dt = Q$ coulombs, which is the total quantity of electricity to flow into the capacitor in time $(t_2 - t_1)$, then

$$C = \frac{Q}{E'} \quad \text{coulomb/volt (farad)} \tag{2.7b}$$

which is a useful definition of capacitance.

Note from Eq. 2.7 that the actual voltage within the capacitor is the sum of the original voltage E_1 at $t = t_1$ and the change in voltage E' which occurs in $(t_2 - t_1)$.

The concept of a capacitor is that it stores energy.

2.3.3 Inductance

The voltage drop across a linear inductor is related to the current flowing in the inductor by Henry's law (Fig. 2.4c),

$$\Delta E = L\frac{di}{dt} = L\,Di \tag{2.8}$$

where ΔE is the voltage drop; L is the inductance of the inductor, volt sec/amp or henry.

The concept of an inductor is that potential drop across it causes acceleration of flow rate through it.

2.3.4 Continuity; Conservation

Kirchhoff's laws for electrical circuits state:

1. The algebraic sum of all currents flowing at a junction is zero:

$$\sum i = 0 \quad \text{at all junctions} \tag{2.9}$$

For the example of Fig. 2.4(d),

$$\sum i = i_1 - i_2 - i_3 + i_4 = 0$$

2. The algebraic sum of the voltage drops around a closed loop is zero:

$$\sum \Delta E = 0 \quad \text{around all closed paths} \tag{2.10}$$

For the example of Fig. 2.4(e),

$$\sum \Delta E = \Delta E_i - \Delta E_1 - \Delta E_2 - \Delta E_3 = 0$$

2.4 THERMAL RELATIONSHIPS

2.4.1 Conduction

Ignoring heat losses to the surrounding medium, heat flows from one point in a homogeneous body (Fig. 2.5a) to another point according to the relationship

$$q = \frac{KA \, \Delta T}{x} \quad \text{BTU/min} \tag{2.11a}$$

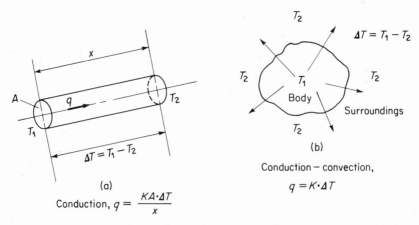

Fig. 2.5 Some basic heat transfer situations.

where A is the cross-sectional area of the body (assumed constant here); x is the length of the heat flow path; ΔT is the temperature difference inducing heat flow; K is the coefficient of heat transfer (thermal conductivity) of the material of the body, BTU/min per ft per °F.

For a particular conductor, K, A, and x are constants and Eq. 2.11(a) can be written

$$q = K_1 \, \Delta T \tag{2.11b}$$

where K_1 is the thermal conductance of the body, BTU/min per °F.

Conduction — convection

For simple heat transfer cases, the rate of heat transfer from (or to) a body to (or from) a surrounding medium, or between two adjacent bodies, is governed by the relationship

$$q = K_2 \, \Delta T \quad \text{BTU/min} \tag{2.11c}$$

where K_2 is the heat transfer coefficient existing and includes the effect of interface films, BTU/min °F; ΔT is the temperature difference inducing heat transfer (Fig. 2.5b).

For the cases of both Eqs. 2.11(b) and (c), the heat transfer relationship can be written in the form

$$\frac{\Delta T}{q} = R \tag{2.11}$$

where $R = 1/K$, the thermal resistance of the body considered, °F min/BTU.

Note that thermal resistance is simply the inverse of the thermal conductivity or heat transfer coefficients. Note also the direct analogy between Eq. 2.11 and Ohm's law (Eq. 2.6), with

(a) temperature drop corresponding to voltage drop, the motivating influences for flow;
(b) heat flow rate corresponding to current (electricity flow rate);
(c) thermal resistance corresponding to electrical resistance.

2.4.2 Energy

The rate at which heat is transferred to a body from its environment (or vice versa) equals the rate of increase of the internal energy of the body;

$$q = \frac{d}{dt} cWT \quad \text{BTU/min} \tag{2.12}$$

where c is the specific heat, BTU/lb °F; W is the weight, lb; T is the temperature, °F, of the body. Commonly, c and W are constants, and Eq. 2.12 becomes

$$q = cW \frac{dT}{dt} \tag{2.12a}$$

Hence

$$q \, dt = cW \, dT \qquad \text{and} \qquad dT = \frac{1}{cW} q \, dt \tag{2.12b}$$

Integrating both sides of Eq. 2.12(b) yields

$$\left[T \right]_{T_1}^{T_2} = T' = \frac{I}{cW} \int_{t_1}^{t_2} q \, dt \tag{2.12c}$$

where T_1 and T_2 are the temperatures of the body at times t_1 and t_2 respectively; T' is the change in temperature, $T_2 - T_1$.

Equation 2.12(c) is directly analogous to Faraday's law (Eq. 2.7), with temperature change T' corresponding to voltage change E', heat flow rate q corresponding to current i (electricity flow rate), and the constant cW corresponding to electrical capacitance. The product cW is called the thermal capacity of the body, BTU/°F, and Eq. 2.12(c) can be written,

$$T' = \frac{1}{C} \int q \, dt \tag{2.12d}$$

2.5 FLUID PRESSURE RELATIONSHIPS

2.5.1 Introduction

Fluid pressure components and systems are widely used in control systems. Where large thrusts or torques are required, as in servomechanisms, oil hydraulic systems using pressures of up to 5000 psi are common. High pressures can be used in conjunction with small piston areas — and hence with small and light components — to generate large forces. Low pressure air (about 15 psi) components are widely used in process control systems, due to the inherent simplicity, low price, and safety of low pressure air. Figure 2.10 (and Fig. 3.8) shows a typical low-pressure air-operated valve, which can be remote-controlled.

The laws of fluid flow are essentially nonlinear. All fluids have a degree of compressibility, which also has a nonlinear effect on the dynamic action of fluid pressure components. However, the actions of many fluid pressure components can be linearized to give a reasonably acceptable linear model of their dynamic characteristics. In the manner illustrated in Section 1.5, it is usually necessary to confine the analysis to relatively small changes of the state of the component about a mean condition. Linearization requires the assumption that the fluid used is incompressible.

While this is a common assumption with low-pressure liquids, it becomes less accurate when high pressures are involved. Air and other gases are highly compressible. However, with slow-response low-pressure air systems of the types used in process control, an assumption that flow is incompressible is often satisfactory.

The assumptions of fluid incompressibility, and of linear approximations to the fluid flow laws, will be used in most of the work of the present text.

2.5.2 Continuity; Conservation

For steady flow in a nonbranching fluid conduit, the mass flow rate is constant at all points. For incompressible flow (steady or unsteady), the volumetric flow rate is constant at all points in such a conduit. The latter condition can be described by

$$q = Av \tag{2.13}$$

where q is the volumetric flow rate of the fluid, ft^3/sec or in.^{3}/min; A is the area of the flow conduit at the point considered, ft^2 or in.^{2}; v is the mean velocity of flow at the point considered, ft/sec or in./min. For example, in the pipe line in Fig. 2.6(a),

$$q = A_1v_1 = A_2v_2 = A_3v_3$$

Consider the piston and cylinder of Fig. 2.6(b). If the flow rate of (incompressible) fluid into the cylinder is q, then

$$q = Av \quad \text{or} \quad v = \frac{q}{A} \tag{2.13a}$$

where v is the velocity of the piston in the cylinder; A is the area of the piston. Note that Av in this case is the rate of change of the volume of the inflow end of the cylinder.

For incompressible flow in a branching system of conduits (Fig. 2.6c):

1. The algebraic sum of the flow rates at any junction is zero:

$$\sum q = 0 \quad \text{at any junction} \tag{2.14}$$

In Fig. 2.6(c), $\sum q = 0$ at the junction yields

$$q_1 = q_2 + q_3 \quad \text{or} \quad A_1v_1 = A_2v_2 + A_3v_3$$

2. In any closed fluid circuit, the algebraic sum of the pressure drops around the circuit is zero:

$$\sum \Delta P = 0 \quad \text{around a closed path} \tag{2.15}$$

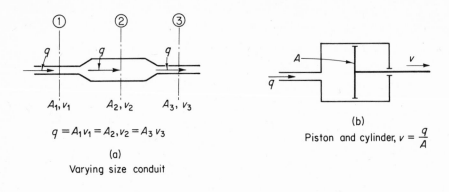

$$q = A_1 v_1 = A_2 v_2 = A_3 v_3$$

(a)

Varying size conduit

(b)

Piston and cylinder, $v = \dfrac{q}{A}$

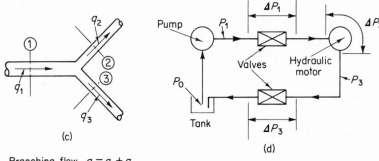

(c)

Branching flow, $q_1 = q_2 + q_3$

(d)

Pressure drop around a hydraulic circuit,
$$(P_1 - P_0) = \Delta P = \Delta P_1 + \Delta P_2 + \Delta P_3$$

Fig. 2.6 Fluid pressure situations.

Figure 2.6(d) shows a fluid pump-valve-motor circuit, in which

$$\Delta P = \Delta P_1 + \Delta P_2 + \Delta P_3$$

The two laws are directly analogous to Kirchhoff's laws (Section 2.3.4), with

flow rate q corresponding with current (flow rate of electricity);

pressure drop ΔP corresponding with voltage drop (potential drop).

2.5.3 Flow Through Restrictions

Valves, orifices, venturis, capillaries, and many other flow controlling or measuring devices act as restrictions in the fluid line. In effect, they offer resistance to flow through themselves, in the manner of electrical resistors.

If flow through the restriction is laminar, then flow rate is proportional to pressure drop (see standard derivations for laminar flow in pipes, annular passages, etc.), i.e.,

$$q \propto \Delta P \quad \text{for laminar flow} \tag{2.16}$$

$$\frac{q}{\Delta P} = K \quad \text{or} \quad \frac{\Delta P}{q} = \frac{1}{K} = R \tag{2.16a}$$

where K (a constant) is called the flow conductance of the restriction, $ft^5 \ sec^{-1} \ lb^{-1}$; R (a constant) is called the resistance of the restriction, sec lb ft^{-5}.

R and K are absolute constants for a particular fluid flowing through a fixed geometry restriction. However, R and K vary with the degree of opening of variable restrictions, such as valves.

Equation 2.16 is linear, and is directly analogous to Ohm's law (Eq. 2.6), with ΔP, q, and R corresponding to ΔE, i, and R respectively.

If flow through the restriction is turbulent, the flow rate is proportional to the square root of the pressure drop across the restriction (see standard derivations for turbulent flow in pipes, venturis, etc.), i.e.,

$$q \propto \Delta P^{1/2} = K \ \Delta P^{1/2} \quad \text{for turbulent flow} \tag{2.17}$$

Figure 1.6 showed a typical flow rate-pressure drop curve for turbulent flow through a fluid restriction. As shown, the nonlinear relationship can be linearized over relatively narrow ranges of working pressure, to give a relationship of the form

$$\frac{q'}{\Delta P'} \approx K \approx \frac{1}{R} \tag{2.17a}$$

where q' is the change in flow rate due to the change in pressure drop $\Delta P'$; K, the flow conductance of the restriction, is the slope of the $q - \Delta P$ curve at the point considered; $R = 1/K$ is the resistance of the restrictor at the point considered.

Equation 2.17(a) is similar to the laminar flow expression 2.16(a), except that changes in q and ΔP are related, rather than the absolute values of q and ΔP. Bearing in mind this latter condition, one sees that Eq. 2.17(a) is also analogous to Ohm's law. Contrary to the laminar flow case, both K and R vary with the mean operating pressure drop considered, even for fixed restrictors. For variable restrictors such as valves, it is usual to present the flow rate-pressure drop characteristics as a family of curves such as is shown in Fig. 2.7. In any particular analysis, the mean working pressure and the degree of opening of the valve have to be specified before any attempt is made to designate its resistance or conductance. It should be kept in mind that methods of nonlinear analysis exist where the true nonlinear characteristics of flow restrictions can be handled.

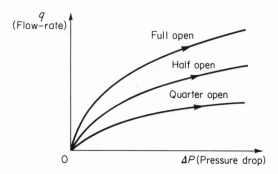

Fig. 2.7   Typical valve characteristic.

2.5.4 Flow Into Chambers

If air flows into a chamber of fixed volume, the pressure in the chamber must rise, and vice versa. This concept is directly analogous to electrical capacitance, in which current flowing into a capacitor causes an increase of potential within it. Except for the ideal isothermal case, the inflow rate-pressure change relationship for a chamber is nonlinear, due to heating effects during compression. However, for small changes of pressure about a mean value in the chamber,

$$\frac{Q}{P'} = C \tag{2.18}$$

where $Q = \int_{t_1}^{t_2} q \, dt$, the volume of air at the mean pressure and temperature which has entered the chamber in time $(t_2 - t_1)$; P' is the pressure change in the chamber due to Q; C (a constant) is called the capacitance of the chamber, ft^5/lb. Equation 2.18 can be expressed

$$P' = \frac{1}{C} \int q \, dt \tag{2.18a}$$

which is analogous to Faraday's law (Eq. 2.7), while Eq. 2.18 is analogous to Eq. 2.7(b). Again, pressure and flow rate correspond to voltage and current respectively.

The concept of capacitance is not meaningful for incompressible fluids flowing into a fixed chamber. In reality, a liquid at high pressures is governed by the bulk modulus relationship,

$$\Delta P = \beta \frac{\Delta V}{V} \tag{2.19}$$

where β is the bulk modulus of the fluid, lb/ft²; V is the volume of fluid considered; ΔV is the change in volume due to ΔP. Equation 2.19 can be written

$$\Delta V = \frac{V}{\beta} \Delta P$$

Introducing a time increment Δt,

$$\frac{\Delta V}{\Delta t} = \frac{V}{\beta} \frac{\Delta P}{\Delta t}$$

Taking the limit as $\Delta t \to 0$,

$$\frac{dV}{dt} = \frac{V}{\beta} \frac{dP}{dt} = q$$

as

$$\frac{dV}{dt} = q \quad \text{(the flow rate)}$$

Hence

$$dP = \frac{\beta}{V} q \, dt$$

and

$$\int dP = P' = \frac{\beta}{V} \int q \, dt = \frac{1}{C} \int q \, dt \tag{2.19a}$$

where $C = V/\beta$ is the fluid capacitance of the fluid volume V.

Equation 2.19(a) is directly analogous to Faraday's law of capacitance and can be expressed

$$\frac{Q}{P'} = C \tag{2.19b}$$

where $Q = \int q \, dt$, which is identical with Eq. 2.18 and analogous to Eq. 2.7(b).

2.5.5 Liquid Level in Tanks

Control of the level of liquid in tanks is a common requirement. Such tanks can be regarded as a special fluid pressure situation. Figure 2.8 shows a simple tank, with one inflow rate q_i and one outflow rate q_o. For continuity,

$$q = q_i - q_o \tag{2.20}$$

where q is the net flow rate into the tank itself.

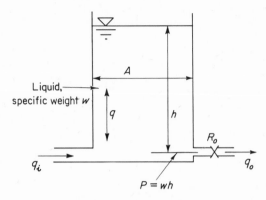

Fig. 2.8 A simple tank.

For steady state operation (equilibrium), head h is constant, yielding

$$q = 0 \qquad \text{and} \qquad q_i = q_o$$

Flow through the discharge valve is due to pressure drop across the valve. Using the linear notion of Eq. 2.17(a)

$$q_o' = \frac{\Delta P'}{R_o} \tag{2.21}$$

where R_o is the resistance of the valve.

It is more common to talk of the head in a tank, than of the pressure. The pressure upstream of the discharge valve is related to the head in the tank by

$$P = wh \tag{2.22}$$

where w is the specific weight of the liquid in the tank, lb/ft³. Hence Eq. 2.21 can be written

$$q_o' = \frac{wh'}{R_o} = \frac{h'}{R_o/w} = \frac{h'}{R_{o1}} \tag{2.21a}$$

where $R_{o1} = R_o/w$ is the resistance of the valve in units compatible with expressing pressure as head.

If the net flow rate into the tank, $q = q_i - q_o$, is finite, then the head is changing according to the continuity expression

$$q = A\dot{h} = A\,Dh = A\,\frac{dh}{dt} \tag{2.22}$$

where A is the cross-sectional area of the tank; $\dot{h}$ is the velocity of the head level.

Hence

$$dh = \frac{1}{A} q \, dt$$

and

$$h' = \frac{1}{A} \int_{t_1}^{t_2} q \, dt \tag{2.22a}$$

where h' is the change in head due to flow rate q over time $(t_2 - t_1)$.

Equation 2.22(a) is obviously analogous to Eqs. 2.18(a) and 2.19(a), and hence to Faraday's law. In this case, head corresponds to pressure and hence to voltage, while the capacitance of the tank is simply its area of cross-section.

It should be appreciated that tank systems can be modeled in terms of pressure rather than head, in which case they are treated in the same manner as other fluid pressure systems.

2.5.6 Some Additional Fluid Pressure Elements

Some additional elements which are in common use in fluid pressure control components will be introduced, so that little further explanation of them is required in the text.

Linear flow — displacement valves

Many valves, piston and seated types, are designed so that the flow rate through them changes linearly with the degree of opening of the valve. Figures 2.9(a) and (b) show a piston and a seated valve. For each to be linear, they must satisfy the condition

$$q \propto x, \qquad q = k_v x \tag{2.23}$$

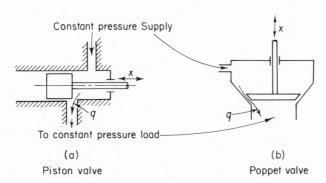

(a)
Piston valve   (b)
Poppet valve

Fig. 2.9 Linear flow — displacement valves, $q' = k_v x'$.

where x is the axial displacement of the valve from its initial position; k_v is the volumetric flow coefficient of the valve, in.³/min per in. of opening, or in.²/min.

In systems analysis situations, Eq. 2.23 is more commonly used in the form

$$q' = k_v x' \tag{2.23a}$$

where q' and x' are the changes in q and x respectively from initial steady state values.

Equation 2.23 essentially applies to constant pressure drop situations. For a particular valve, a family of flow rate-displacement curves for various constant pressure drops can be obtained, from which a value of k_v for given mean operating conditions of ΔP and x can be taken.

Valves which have approximately linear relationships between flow rate, displacement, and pressure drop can also be obtained.

For this case

$$q' = k_p x' \tag{2.24}$$

where k_p is a pressure flow coefficient of the valve, psi/in. of opening, or lb/in.³. As for k_v, the family of flow rate-pressure-constant flow rate curves for the valve would be required to enable correct selection of k_p for a particular situation.

Spring bellows and spring diaphragms

Figures 2.10(a) and (b) illustrate the spring bellows and the spring-supported diaphragm, which are both commonly used to convert pressure to displacement or force. For both configurations:

1. If the end plate is fixed or if the spring strength is negligible, then a change in internal pressure p' generates an additional force on the end plate

$$F' = p'A \quad \text{lb} \tag{2.25}$$

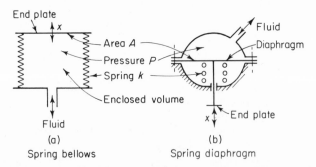

(a) Spring bellows   (b) Spring diaphragm

Fig. 2.10   Fluid pressure—displacement or pressure-force devices.

2. If the end plate is free to move axially under the action of internal pressure,

$$x' = \frac{F'}{k} = \frac{p'A}{k} \quad \text{in.} \tag{2.26}$$

It will be shown in examples in Chapter 3 that both the bellows and the diaphragm chamber can exhibit capacity effects on incoming pressure changes.

Flapper nozzles

The flapper nozzle, Fig. 2.11, is a very fast and sensitive device for relating a displacement input to a pressure output. The nozzle is supplied with a fluid (commonly air) from a constant pressure supply. The input

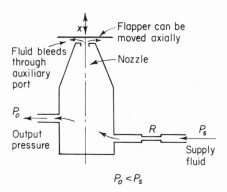

Fig. 2.11   A flapper-nozzle unit, $P'_o = Kx'$.

pressure line includes a restriction which provides a resistance R to flow into the nozzle. The nozzle has a discharge port with a corresponding discharge pressure line. The nozzle also has an additional discharge port, discharging directly to waste. A flat strip, known as the flapper, is adjacent to the port and can be moved axially relative to it. If the flapper covers the port, then fluid can discharge only through the main discharge port. For this condition, the pressure in the nozzle and in the discharge line assumes a certain value. If the flapper is moved away from the auxiliary discharge port, fluid can escape through this port and the pressure in the nozzle will drop. The farther the flapper is moved away from the nozzle, the easier it is for fluid to escape from the nozzle, and the lower the nozzle pressure will be. In this manner, the pressure in the nozzle and in the main discharge line is dependent on the position of the flapper. Flapper nozzles are easily designed to have the linear relationship

$$P_o = Kx \qquad \text{or} \qquad \frac{P_o}{x} = K \qquad \text{or} \qquad \frac{P'_o}{x'} = K \qquad (2.27)$$

where K is the gain constant of the unit, psi/in.

A typical flapper nozzle unit in a pneumatic controller would have physical specifications of the order:

$P_s = 20$ psi; volume of nozzle $= 0.01$ in.^{3}; range of $x = 0.008$ in.; linear range of $P_o = 3$–15 psi; gain $K = 1500$ psi/in.

Flapper nozzles are also used with high-pressure gas systems and with oil hydraulic systems. The flapper nozzle is essentially an amplifying transducer, which accepts a small displacement signal as its input and generates a relatively large pressure signal as its output. The flapper nozzle unit is usually too small to perform any work with its output pressure. To overcome this, the unit commonly discharges into a 1:1 relay, which generates the same output pressure P_o but supplies a flow rate of fluid at this pressure which is large enough to provide the necessary power.

2.6 SUMMARY OF DIRECT ANALOGIES

A direct analogy between the basic dynamic natures of simple electrical, thermal, and fluid pressure situations can be formed using the concepts of potential and potential drop, flow rate, resistance, and capacitance.

The concept of linear resistance is that potential drop across a resistor causes flow rate through it according to Ohm's law:

$$\Delta E = qR \qquad \text{or} \qquad R = \frac{\Delta E}{q}$$

If there is no potential drop across a resistor, there is no flow through it.

The concept of capacitance is that flow into a capacitor causes potential rise within it according to Faraday's law:

$$E' = \frac{1}{C} \int_{t_1}^{t_2} q \, dt$$

while for a total flow of Q into the capacitor,

$$E' = \frac{Q}{C}$$

If there is no flow into a capacitor, there is no change of potential within it.

Using these two conceptions, Table 2.1 can be compiled. The most common dimensions are used in each case.

TABLE 2.1: *Analogies between Electrical, Thermal, and Fluid Pressure Actions*

	Type of system			
Dimension	Electrical	Thermal	Fluid pressure	Liquid level
Flow quantity $Q = qt$	coulomb	BTU	in.^{3}	ft^3
Flow rate q	coulomb/sec (amp)	BTU/min	in.^{3}/min	ft^3/sec
Potential E	volt	°F	lb/in.^{2}	ft (head)
Resistance $R = \dfrac{\Delta E}{q}$	volt/amp (ohm)	°F min/BTU	lb min/in.^{5}	sec/ft^2
Capacitance $C = \dfrac{Q}{E}$,	coulomb/volt (farad)	BTU/°F	in.^{5}/lb	ft^2

Note that the product $R \cdot C$ has units of time, this being the origin of the "time constants" which appear in control theory.

The analogy between electrical and thermal phenomena is good, thermal resistance being the reverse of thermal conductivity. The thermal capacity of a body is the product of its specific heat and weight.

The analogy between electrical and fluid pressure phenomena is less accurate, due to the inherent nonlinearity of most fluid pressure relationships. However, for conditions of small changes in the fluid pressure variables about mean values, the relationships can be linearized and the analogies used.

Mechanical systems containing inertia, damping, and elasticity are less obviously analogous to electrical laws, and are best solved by direct use of Newton's law and its derivatives. However, electrical analogies of mechanical systems can be drawn. One technique is to use displacement for quantity $Q = q\, dt$, the viscous friction coefficient for resistance, elasticity for capacitance (energy storage), and inertia for inductance (because it controls the acceleration).

Analogies are useful, particularly for students new to engineering systems analysis. However, an engineer should aim to work directly in the quantities and units of the particular system whose dynamic performance he is investigating.

2.7 SUMMARY

The basic laws describing the dynamic behavior of electrical, heat transfer, mechanical, and fluid power systems have been reviewed and discussed. The technique of linearizing nonlinear fluid pressure relationships has been introduced, and its limitations discussed. The relationships presented are the basic building blocks for linear dynamic analysis, and will be used extensively in the present text.

3   *The derivation of system*
*equations**

3.1 INTRODUCTION

An engineering system exists when two or more engineering elements are interconnected in such a manner that the behavior of each element affects the behavior of the other elements and that each element contributes to the behavior of the system as a whole. For example, the mass and spring of Fig. 3.1 each affect the other and both contribute to the behavior of the spring-mass unit, which is an engineering system.

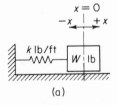

(a)

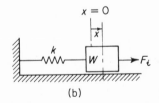

(b)

Fig. 3.1

*Transfer functions; mathematical models.

40

Each component of an automatic control system [the load, the controller, the regulator, the detector, etc. (Fig. 1.2)] is itself an engineering system comprising a set of interconnected basic engineering elements (springs, masses, resistors, capacitors, etc.). Thus an automatic control system consists of a set of interconnected engineering systems, which together provide the desired control.

The first requirement for control systems analysis and synthesis is that one must be able to describe accurately each physical component of a system by a mathematical function. These mathematical models of the components must then be combined to produce the mathematical model of the control system. The manner in which a component or system behaves when going from one equilibrium condition to another equilibrium condition is as important as the magnitude of the change achieved. Hence, where appropriate, the mathematical models must be dynamic functions of time. In its simplest form, a mathematical model may be a constant, whereas in general it will be a differential equation with time as the independent variable. It is usual to express the model (be it an engineering system or a complete control system) in the form

$$\frac{\text{system output (response)}}{\text{system input (disturbance or forcing function)}} = \frac{\theta_o(t)}{\theta_i(t)} = f(D) \qquad (3.1)$$

where θ_i is the variable to which the input $\theta_i(t)$ is applied; θ_o is the variable whose response $\theta_o(t)$ to the input $\theta_i(t)$ is being sought; $f(D)$ is the function of operator $D = d/dt$ which relates $\theta_i(t)$ to $\theta_o(t)$; $\theta_i(t)$ and $\theta_o(t)$ are usually written as simply θ_i and θ_o respectively; $\theta_o/\theta_i = f(D)$ is called the **transfer function** of the system, and is simply a convenient and descriptive operational method of expressing the differential equation which relates the response variable θ_o to the input variable θ_i.

For example, consider the spring-restrained mass shown in Fig. 3.1. The mass is initially lying in equilibrium on a smooth (frictionless) table, so that the spring is exerting zero force on it (Fig. 3.1a). To reveal the nature of the spring-mass system, a disturbing force F_i is applied to the mass and the resulting displacement $x(t)$ of the mass from its initial position $x = 0$ is studied (Fig. 3.1b). In the position shown, the spring force F_s acts in the opposite direction to F_i. Applying Newton's law, $\sum F = ma = (W/g) \cdot D^2 x$,

$$F_i - F_s = \frac{W}{g} D^2 x$$

Using $F_s = kx$ for the spring force,

$$\frac{W}{g} D^2 x + kx = F_i$$

is the differential equation relating response x to input F_i, which can be solved to give response $x(t)$. The equation can be rearranged to

$$\left(\frac{W}{g} D^2 + k\right)x = F_i$$

or

$$\frac{x}{F_i} = \frac{1}{(W/g)\,D^2 + k} = \frac{1/k}{(W/gk)\,D^2 + 1} \tag{3.2}$$

which is the transfer function of the system.

This example illustrates the important fact that the transfer function of a linear system is completely independent of the magnitude and nature of the input disturbance. F_i was an unspecified force. In deriving a transfer function, it is necessary only to select an appropriate variable as the input disturbance, without defining the size or nature of the disturbance. It will be demonstrated in later examples that the transfer function is also completely independent of any initial values of the system variables. The $f(D)$ side of a transfer function contains only system constants plus the operator D, which represents time.

When deriving the transfer function of a physical system one must

(a) select an appropriate system variable as the response variable θ_o;
(b) select an appropriate system variable as the input variable θ_i.

It is convenient, though not necessary, to

(c) consider the system to be in equilibrium (this includes a steady-state operating condition) at the instant $t = 0$ when the arbitrary input disturbance is introduced; this means that all of the system variables are in equilibrium at $t = 0$, and that all of their time derivatives are zero;
(d) arbitrarily choose the value of all system variables as zero at $t = 0$, the instant the input is introduced. Hence changes in the system variables are related during formation of a transfer function, rather than their absolute values. This means that all initial values of the variables are neglected. This simplification is valid, as demonstrated in later examples, as the initial values do not affect the form of a system's transfer function.

Use of conditions (c) and (d) eliminates the need to apply initial conditions to the equations used to form a transfer function, and allows algebraic manipulation of the operator D. The manipulations necessary to the formation of a transfer function are simplified, without altering the final form. The conditions were observed in the example of Fig. 3.1: the mass was in equilibrium, and the only system variables, x and F_s and F_i, were zero when the disturbance was introduced at time $t = 0$.

With simple engineering systems, the variables which are most suitable for use as the response and the input are usually obvious. For complex systems or for complete automatic control systems, a choice often exists in the selection of the input and response variables. With a control system, the response variable is the variable which is being controlled. Input disturbances usually can be introduced at one of several points in a control system. The two most useful input points for analysis purposes are:

(a) At the desired value of the controlled variable. That is, consider a change in θ_i, the desired value, and relate to it dynamically the corresponding change in θ_o, the actual value of the controlled variable, as it seeks to attain the new desired value condition. A typical system block diagram for this situation would be as shown in Fig. 3.2(a). For this case, the transfer function $\theta_o/\theta_i = f(D)$ is required.

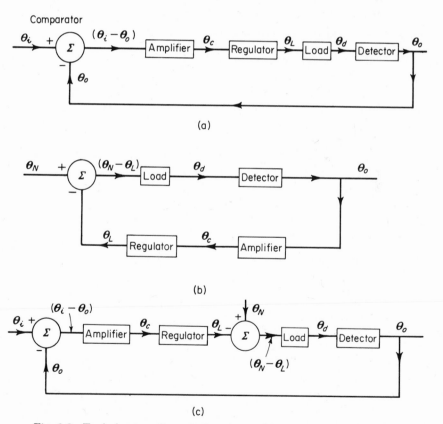

(a)

(b)

(c)

Fig. 3.2 Typical automatic control system, subjected to: (a) a disturbance θ_i' at the desired value, θ_i; (b) a disturbance θ_N at the load; (c) disturbances at both desired value and load.

(b) At the load or process being controlled. That is, consider an external disturbance θ_N at the load being controlled, and relate to it the corresponding dynamic change (i.e., the response) of the controlled variable as the system seeks to regain equilibrium. A typical system block diagram for this situation would be as shown in Fig. 3.2(b), in which case the transfer function $\theta_o/\theta_N = f_L(D)$ is required.

Both locations of the input disturbance can be illustrated in the general system diagram of Fig. 3.2(c). For case (a) — the disturbance to the desired value — the load disturbance θ_N is zero and its summing sign can be eliminated to give Fig. 3.2(a). For case (b) — the disturbance at the load — the desired value is unchanged and its summing sign can be eliminated and the diagram rearranged to yield Fig. 3.2(b).

Where possible, it is normal practice to present a transfer function in the form of dimensionless factors $(1 + T\,D)$, where T is a parametric constant, e.g.,

$$\frac{\theta_o}{\theta_i} = f(D) = \frac{K}{1 + T_1\,D}, \quad \text{or} \quad \frac{K(1 + T_1\,D)}{(1 + T_2\,D)(1 + T_3\,D)}, \quad \text{etc.}$$

Dimensional compatability must be maintained. Operator $D = d/dt$ has units sec^{-1}, and hence the dimensions of T must be seconds to ensure that the product $T\,D$ is dimensionless. T constants of this form are known as **time constants,** and a transfer function in such a factored form is said to be in time constant form. The numerator constant K associated with a transfer function in the time constant form is referred to as the **system gain constant.** The system gain constant equals the static (steady-state or equilibrium) relationship between the response and input variables in the sense that

$$\left(\frac{\theta_o}{\theta_i}\right)_{\text{steady-state}} = K \quad \text{(system gain constant)} \tag{3.3}$$

This relationship is clearly illustrated or obtained by substituting 0 for D in a transfer function, i.e., for

$$\frac{\theta_o}{\theta_i} = \frac{K(1 + T_1\,D)}{1 + T_2\,D}$$

$D = 0$ yields

$$\frac{\theta_o}{\theta_i} = \frac{K(1 + 0)}{1 + 0} = K$$

Use of $D = 0$ simply indicates an equilibrium relationship, as all time derivatives of θ_o and θ_i will be zero for equilibrium.

For example, Eq. 3.2 can be written

$$\frac{x}{F_i} = \frac{K}{1 + T\,D}$$

where T, the time constant, is equal to W/gk sec and K, the system gain constant, is equal to $1/k$ in./lb, for the spring-mass system of Fig. 3.1.

Two methods for deriving a transfer function will be demonstrated in the following work. The methods are:

(1) The direct combination of the elementary simultaneous equations associated with a physical setup.
(2) The use of block diagram algebra to first produce the signal flow diagram of a physical setup, and then to obtain the required transfer function.

A variety of examples will be used to illustrate the dynamic similarity between physically different components and systems.

3.2 THE SIMULTANEOUS EQUATION METHOD

The simple well-established relationships for a component or system can be written down as simultaneous equations and combined to give the required relationship. In combining the basic equations, one should seek to eliminate all variables other than the two variables chosen as input and response, and to relate these last two variables in a function of time (D) and the equation constants. The following worked-out examples demonstrate the method. A primed symbol (i.e., q_o', F', etc.) denotes a change in the variable from its equilibrium value.

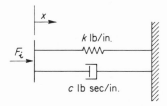

Fig. 3.3

Example 3.1: Derive the transfer function describing the light damped-spring component shown in Fig. 3.3, with applied force F_i as the input disturbance and displacement x of the light (weightless) end member as response.

Assumed: The system is in equilibrium at the instant $t = 0$ when F_i is applied, i.e., $x = 0$, $Dx = 0$, $D^2x = 0$, $F_s = 0$, $F_f = 0$ at $t = 0$, where F_s and F_f are the spring and viscous damper forces respectively.

Known: After F_i is applied,

$$F_s = kx \tag{1}$$

$$F_f = c\dot{x} = c\, Dx \tag{2}$$

$$F_{\text{net}} = m\ddot{x} = m\, D^2x \quad \text{(Newton)} \tag{3}$$

Solution: Net force acting is $F_i - F_s - F_f = F_i - kx - c\, Dx$.
As mass is negligible, $m\, D^2x = 0$ and $F_i - kx - c\, Dx = 0$, i.e., $F_i = (k + c\, D)x$:

$$\therefore \frac{x}{F_i} = \frac{1}{k + c\, D} = \frac{1/k}{1 + (c/k)\, D} = \frac{1/k}{1 + T\, D}$$

where $T = c/k$ sec.

Note that the above transfer function can be converted to an ordinary differential equation by crossmultiplication:

$$(1 + T\, D)x = F_i \frac{1}{k}, \qquad T\, Dx + x = F_i \frac{1}{k}, \qquad T\frac{dx}{dt} + x = F_i \frac{1}{k}$$

Example 3.2: Obtain the transfer function of the simple resistance-capacity electrical network shown in Fig. 3.4, selecting voltages E_1 and E_2 as the input and response respectively, i.e., get $E_2/E_1 = f(D)$.

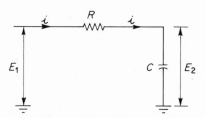

Fig. 3.4

Assumed: The network is in equilibrium at the instant $t = 0$ when a voltage E_1 is applied; E_2 is the voltage across the capacitor C due to E_1.

Known:

$$E_1 - E_2 = iR \quad \text{(Ohm)} \tag{1}$$

$$E_2 = \frac{1}{C}\int i\, dt = \frac{i}{C\, D} \quad \text{(Faraday)} \tag{2}$$

Solution:

$$E_2 = \frac{i}{C\, D} = \frac{(E_1 - E_2)/R}{C\, D}$$

$$E_1 = (RC\, D + 1)E_2$$

$$\frac{E_2}{E_1} = \frac{1}{1 + T\, D}$$

where $T = RC$ sec.

Example 3.3: Find the dynamic relationship between inflow rate q_i and outflow rate q_o for the tank shown in Fig. 3.5; q_{ii} and q_{oi} are the initial inflow and initial outflow rates respectively.

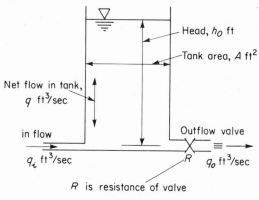

Head, h_0 ft

Tank area, A ft^2

Net flow in tank, q ft^3/sec

in flow

q_i ft^3/sec

Outflow valve

R q_o ft^3/sec

R is resistance of valve

Fig. 3.5

Assumed: The tank is initially in equilibrium, so that $q_{oi} = q_{ii}$ and $q = 0$. Consider the effect on q_o of a change q_i' in the inflow rate.

Known: After q_i' is applied, net flow into or from the tank is

$$q = q_i - q_o = (q_{ii} + q_i') - (q_{oi} + q_o') = q_i' - q_o', \quad \text{as} \quad q_{ii} = q_{oi} \quad (1)$$

$$\frac{q}{A} = D\,(h_{oi} + h_o') = Dh_o' \quad \text{as} \quad h_{oi} \quad \text{is a constant} \quad (2)$$

$$q_o = \frac{h_o}{R} \quad \text{and} \quad q_o' = \frac{h_o'}{R} \quad (3)$$

Solution:

$$q_o' = q_i' - q = q_i' - A\,Dh_o' = q_i' - A\,DR\,q_o'$$

$$\therefore (1 + AR\,D)q_o' = q_i' \quad \text{or} \quad \frac{q_o'}{q_i'} = \frac{1}{1 + TD}$$

where $T = AR$ sec.

Note that for steady-state operation, $q_o' = q_i'$ and $q = 0$. This is apparent if $D = 0$ is substituted in the transfer function, which is equivalent to saying that $Dq_o = dq_o/dt = 0$ as the time after introduction of disturbance q_i' becomes large, and q_o reaches its new final or steady-state value $q_o = q_{oi} + q_o'$.

Example 3.4: The simple gas-filled thermometer shown in Fig. 3.6 has a thermal conductivity of B BTU/sec °F, and is filled with a gas the thermal capacity of which is C BTU/°F. Find the transfer function relating the temperature of the gas in the thermometer (θ_o) to the temperature of the medium in which the thermometer is inserted (θ_i). Neglect the capacity effect of the material of the thermometer casing.

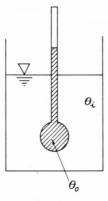

Fig. 3.6

Assumed: The temperature of the medium is in equilibrium when the thermometer is inserted in it. The rate of heat flow from medium to gas is

$$q = B(\theta_i - \theta_o) \quad \text{BTU/sec}$$

The rate of change of gas temperature is

$$D\,\theta_o = \frac{q}{C} \quad \left(\text{i.e., } \theta_o = \frac{1}{C}\int q\,dt\right)$$

Solution:

$$D\,\theta_o = \frac{B(\theta_i - \theta_o)}{C}$$

$$\theta_i = \left(\frac{C}{B}D + 1\right)\theta_o$$

$$\frac{\theta_o}{\theta_i} = \frac{1}{(C/B)D + 1} = \frac{1}{1 + T\,D}$$

where $T = \dfrac{C}{B}$ sec.

Note that as time after insertion becomes large, $\theta_o = \theta_i$ as indicated by putting $D = 0$ in the transfer function. Note also that thermal resistance $= 1/B$ °F sec/BTU.

Example 3.5: Figure 3.7 shows a spool-valve controlled hydraulic ram. The unit is in static equilibrium when the spool valve is in mid-position such that it blocks off flow to or from both ends of the cylinder. If the spool valve is moved to one side of its neutral position, one port is opened to permit flow of high-pressure oil to one end of the cylinder; at the same time the other port is opened to permit

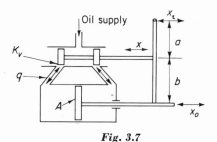

Fig. 3.7

flow from the other end of the cylinder to drain. Thus deflection of the spool valve from neutral position causes movement of the ram. The spool-valve spindle and the ram piston rod are connected to a common lever via pin joints.

Derive the transfer function relating the displacement of the extended end of the lever (x_i) to the resulting movement of the ram (x_o).

Known:

$$q = x \cdot K_v \qquad\qquad (1)$$

$$\frac{q}{A} = \dot{x}_o = D x_o \qquad\qquad (2)$$

Solution: The unit is initially in equilibrium, the spool being centralized so that both ports are blocked and the piston is locked in position. When displacement x_i is introduced at the end of the lever, the lever initially pivots about its lower joint, displacing the spool by an amount $x_1 = x_i \cdot [b/(a + b)]$. Immediately after x_1 becomes finite, oil flows to one side of the ram, causing movement x_o; x_o in turn acts to move the spool an amount $x_2 = x_o \cdot [a/(a + b)]$ (i.e., now consider the lever pivot about its upper joint at x_i). The net movement of the spool is the algebraic sum of x_1 and x_2, which are of opposite sign:

$$x = \left(\frac{b}{a+b}\right) x_i - \left(\frac{a}{a+b}\right) x_o$$

and using Eqs. (1) and (2) to eliminate x and then q,

$$\left[\left(\frac{b}{a+b}\right) x_i - \left(\frac{a}{a+b}\right) x_o\right] \frac{K_v}{A\,D} = x_o$$

which is rearranged to

$$\frac{x_o}{x_i} = \frac{b/a}{1 + [(a + b)/a](A/K_v) D} = \frac{b/a}{1 + T D}$$

where $T = [(a + b)/a] \cdot (A/K_v)$ sec.

Example 3.6: The pneumatic diaphragm valve shown in Fig. 3.8 is used to adjust the rate of flow of liquid to a tank. It is actuated by a pressure signal P_i applied to the end of the capillary tube. An increase in P_i causes pressure in the diaphragm chamber to increase, which acts on the diaphragm to generate a force tending to close the valve against the spring force. When in equilibrium, the pressure force and the spring force are balanced. The valve is a low-pressure device and operates over a small pressure range (say, 5–15 lb/in.²).

Neglecting compressibility of the air,* show that the transfer function relating dynamically the flow rate of liquid and the pressure signal at the inlet to the capillary is

$$\frac{q'_o}{P'_i} = \frac{A K_v/k}{1 + T D}$$

where A is the area of the diaphragm; K_v is the flow characteristic of the valve; k is the spring constant; $T = RC$ sec; R is the pneumatic resistance of the capillary; C is the pneumatic capacity of the diaphragm chamber; q'_o is the change in flow rate of liquid through the valve for a change P'_i in the pressure signal.

Assumed: The valve is initially in equilibrium, i.e., steady-state operating condition, such that pressure in the chamber $p = P_i$, and no air is flowing to or from the chamber, i.e., $P_iA = kx_i$ and $Dx = D^2x = 0$. Then a change P'_i is introduced causing air to flow at q_{air} in the capillary.

Known:

$$q_{air} = \frac{P'_i - p'}{R} \quad \text{(Ohm analogy)} \tag{1}$$

$$p' = \frac{1}{C}\int q_{air}\, dt = \frac{q_{air}}{C D} \quad \text{(Faraday analogy)} \tag{2}$$

$$x' = \frac{p'A}{k} \quad \text{(Newton, with mass neglected)} \tag{3}$$

$$q'_o = x'K_v \tag{4}$$

Solution: From (1) and (2),

$$\frac{P'_i - p'}{R} = C\, Dp'$$

and

$$P'_i = p'(1 + RC\, D) = p'(1 + T\, D)$$

where $T = RC$ sec.

*This is justified if P'_i is small and the response of the unit is relatively slow.

Using (3),

$$P_i' = \frac{kx'}{A} (1 + T D)$$

Using (4),

$$P_i' = q_o \frac{k}{K_v A} (1 + T D) \qquad \text{and} \qquad \frac{q_o'}{P_i'} = \frac{K_v A / k}{1 + T D}$$

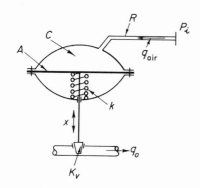

Fig. 3.8

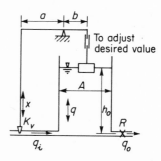

Fig. 3.9

Example 3.7: The head h_o in the tank shown in Fig. 3.9 is controlled to a desired value h_i by the float-operated inlet valve. If the head tends to increase, the valve reduces flow rate to the tank, and vice versa. The turn screw in the float lever mechanism is used to adjust the desired value of head as required.

Derive the transfer function describing the dynamic response of the system, by relating the change in head h_o' for a deliberate change in the desired value setting h_i', i.e., find $h_o'/h_i' = f(D)$.

Known: In initial equilibrium, $q_o = q_i$ and $q = 0$; $h_o = h_i$. After h_i' is introduced at time $t = 0$,

Error in float position: $h = h_i - h_o = h_i' - h_o'$ (1)

Regulator valve movement: $x' = h(a/b)$ (2)

Change of inflow rate: $q_i' = x' \cdot K_v$ (3)

Net flow into tank: $q = q_i - q_o = q_i' - q_o'$ (4)

Rate of change of head: $q/A = Dh_o'$ (5)

Change of discharge rate: $q_o' = h_o'/R$ (6)

Solution: From (6), $h_o' = q_o'R$; using (4), $h_o' = (q_i' - q)R$; using (3) and (5), $h_o' = (x'K_v - A Dh_o')R$; using (2)

$$h_o' = \left(h \frac{a}{b} K_v - A Dh_o' \right) R$$

Using (1)

$$h'_o = \left[\frac{a}{b} K_v (h'_i - h'_o) - A Dh'_o\right]R$$

$$\left(1 + \frac{a}{b} K_v R + A DR\right)h'_o = \frac{a}{b} K_v Rh'_i$$

and

$$\frac{h'_o}{h'_i} = \frac{(a/b)K_v R}{1 + (a/b)K_v R + AR D} = \frac{(a/b)K_v R/[1 + (a/b)K_v R]}{1 + \{AR/[(a/b)K_v R + 1]\} D} = \frac{K}{1 + T D}$$

where

$$K = \frac{(a/b)K_v R}{1 + (a/b)K_v R} \quad \text{and} \quad T = \frac{AR}{(a/b)K_v R + 1} \text{ sec}$$

Note that as time after the disturbance becomes large and $D = 0$ can be substituted to represent the steady-state condition reached, h'_o does not equal h'_i. This phenomena, known as offset, is a characteristic of the proportional type of control system which is discussed fully in Chapter 9. Offset can be minimized by making $(a/b)K_v R \gg 1$, thus reducing K towards unity.

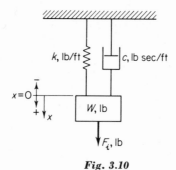

Fig. 3.10

Example 3.8: For the damped spring-mass component shown in Fig. 3.10, derive the dynamic equation in time relating the displacement x of the mass due to the disturbing force $F_i = f(t)$.

Assumed: The component is in equilibrium (steady-state) at the instant that F_i is introduced; x is measured from this equilibrium position.

Known: Initially, $F_{si} = W$, where F_{si} is the initial spring force, lb; W is the weight of the mass, lb.

When F_i is applied, the net force on the mass is $F_i + W - F_s - F_f$, where F_s is the force exerted by the spring at any instant, and F_f is the viscous damping force exerted on the mass at any instant, and

$$F_{\text{net}} = m\ddot{x} = \frac{W}{g} D^2 x \qquad (\text{Newton})$$

Solution: $F_s = F_{si} + kx$ and $F_f = c\dot{x} = c\,Dx$; $F_{\text{net}} = F_i + W - (F_{si} + kx) - c\,Dx = m\ddot{x}$ (Newton); i.e.,

$$F_i - kx - c\,Dx = \frac{W}{g} D^2 x, \qquad \text{as} \qquad W = F_{si} \qquad \text{and} \qquad \ddot{x} = D^2 x$$

$$\left(\frac{W}{g} D^2 + c\,D + k\right)x = F_i$$

and

$$\frac{x}{F_i} = \frac{1}{(W/g)\,D^2 + c\,D + k} = \frac{1/k}{(W/gk)\,D^2 + (c/k)\,D + 1}$$

Note that the condition that all variables are chosen as zero at the instant $t = 0$ when the disturbance is introduced was not used throughout this solution. An initial spring force F_{si} due to the weight of the mass was included. This had no effect on the resulting dynamic equation or transfer function, and could have been eliminated completely from the solution by fully using the condition that only changes in system variables are considered when forming transfer functions, i.e., $W' = 0$, $F'_s = kx$, and $F_{\text{net}} = F_i - F'_s - F_f = W/g\,D^2 x$.

Example 3.9: Derive the dynamic relationship existing between the voltages E_i and E_o for the resistance-capacity circuit shown in Fig. 3.11.

Assumed: The system is in steady-state operating condition when a change E'_i to the input voltage is introduced, i.e., find

$$\frac{E'_o}{E'_i} = f(D)$$

in which $f(D)$ contains only operator D and system constants such as R_1, R_2, C_1, C_2.

Known:

$$E'_i - E' = i_1 R_1 \qquad (\text{Ohm}) \tag{1}$$

$$i_1 = i_2 + i_3 \qquad (\text{Kirchhoff}) \tag{2}$$

$$E' - E'_o = i_2 R_2 \qquad (\text{Ohm}) \tag{3}$$

$$E' = \frac{1}{C_1} \cdot \frac{i_3}{D} \qquad (\text{Faraday}) \tag{4}$$

$$E'_o = \frac{1}{C_2} \cdot \frac{i_2}{D} \qquad (\text{Faraday}) \tag{5}$$

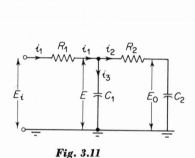

Fig. 3.11

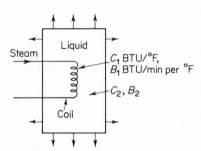

Heat lost to atmosphere, q_o
(ambient temperature remains constant)

Fig. 3.12

Solution: From (1), $E'_i = i_1 R_1 + E'$; using (2), $E'_i = (i_2 + i_3) R_1 + E'$. Using (3) for E', $E'_i = i_2 R_1 + i_3 R_1 + i_2 R_2 + E'_o = i_2 (R_1 + R_2) + i_3 R_1 + E'_o$. Using (4) for i_3 and (5) for i_2,

$$E'_i = E'_o C_2 D (R_1 + R_2) + E' C_1 D R_1 + E'_o$$

Using (3) to eliminate E',

$$E'_i = E'_o C_2 D (R_1 + R_2) + (E'_o + i_2 R_2) C_1 R_1 D + E'_o$$

Using (5) to eliminate i_2,

$$E'_i = E'_o C_2 (R_1 + R_2) D + E'_o R_1 C_1 D + E'_o C_2 D R_2 C_1 R_1 D + E'_o$$

from which

$$E'_i = [(R_1 C_2 + R_2 C_2 + R_1 C_1) D + R_1 C_1 R_2 C_2 D^2 + 1] E'_o$$

and

$$\frac{E'_o}{E'_i} = \frac{1}{T_1 T_2 D^2 + (T_1 + T_2 + T_3) D + 1}$$

where $T_1 = R_1 C_1$, $T_2 = R_2 C_2$, and $T_3 = R_1 C_2$ are time constants.

Note that this transfer function is the operational form of the differential equation

$$T_1 T_2 D^2 E_o + (T_1 + T_2 + T_3) D E_o + E_o = E_i$$

found by cross-multiplication.

Note also that for the steady-state condition (i.e., equilibrium), all time derivatives are zero and $E'_o = E'_i$, which is established by putting $D = 0$ in the transfer function.

Example 3.10: For the thermostatic tank unit shown in Fig. 3.12, it is desired to maintain constant the temperature of the liquid in the tank by passing steam through the immersed coil. The liquid is stirred so that its temperature can be considered uniform and equal to the temperature of the tank itself.

Thermal capacity of the coil pipes is C_1 BTU/°F and the coefficient of heat transfer between pipes and liquid is B_1 BTU/min/°F.

Thermal capacity of the liquid and tank is C_2 BTU/°F, whereas the unit's coefficient of heat transfer to the atmosphere is B_2 BTU/min/°F.

Obtain the dynamic relationship

$$\frac{T'_o}{q'_i} = f(D)$$

where T_o is the actual temperature of liquid and tank, °F; q_i is the rate of heat supplied to the tank system from the steam, BTU/min.

Known: For a change q'_i in the heat rate of steam,

Rate of heat absorbed by liquid and tank:

$$q'_T = q'_i - q'_o\,(1) \qquad - q'_p \tag{1}$$

where q'_p = rate of heat absorbed by coil pipes.

Instant temperature of pipe:

$$T'_p = \frac{1}{C_1}\frac{q'_p}{D} \quad \text{(Faraday analogy)} \tag{2}$$

Rate of heat flow from coil to liquid:

$$q'_o + q'_T = B_1\,(T'_p - T'_o) \quad \text{(Ohm analogy: thermal resistance is } 1/B_1) \tag{3}$$

Dynamic temperature of liquid and tank:

$$T'_o = \frac{1}{C_2}\frac{q'_T}{D} \quad \text{(Faraday analogy)} \tag{4}$$

Rate of heat flow from tank to surroundings:

$$q'_o = B_2 T'_o \tag{5}$$

Solution: The five simultaneous equations can be solved to yield $T'_o/q'_i = f(D)$. The priming of symbols will be dropped for convenience. Thus q_T means q'_T, T_o means T'_o, etc.

From (4),

$$q_T = T_o\,C_2\,D \tag{6}$$

From (2),

$$q_P = T_P C_1\,D \tag{7}$$

From (3),

$$T_P = \frac{q_o + q_T}{B_1} + T_o$$

and using (5) and (6) for q_o and q_T,

$$T_P = \frac{B_2 T_o + C_2\,D T_o}{B_1} + T_o = T_o\left(1 + \frac{B_2}{B_1} + \frac{C_2\,D}{B_1}\right) \tag{8}$$

(8) can be used in (7) to give

$$q_P = C_1 \, DT_o\left(1 + \frac{B_2}{B_1} + \frac{C_2 \, D}{B_1}\right) \tag{9}$$

Using (5), (6), and (9) in (1) gives

$$T_o C_2 \, D = q_i - B_2 T_o - C_1 \, DT_o\left(1 + \frac{B_2}{B_1} + \frac{C_2 \, D}{B_1}\right)$$

which contains only q_i and T_o as dependent variables. Then

$$\left\{\frac{C_1 C_a}{B_1} \, D^2 + \left[C_1\left(1 + \frac{B_2}{B_1}\right) + C_2\right] D + B_2\right\} T_o = q_i$$

and

$$\frac{T_o}{q_i} = \frac{1}{(C_1 C_2 / B_1) \, D^2 + \{C_1 \, [1 + (B_2/B_1)] + C_2\} \, D + B_2}$$

$$= \frac{1/B_2}{(C_1 C_2 / B_1 B_2) \, D^2 + [(C_1/B_2) + (C_1/B_1) + (C_2/B_2)] \, D + 1}$$

i.e.,

$$\frac{T_o'}{q_i'} = \frac{1/B_2}{T_1 T_2 \, D^2 + (T_1 + T_2 + T_3) \, D + 1}$$

where $T_1 = C_1/B_1$, $T_2 = C_2/B_2$, and $T_3 = C_1/B_2$ are time constants.

Example 3.11: The head in the tank shown in Fig. 3.13 is to be controlled automatically, using a pneumatic diaphragm valve, of the type analyzed in Example 3.6, to adjust the inflow rate (q_i) to the tank. A pneumatic flapper nozzle, of the

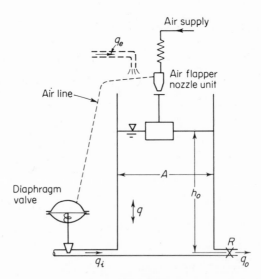

Fig. 3.13

type discussed in Section 2.4, is used to sense the actual value of the head by sensing the float position. The flapper unit generates an output air pressure proportional to the error h'_o between the actual head $(h_o + h'_o)$ and the required equilibrium value of the head h_o, i.e.,

$$\frac{P'_a}{h'_o} = G$$

where G is a constant.

Thus if head tends to increase from its equilibrium (steady-state) operating condition, the air pressure to the regulating valve is increased and acts to close the inlet valve. Thus inflow to the tank will be reduced and the head will decrease toward its required equilibrium value.

Find the transfer function describing the system by relating the change in head h'_o due to an external flow rate q_e directed into the tank as shown, i.e., find

$$\frac{h'_o}{q_e} = f(D)$$

Assumed: The system was in steady-state operating condition at the instant that the external disturbance q_e was introduced, i.e., at time $t = 0$, $q_i = q_o$, and $q = 0$.

Known: For the head sensing unit,

$$\frac{P'_a}{h'_o} = G \tag{1}$$

For the flow regulating unit,

$$\frac{q'_i}{P'_a} = \frac{K_1}{1 + TD} \tag{2}$$

(See Example 3.6 for derivation.)

For the tank process, after q_e is introduced,

$$q = q_e - q'_o - q'_i \tag{3}$$

and

$$q'_o = \frac{h'_o}{R} \tag{4}$$

and

$$h'_o = \frac{q}{A D} \tag{5}$$

Solution (omit prime from symbols for convenience): From (1) and (2),

$$q_i = \frac{h_o\, GK_1}{1 + T D} \tag{6}$$

From (5),

$$q = h_o\, A\, D \tag{7}$$

Substituting (4), (6), and (7) in (3) yields

$$A \, D \, h_o = q_e - \frac{h_o}{R} - \frac{h_o \, GK_1}{1 + T \, D} \quad \text{and} \quad \left(A \, D + \frac{1}{R} + \frac{GK_1}{1 + T \, D} \right) h_o = q_e$$

from which

$$\frac{h'_o}{q_e} = \frac{1}{A \, D + 1/R + GK_1/(1 + T \, D)} = \frac{K \, (1 + T \, D)}{TT_2 \, D^2 + (T_1 + T_2) \, D + 1}$$

where $K = R/(1 + RGK_1)$; $T_2 = AR/(1 + RGK_1) = AK$ sec; $T_1 = T/(1 + RGK_1)$

Note: The significance of the numerator term $(1 + T \, D)$ in the transfer function will be investigated in Chapter 9.

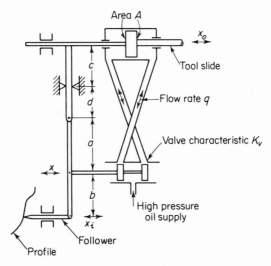

Fig. 3.14

Example 3.12: Figure 3.14 shows the essential elements of a profile-actuated lathe tool slide. With the longitudinal feed set at constant speed and the lateral position of the tool dictated by the position of the profile follower, the work piece is machined to the desired shape.

Describe the primary dynamic characteristics of the device by relating the position of the tool to the position of the profile follower, i.e., find

$$\frac{x_o}{x_i} = f(D)$$

where x_o is the change in cutting tool position resulting from a displacement x_i of the follower.

Assumed: The device is in static equilibrium when the displacement x_i to the profile follower is introduced.

Known: (1) The net displacement x of the spool valve from its equilibrium position, where both ports to the hydraulic cylinder are blocked, is the algebraic sum of two movements:

(a) the movement of the spool (x_1) due to x_i, when the ram and tool are considered locked by the oil in the cylinder;
(b) the movement of the spool (x_2) due to the subsequent motion of the ram and cutting tool, with the profile follower considered locked. It is apparent that these two motions are of opposite direction, i.e.,

$$x = x_1 - x_2 \tag{1}$$

(2) The velocity of the ram and cutting tool is given by

$$\dot{x}_o = \frac{xk_v}{A} \qquad \left(\text{i.e.,} \qquad q = xk_v, \qquad v_o = \dot{x}_o = \frac{q}{A}\right) \tag{2}$$

(3) The position of the cutting tool is the time integral of its velocity, i.e.,

$$x_o = \frac{xk_v}{A\,D} \tag{3}$$

Solution: Initial movement of spool, due to x_i
(i.e., ram and tool locked):

$$x_1 = x_i \cdot \frac{a}{a+b} \tag{4}$$

Secondary movement of spool, due to x_o
(i.e., follower locked):

$$x_2 = x_o \cdot \frac{d}{c} \cdot \frac{b}{a+b} \tag{5}$$

Net movement of the spool:

$$x = x_1 - x_2 = x_i \frac{a}{a+b} - x_o \frac{bd}{c(a+b)} \tag{6}$$

Using (6) in (3),

$$x_o = \frac{k_v}{A\,D}\left(\frac{a}{a+b}\cdot x_i - \frac{bd}{c(a+b)}\cdot x_o\right)$$

$$x_o\left[1 + \frac{k_v}{A\,D}\cdot\frac{bd}{c(a+b)}\right] = \frac{k_v}{A\,D}\cdot\frac{a}{a+b}\,x_i$$

$$\frac{x_o}{x_i} = \frac{(k_v/A\,D)[a/(a+b)]}{1 + (k_v/A\,D)[bd/c(a+b)]} = \frac{ac/bd}{[c(a+b)/bd](A/k_v)\,D + 1} = \frac{K}{1 + T\,D}$$

where $K = ac/bd$; $T = [c(a+b)/bd]\cdot(A/k_v)$.

3.3 THE BLOCK DIAGRAM METHOD

3.3.1 The Nature and Formation of Mathematical Block Diagrams

To obtain by analysis the transfer function of a component or system, a clear picture of the physical setup is essential. A block diagram is a convenient link between the physical setup and its mathematical model. The concept of a block diagram is illustrated in Fig. 3.2, which shows signal flow diagrams representing a typical automatic control system. The diagram consists of a series of boxes representing the system components, and summing units representing addition or subtraction of signals. If each component can be represented by its mathematical model, by placing that model in the appropriate box the diagram becomes the mathematical block diagram representing the system. The function contained in a box relates the signal flowing into the box (its input) to the signal flowing from it (its response or output), and hence is the transfer function of the particular component represented.

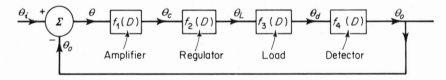

Fig. 3.15

Figure 3.15 shows the mathematical block diagram corresponding to Fig. 3.2(a), where θ_i and θ_o are signals representing the desired value and actual value respectively of the controlled variable; $\theta_c/\theta = f_1(D)$ is the

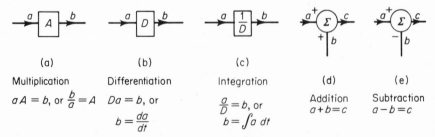

Fig. 3.16   Basic block diagram operations.

transfer function of the amplifier unit; $\theta_L/\theta_c = f_2(D)$ is the transfer function of the regulator unit; $\theta_d/\theta_L = f_3(D)$ is the transfer function of the load or process being controlled; $\theta_o/\theta_d = f_4(D)$ is the transfer function of the detector unit.

Any component can be reduced to its basic mathematical elements and represented by a block diagram. The basic operations involved, illustrated in Fig. 3.16, are (a) multiplication, (b) differentiation, (c) integration, (d) addition, (e) subtraction.

As an example, consider the spring-mass component in Fig. 3.1. It is required to relate the disturbing force F_i and the resulting displacement x of the mass. It is apparent that the spring force $F_s = kx$ opposes the initial motion of the mass. Thus the net force on the mass, $F_i - F_s$, can be represented by Fig. 3.17(a). Next, it is recognized that mass acceleration can be obtained by using Newton's law,

$$F_\text{net} = \frac{W}{g}\ddot{x} = \frac{W}{g}D^2x$$

which can be added to the diagram to give Fig. 3.17(b). Then, if acceleration D^2x is integrated twice, displacement x is obtained (Fig. 3.17c). Using

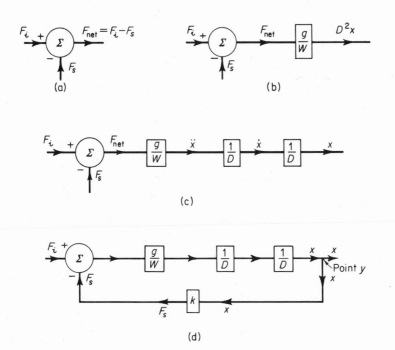

Fig. 3.17 Forming the block diagram of the spring-mass system of Fig. 3.1.

the knowledge that spring force $F_s = kx$, the diagram can be completed to give Fig. 3.17(d), which is the block diagram representing the spring-mass system. It is shown in the most common form, having the input signal fed in at the left and the response projecting from the right. All other signals are connected in a continuous cause-effect sequence. It is essential to realize that the branching of the diagram at point Y is not a division of the signal x. The signal flowing back in the feedback loop toward box k is x, the same as that projecting from the righthand side of the diagram. Signals are divided only where a summing sign is present. In the early stages of formation of the diagram, it was not necessary to know from where the signal F_s would come. It was only necessary that the presence of F_s be appreciated.

3.3.2 Transfer Function from a Block Diagram

A block diagram is in effect a schematic representation of the dynamic simultaneous equations applying to a physical setup. This fact is apparent if the block diagram of the previous spring-mass component is compared with the corresponding example worked out in Section 3.2.

Subject to the two conditions of (1) initial equilibrium, and (2) the relating of changes in the variables, discussed in Section 3.1, a block diagram can be reduced mechanically to yield the transfer function of the setup represented. The algebraic relationships required to perform the reduction are as follows. Proofs are included where necessary.

1. Elements in series: Figure 3.18(a) shows three blocks in series. It is apparent that

(a) the output from block A is aA, which becomes the input to block B;
(b) the output from block B is aAB, which becomes the input to block C;
(c) the output from block C is $b = aABC$,

$$\therefore \frac{b}{a} = ABC$$

and elements in series can be combined into a single box containing their product.

2. Negative feedback loop: Figure 3.18(b) shows a negative feedback loop, in which the output b is fed back toward the input summing sign.

Performing the summation yields

$$a - Bb = c \qquad (1)$$

Also,

$$cA = b \qquad (2)$$

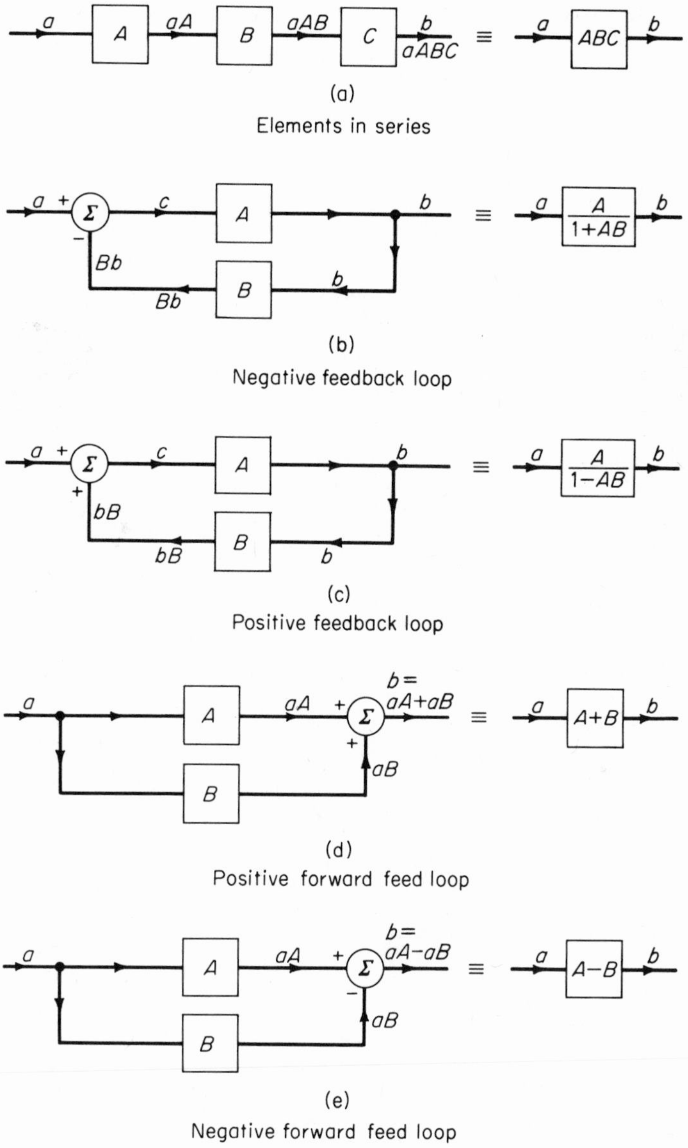

a
A
aA
B
aAB
C
b
aABC
≡
a
ABC
b
(a)
Elements in series
a
+
Σ
c
A
b
−
Bb
Bb
B
b
≡
a
A/(1+AB)
b
(b)
Negative feedback loop
a
+
Σ
c
A
b
+
bB
bB
B
b
≡
a
A/(1−AB)
b
(c)
Positive feedback loop
a
A
aA
+
Σ
b= aA+aB
+
aB
B
≡
a
A+B
b
(d)
Positive forward feed loop
a
A
aA
+
Σ
b= aA−aB
−
aB
B
≡
a
A−B
b
(e)
Negative forward feed loop

Fig. 3.18 Basic procedures for reducing block diagrams.

Substituting $c = b/A$ in (1) yields

$$a = b\left(\frac{1}{A} + B\right)$$

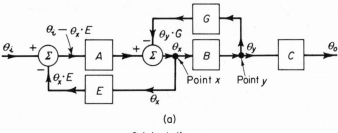

(a)

Original diagram

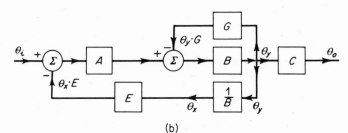

(b)

Shifting lower loop take-off point from x to y

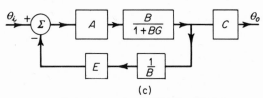

(c)

Reducing upper negative feedback loop

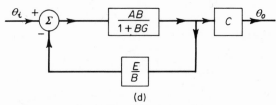

(d)

Combining elements in series

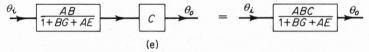

(e)

Reducing lower negative feed back loop, and final reduction

Fig. 3.19 Adjusting and reducing a block diagram to get the transfer function.

from which

$$\frac{b}{a} = \frac{1}{1/A + B} \quad \text{or} \quad \frac{A}{1 + AB}$$

3. Positive feedback loop: Figure 3.18(c) shows a positive feedback loop. Performing the summation yields

$$a + Bb = c$$

From the forward feed,

$$cA = b$$

$$\therefore a + Bb = \frac{b}{A}$$

$$a = b\left(\frac{1}{A} - B\right)$$

$$\frac{b}{a} = \frac{1}{1/A - B} = \frac{A}{1 - AB}$$

4. Positive forward feed loop: Figure 3.18(d) shows a positive forward feed loop. Performing the summation yields

$$aA + aB = b \quad \text{or} \quad b = a(A + B)$$

$$\therefore \frac{b}{a} = A + B$$

5. Negative forward feed loop: Figure 3.18(e) shows a negative forward feed loop. Performing the summation yields

$$aA - aB = b \quad \text{or} \quad b = a(A - B)$$

$$\therefore \frac{b}{a} = A - B$$

To make a block diagram suitable for reduction

Elements in series can be combined by Rule 1 only if there are no summing units or loop takeoff points between them. The loop reduction Rules 2, 3, and 4 can be used only when there are no other summing units or loop takeoff points involved in the section being reduced. It is commonly necessary that loop takeoff points be moved before reduction can commence. The loop positions can be manipulated so long as the diagram is compensated accordingly.

Consider Fig. 3.19(a), which includes two overlapping negative feedback loops. There is no significance in one loop being shown on top of the diagram. Due to the overlapping of the loops, the diagram cannot be reduced while in its present form. If the takeoff point of the lower loop is moved from point x to point y, as shown in Fig. 3.19(b), the upper loop will be completely clear. In effect, the move means that signal θ_y is being fed back in the lower loop instead of the required θ_x. However, $\theta_y = B\theta_x$ and hence, if $1/B$ is added into the lower loop, the original signal is fed into box E and the diagram is equivalent to the original. Then,

(a) the upper negative feedback loop is now clear and can be eliminated using Rule 2 to give Fig. 3.19(c);
(b) the elements in series and clear of loops can be combined to give Fig. 3.19(d);
(c) the negative feedback loop can be eliminated using Rule 2 to give Fig. 3.19(e), from which

$$\frac{\theta_o}{\theta_i} = \frac{ABC}{1 + BG + AE}$$

is the transfer function of the system represented by the original diagram.

Loop takeoff points can be manipulated as required if

(a) the loops are not taken past a summing sign;
(b) the moved loop is compensated to restore the original signal flow in the loop.

3.3.3 Examples of the Formation and Reduction of Block Diagrams

Example 3.13: Use the block diagram method to obtain the transfer function for the spring-mass component of Fig. 3.1, Section 3.1.

The block diagram of the system was shown in Section 3.3.2 to be as illustrated by Fig. 3.20(a). The three blocks in series in the forward feed are clear of summing signs and loop takeoff points, and can be combined to give Fig. 3.20(b). The diagram can be reduced using the negative feedback rule to give Fig. 3.20(c), from which,

$$\frac{x}{F_i} = \frac{1/k}{1 + (W/gk)\,D^2}$$

Note again that the transfer function is simply the operational form of the differential equation found by cross multiplication,

$$\frac{W}{gk}\,D^2x + x = \frac{1}{k}F_i \qquad \text{or} \qquad \frac{W}{g}\,D^2 + kx = F_i$$

Example 3.14: Find, by block diagram methods, the transfer function of the damped spring-mass system of Example 3.8. The block diagram is built up in

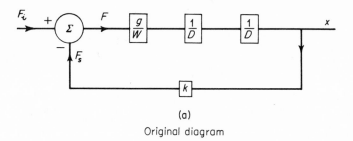

(a)

Original diagram

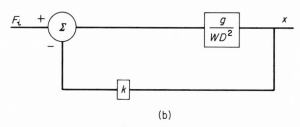

(b)

Combining elements in series

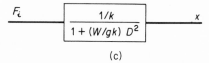

(c)

Reducing negative feedback loop

Fig. 3.20 Getting the transfer function of Example 3.1.

sections by considering the physical phenomena occurring, i.e., the net force acting on the mass can be expressed by Fig. 3.21(a), which means $F_i - F_s - F_f = \Sigma F$. Then,

(a) Figure 3.21(b) expresses Newton's law for the mass,

$$\Sigma F \cdot \frac{g}{W} = \ddot{x} = D^2 x \quad \text{or} \quad \Sigma F = \frac{W}{g} \ddot{x}$$

(b) Figure 3.21(c) reduces $\ddot{x}$ to $\dot{x}$ by integration;

(c) Figure 3.21(d) reduces $\dot{x}$ to x, the desired response variable, by integration.

Displacement x is the required response and hence the forward feed of the diagram is complete. It remains now to complete the loops required to generate the unconnected signals F_s and F_f. It is known that $F_s = kx$ and $F_f = c\dot{x} = c\,Dx$. The signals $\dot{x}$ and x in the forward feed can be tapped and fed back through c and k respectively to generate F_f and F_s respectively. The complete system block dia-

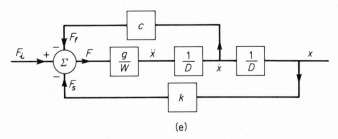

(a)   (b)

(c)   (d)

Progressively building the block diagram

(e)

Completed block diagram

Fig. 3.21 Deriving the transfer function for the damped-spring-mass (Fig. 3.10). (*Continued on p. 69.*)

gram, formed from the component blocks, is shown in Fig. 3.21(e). It can be seen that the block diagram is simply a diagramatic representation of the equations written for simultaneous solution in Example 3.8.

The block diagram can be reduced systematically to obtain the transfer function $x/F_i = f(D)$:

Step 1 (Fig. 3.21f) the first two blocks in the forward feed are clear of loops and summing signs and can be combined;
Step 2 (Fig. 3.21g) the upper negative feedback loop can be eliminated;
Step 3 (Fig. 3.21h) the two blocks in the forward feed can be combined;
Step 4 (Fig. 3.21i) the negative feedback loop can be eliminated;

hence the transfer function is

$$\frac{x}{F_i} = \frac{1/k}{(W/gk)\,D^2 + (c/k)\,D + 1}$$

Example 3.15: Construct the block diagram representing the oil hydraulic

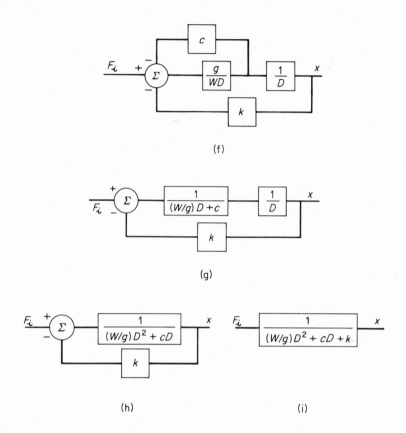

(f)

(g)

(h)   (i)

Progressively reducing the block diagram to get the transfer function

Fig. 3.21   (*Cont.*)

positioning device of Example 3.5. Reduce the diagram to obtain the system transfer function $x_o/x_i = f(D)$.

Solution requires recognition that the opening of the spool valve is affected by both input displacement x_i and the consequent output displacement x_o, according to the relationship shown in Fig. 3.22(a), which means

$$x = \frac{x_i b}{a + b} - \frac{x_o a}{a + b}$$

Then,

(a) recognize that $xk_v = q$, to yield Fig. 3.22(b);
(b) recognize that $q(1/A) = \dot{x}_o$, to yield Fig. 3.22(c);
(c) recognize that $\dot{x}_o/D = x_o$, to yield Fig. 3.22(d).

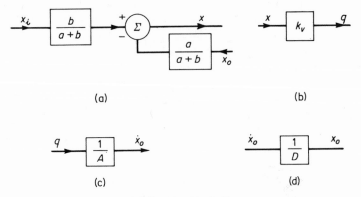

(a)   (b)

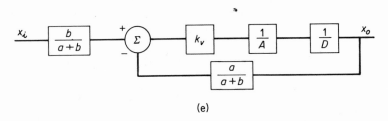

(c)   (d)

Building the block diagram

(e)

The completed block diagram

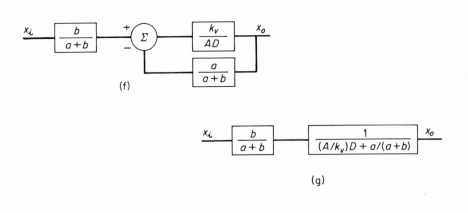

(f)

(g)

(h)

Fig. 3.22 Deriving the transfer function for the spool-ram of Fig. 3.7.

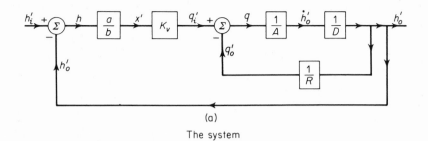

(a)

The system

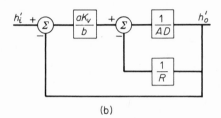

(b)

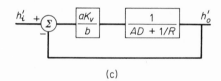

(c)

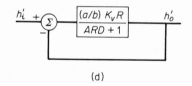

(d)

(e)

Reducing the block diagram

Fig. 3.23 Getting the transfer function of the tank system of Fig. 3.9.

Thus the forward feed is completed, with the desired input x_i at the left and the response x_o at the right. The feedback loop can be completed to give Fig. 3.22(e).

The diagram can be reduced by

(d) combining the 3 blocks in series in the forward feed, to give Fig. 3.22(f);
(e) eliminating the negative feedback loop, yielding Fig. 3.22(g);
(f) combining the remaining 2 blocks in series, yielding Fig. 3.22(h).

Thus the transfer function is

$$\frac{x_o}{x_i} = \frac{b/a}{[(a+b)/a](A/k_v)\,D+1} = \frac{b/a}{1+T\,D}$$

where $T = (a+b)A/ak_v$.

Example 3.16: The tank level control system of Example 3.7 can be represented by the block diagram of Fig. 3.23, which is built up systematically by considering each action after a change h_i' in the desired value of head is introduced. The diagram can be reduced progressively by

(a) combining the blocks in series after each summing unit, to give Fig. 3.23(b);
(b) eliminating the inner negative feedback loop, which is clear of any interacting loops, yielding Fig. 3.23(c);
(c) combining the two blocks in series, yielding Fig. 3.23(d);
(d) reducing the remaining negative feedback loop, noting that the loop contains unity, yielding Fig. 3.23(e).

Then,

$$\frac{h_o'}{h_i'} = \frac{K}{1+T\,D}$$

where

$$K = \frac{(a/b)\cdot k_v R}{1+(a/b)\cdot k_v R} \quad \text{and} \quad T = \frac{AR}{1+(a/b)\cdot k_v R}$$

Example 3.17: Solve Example 3.10 by the block diagram method, i.e., get

$$\frac{T_o'}{q_i'} = f(D)$$

where T_o is the temperature of the liquid in the tank; q_i is the rate of heat supplied to the system.

All symbols are defined in Fig. 3.12.

(a) Recognize that q_i' and T_o' are the input and response which should appear at the left and righthand extremes respectively of the diagram.

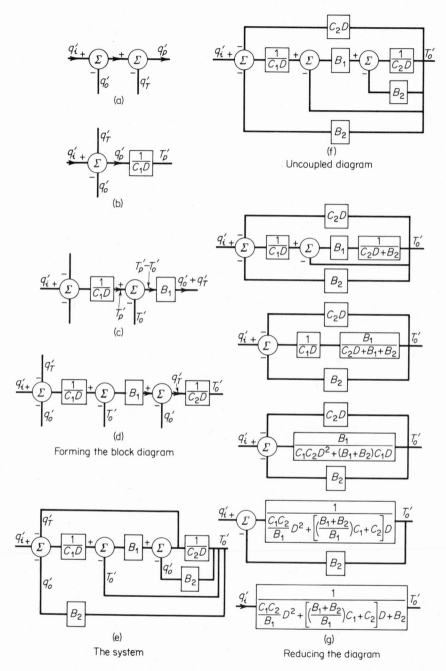

(a)

(b)

(c)

(d)

Forming the block diagram

(e)

The system

(f)

Uncoupled diagram

(g)

Reducing the diagram

Fig. 3.24 Forming and reducing the block diagram of the thermostatic tank system shown on Fig. 3.12.

(b) Recognize that the first part of the system to absorb a portion of the heat input is the coil pipe, and then form the heat dispersion relationship,

$$q'_P = q'_i - q'_o - q'_T$$

which is shown in Fig. 3.24(a).

(c) Recognize that the temperature rise in the coil pipe is given by

$$T'_P = \frac{q'_P}{C_1 D}$$

and hence extend the diagram as shown in Fig. 3.24(b).

(d) Recognize that the rate of heat flowing from the coil pipe to the liquid is

$$q'_o + q'_T = B_1 (T'_P - T'_o)$$

and extend the diagram to Fig. 3.24(c).

(e) Subtract q'_o to get q'_T, and recognize that

$$T'_o = \frac{q'_T}{C_2 D}$$

to give Fig. 3.24(d), which completes the forward feed part of the diagram, as T'_o is the desired output. It remains now to complete the loops.

(f) (Figure 3.24e). The output T'_o can be fed back directly to the middle summing sign. The relationship

$$q'_o = B_2 T'_o$$

is used to complete feedbacks to both outer summing signs. The signal q'_T existing after the third summing sign can be fed back directly to complete the upper feedback to the lefthand summing sign. Figure 3.24(e) is the block diagram of the system.

Figure 3.24(e) cannot be reduced due to the coupling (interaction) effect of the upper loop, which extends past the second and third summing units. To render the diagram suitable for reduction, move the takeoff point of the upper loop past the $1/C_2 D$ block, and add $C_2 D$ in the upper loop for compensation, as shown in Fig. 3.24(f).

The uncoupled diagram can now be reduced progressively, as shown in Fig. 3.24(g), to yield the transfer function

$$\frac{T'_o}{q'_i} = \frac{1/B_2}{T_1 T_2 D^2 + (T_1 + T_2 + T_3) D + 1}$$

where $T_1 = C_1/B_1$, $T_2 = C_2/B_2$, and $T_3 = C_1/B_2$ are time constants.

Example 3.18: Construct the block diagram for the level control system of Example 3.11, and reduce it to get the transfer function

$$\frac{h'_o}{q_e} = f(D)$$

where h'_o is the change of head in the tank produced by the externally applied flow rate q_e.

(a) Recognize that q_e and h'_o are the input and response required at the left and righthand sides of the block diagram respectively.

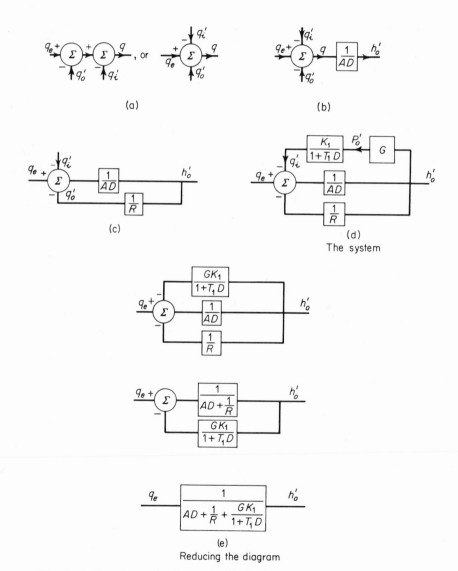

Fig. 3.25 Forming and reducing the block diagram of the tank system of Fig. 3.13.

(b) Recognize that the net flow into the tank after q_e is introduced is

$$q = q_e - q_i' - q_o'$$

as shown in Fig. 3.25(a).

(c) Extend the diagram by recognizing that $q/A\,D = h_o'$ (Fig. 3.25b), to complete the forward feed.

(d) Recognize that $h_o'/R = q_o'$ to allow completion of the lower feedback loop, Fig. 3.25(c).

(e) Recognize that $h_o'\,G = P_a$ and that $P_a'[K_1/(1 + T\,D)] = q_i'$, to complete the upper feedback loop, yielding the system block diagram of Fig. 3.25(d).

The block diagram is uncoupled and can be immediately reduced, as shown in Fig. 3.25(e), to yield the transfer function

$$\frac{h_o'}{q_e} = \frac{K(1 + T\,D)}{TT_2\,D^2 + (T_1 + T_2)\,D + 1}$$

where $K = R/(1 + RK_1G)$ is the system gain constant; $T_1 = T/(1 + RGK_1)$ and $T_2 = AR/(1 + RGK_1)$ are time constants.

Note that Fig. 3.25(d) is a schematic representation of the simultaneous equations written for Example 3.11.

3.4 THE LAPLACE TRANSFORM APPROACH

It has been common practice in automatic control theory to write dynamic equations and transfer functions in terms of the Laplace transform operator, P or s, rather than in terms of the operator $D = d/dt$. The Laplace Transform Method will be examined in Chapter 4, which deals with system response. At present, it is sufficient to accept that the Laplace transform operator and operator D are directly interchangeable in the dynamic equations and transfer functions being used, i.e.,

$$\frac{\theta_o}{\theta_i} = \frac{K}{1 + T\,P} \qquad \text{or} \qquad \frac{K}{1 + T\,s} \qquad \text{corresponds to} \qquad \frac{\theta_o}{\theta_i} = \frac{K}{1 + T\,D}$$

This note is included so that the student can recognize the operator D as P or s in texts written in the Laplace transform domain.

3.5 SUMMARY

The transfer function of a component or system is the dynamic equation relating its response to an input disturbance, written in operational form so that the operator $D = d/dt$ represents time. In general, a transfer function represents a differential equation with time as the independent variable. The transfer function of a component or system describes its nature, and is in fact its mathematical model. For a linear system, it is independent of the magnitude or type of disturbance experienced. Different physical situations can have the same form of transfer function, and are dynamically analogous: they have the same dynamic nature.

A transfer function can be obtained by imagining an arbitrary disturbance to a convenient variable and writing the simple equations governing the subsequent action. The equations can be combined simultaneously to relate the disturbance (i.e. the input) to the variable selected as the response. All variables other than the selected input and response should be eliminated so that input and response are related only in terms of system constants and the operator D.

A physical situation can be represented by a block diagram formed by progressively "thinking out" the system. Formation of a block diagram gives valuable insight into the nature of a system. A mathematical block diagram is in fact a graphic representation of the basic equations governing the action of a physical system. Subject to conditions (a) and (b) below, a mathematical block diagram can be reduced mechanically to yield the transfer function of a system.

A transfer function is normally formed within the following conditions:

(a) The component or system is in equilibrium when the disturbing input is applied to it.
(b) Changes in the system variables from their equilibrium values are related, rather than the absolute values.

These conditions simplify mathematical manipulations by eliminating the need to apply initial conditions to the variables and by permitting operator D to be manipulated algebraically.

When one has become familiar with the techniques for forming transfer functions, it is usual

(a) to omit the symbols used to describe "a change in" the system variables, i.e., to omit the prime symbol used in the present text (thus, p, x, h, etc. are used to designate p', x', h', etc.);
(b) to omit the arrowheads from block diagrams (the direction of signal flow is readily discerned from the positions of the summing signs).

3.6 EXAMPLES WITH OUTLINE SOLUTIONS

Example 3.19: The tank shown in Fig. 3.26 is in steady-state operating condition ($q_o = q_i$, $q = o$) when a hose pipe having flow rate q_e ft³/sec is directed into it. Inflow rate q_i remains constant. Establish the relationship between q_e and change in head h'.

Known:

(1) After q_e is applied, head h will increase and q_o will increase by q_o'. Equilibrium

will be restored when $q_i + q_e = q_o$ and h attains its new (larger) equilibrium value $(h + h')$.

(2) $q'_o = h'/R$ (linear approximation to Ohm's law).

(3) $q = q'_i + q_e - q'_o = q_e - q'_o$ as $q'_i = 0$.

(4) $q/A = \dot{h}'$; $h' = \dot{h}'/D$.

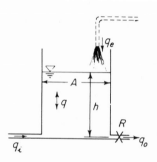

Fig. 3.26

Solution: $h' = q/A\,D$ (from 4) $= (q_e - q'_o)/A\,D$ (from 3) $= (q_e - h'/R)/A\,D$ (from 2), i.e.,

$$\left(A\,D + \frac{1}{R}\right)h' = q_e$$

$$\frac{h'}{q_e} = \frac{R}{1 + T\,D}$$

where $T = AR$ sec.

Note that the new steady-state value of head achieved in time is found by putting $D = 0$ in the transfer function to give $h'_f = q_e R$ and $h_f = h + h'_f = h + q_e R$. Also, the transfer function obtained is of the same form as that obtained for Example 3.3, in which the disturbance was introduced to inflow rate q_i.

Example 3.20: It is required to ascertain the dynamic response characteristics of the two-tank process shown in Fig. 3.27(a).

Solution:

(1) Select the outflow rate q_o as the system response, and the inflow rate q_i as the variable to be disturbed (i.e., as the input).

(2) Assume the system is initially in steady-state operating condition such that the head in each tank is constant (though not equal) and $q_o = q_i = q$, i.e., $q_1 = q_2 = 0$. Introduce an arbitrary change q'_1 to q_i.

(3) Using the block diagram method, the diagram of Fig. 3.27(b) is built up.

(4) The block diagram has three interacting loops, requiring movement of loop takeoff points prior to reduction.

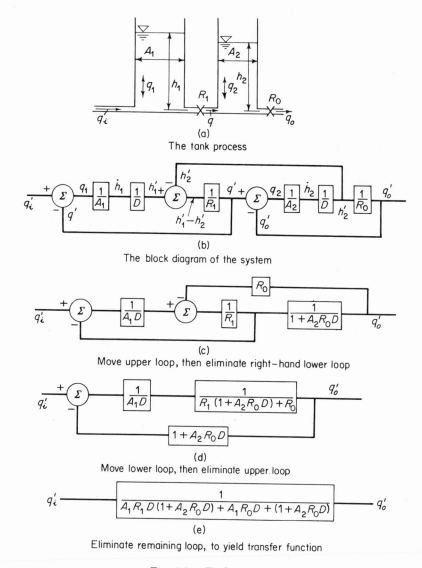

(a)

The tank process

(b)

The block diagram of the system

(c)

Move upper loop, then eliminate right–hand lower loop

(d)

Move lower loop, then eliminate upper loop

(e)

Eliminate remaining loop, to yield transfer function

Fig. 3.27 Tank process.

(a) Move upper loop takeoff point past $1/R_o$ and add R_o into the upper loop. Then combine $1/A_2$, $1/D$, and $1/R_o$ and eliminate the lower righthand loop to give Fig. 3.27(c).

(b) Move the remaining lower loop takeoff point to q_o, putting $1 + A_2 R_o D$ in the lower loop as compensation. Eliminate the upper negative feedback loop, giving Fig. 3.27(d).

(c) Combine the terms in the forward feed loop, and eliminate the remaining negative feedback loop, yielding Fig. 3.27(e).

(5) The required transfer function is

$$\frac{q_o'}{q_i'} = \frac{1}{1 + (T_1 + T_2 + T_3)\,D + T_1 T_2\,D^2}$$

where $T_1 = A_1 R_1$ sec; $T_2 = A_2 R_o$ sec; $T_3 = A_1 R_o$ sec.

Notes:

(1) It is inferred that q_o' and q_i' mean changes in q_o and q_i, respectively.
(2) The presence of three time constants reflects the interaction present in the second-order system;
(3) The new equilibrium condition found by putting $D = 0$ in the transfer function is $q_o' = q_i'$, or $q_o + q_o' = q_i + q_i'$.
(4) The transfer function $q_o'/q_i' = f(D)$ is readily adjusted to give the transfer function $h_2'/q_i' = f_1(D)$ by putting h_2'/R_o for q_o', to yield

$$\frac{h_2'}{q_i'} = \frac{R_o}{1 + (T_1 + T_2 + T_3)\,D + T_1 T_2\,D^2}$$

Example 3.21: A mechanical vibration damper is represented in Fig. 3.28. It is desired to establish the dynamic relationship between an external force F applied to mass M_1, as shown, and the position of the mass.

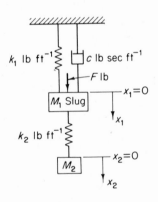

Fig. 3.28

Solution: Consider the system to be at rest in equilibrium when the disturbing force F is applied. As mass M_1 moves downward, its motion is opposed by the spring force $F_{s1}' = k_1 x_1$, the damping force $F_d = c\dot{x}$, and the force exerted on it by spring k_2, i.e.,

$$F - F_{s1}' - F_d - F_{s2}' = M_1\,\ddot{x}_1 \quad \text{(Newton's law)}$$

$$F - k_1 x_1 - c\,Dx_1 - k_2(x_1 - x_2) = M_1 \cdot D^2 x_1$$

$$\text{or} \quad M_1\,D^2 x_1 + c\,Dx_1 + k_1 x_1 + k_2 x_1 - k_2 x_2 = F \tag{1}$$

Mass M_2 experiences the spring force $F'_{s2} = k_2(x_1 - x_2)$

$$\therefore k_2(x_1 - x_2) = M_2 D^2 x_2 \quad \text{(Newton's law)} \tag{2}$$

From (2),

$$x_2 = \frac{k_2 x_1}{M_2 D^2 + k_2}$$

and substituting this in (1) gives

$$\left(M_1 D^2 + c D + k_1 + k_2 - \frac{k_2^2}{M_2 D^2 + k_2}\right) x_1 = F$$

$$\therefore \frac{x_1}{F} = \frac{M_2 D^2 + k_2}{M_1 M_2 D^4 + c M_2 D^3 + (k_2 M_1 + k_1 M_2 + k_2 M_2) D^2 + c k_2 D + k_1 k_2}$$

Note that this system can be represented by two second-order differential equations [(1) and (2) above] or by one fourth-order differential equation (the transfer function).

Example 3.22: Figure 3.29(a) shows a powered relay with which an input force applied to the spool valve F_i causes a displacement of the ram x_o.

Derive the transfer function relating F_i and x_o.

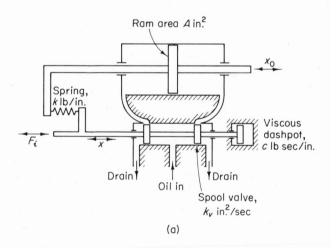

(a)

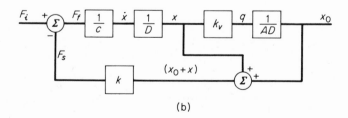

(b)

Fig. 3.29

Assumed: The system is in steady-state condition, with the spool valve in neutral position, i.e., $x = \dot{x} = \ddot{x} = 0$; $\dot{x}_o = \ddot{x}_o = 0$. Introduce an arbitrary force F_i to the spool spindle, and study the resulting change in ram position x_o. Note that x_o then represents the change from the original steady-state position of the ram.

Known: The net force experienced by the valve stem is $F_i - F_s - F_f$, where F_s is the change in spring force due to the application of F_i; F_f is the viscous damping force. If the mass of the valve is considered negligible,

$$F_i - F_s - F_f = 0 \qquad \text{(Newton)} \tag{1}$$

also $\qquad\qquad F_f = c\dot{x} = c\,Dx \quad \text{(viscous friction)} \tag{2}$

$$xk_v = q \qquad \text{(valve flow rate)} \tag{3}$$

$$q/A\,D = x_o \qquad \text{(displacement of ram due to } q\text{)} \tag{4}$$

$$k(x_o + x) = F_s \qquad (x + x_o \text{ is total extension of spring)} \tag{5}$$

Solution: Using (5) and (2) in (1) yields

$$F_i - k(x + x_o) - c\,Dx = 0 \qquad \text{and} \qquad F_i = kx_o - x(k + c\,D)$$

Using (3) and (4),

$$x = \frac{A\,Dx_o}{k_v}$$

and

$$F_i = kx_o + \frac{A\,Dx_o}{k_v}(k + c\,D) = \left(\frac{Ac}{k_v}D^2 + \frac{Ak}{k_v}D + k\right)x_o$$

and

$$\frac{x_o}{F_i} = \frac{1/k}{(Ac/kk_v)\,D^2 + (A/k_v)\,D + 1} = \frac{1/k}{T_1 T_2\,D^2 + T_1\,D + 1}$$

where $T_1 = A/k_v$ sec; $T_2 = c/k$ sec.

Note: The block diagram for the system is shown in Fig. 3.29(b). The diagram can be reduced to yield the transfer function.

Example 3.23: Figure 3.30(a) shows a low-pressure air servomechanism. The unit is operated by a remote pressure signal P_i which acts through the bellows and spring to operate the spool valve. Air from the spool valve actuates the power cylinder and load. The movement of the load causes a feedback displacement via the cam and crank, which acts to restore the spool valve to its neutral position. Thus, a particular input pressure signal P_i results in a particular position of the mass being achieved.

It is required to establish the primary dynamic characteristics of the servomechanism by relating dynamically the input pressure P_i and the resulting load displacement x_o.

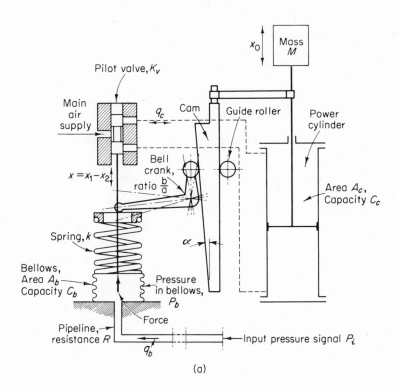

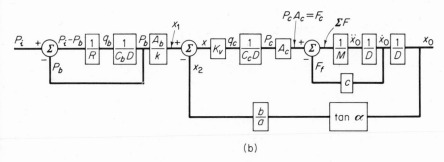

Fig. 3.30 A low-pressure air servomechanism. (a) Diagrammatic arrangement of position-control unit and power cylinder. (b) System block diagram.

Simplifying Assumptions: Neglect compressibility of the air on the grounds that only small pressure changes are likely to occur. Assume that the resistance of the input pressure line, the capacity of the bellows, and the capacity of the cylinder chamber are all constant. Assume that the friction in the power cylinder and load can be lumped together and is viscous, so that frictional resistance $\propto$ velocity of load.

Then, the following simultaneous equations can be written by progressively considering the result of a change in pressure P_i:

Flow rate of air to bellows: $\dfrac{P_i - P_b}{R} = q_b$ (Ohm analogy) $\hspace{2em}$ (1)

Pressure change in bellows: $P_b = \dfrac{q_b}{C_b\,D}$ (Faraday analogy) $\hspace{2em}$ (2)

Initial displacement of spool valve: $\dfrac{P_b A_b}{k} = x_1$ $\hspace{2em}$ (3)

Displacement of spool valve (x_2 is feedback displacement): $x_1 - x_2 = x$ $\hspace{0.5em}$ (4)

Flow rate of air to cylinder: $xK_v = q_c$ $\hspace{2em}$ (5)

Pressure change in cylinder: $P_c = \dfrac{q_c}{C_c\,D}$ (Faraday analogy) $\hspace{2em}$ (6)

$P_c A_c - F_f = M\ddot{x}_o = M\,D^2 x_o$ (Newton: F_f is friction force) $\hspace{2em}$ (7)

$\dfrac{M\,D^2 x_o}{M\,D} = Dx_o = \dot{x}_o$ $\hspace{2em}$ (8)

Viscous friction: $\dot{x}_o c = F_f$ $\hspace{2em}$ (9)

$\dfrac{Dx_o}{D} = x_o$ $\hspace{2em}$ (10)

Feedback movement of spool valve, through cam and bell crank: $x_2 = x_o \tan\alpha \cdot \dfrac{b}{a}$ $\hspace{2em}$ (11)

These equations can be used to get the transfer function

$$\frac{x_o}{P_i} = \frac{aA_b/b \tan\alpha\;k}{(1 + RC_b\,D)[(M/G)\,D^3 + (c/G)\,D^2 + 1]}$$

where $G = A_c K_v\,b \tan\alpha/a\,C_c$

Alternatively, the system block diagram can be progressively formed to obtain Fig. 3.30(b), which can be reduced to yield the transfer function.

PROBLEMS

3.1 Reduce the block diagrams of Fig. 3.31 to find the relationships θ_o/θ_i:

$\textbf{Answer: }$ (a) $\dfrac{AB}{1 - A + ABC}$; (b) $\dfrac{A(1 + B)}{1 + A}$;

(c) $\dfrac{AB(1 + EC)}{1 + EC + AC}$; (d) $\dfrac{ABCE + EG + BEFG}{(1 + BF)\,(1 + EGH)}$.

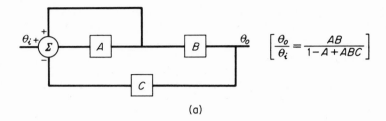

$$\left[\frac{\theta_o}{\theta_i} = \frac{AB}{1 - A + ABC} \right]$$

(a)

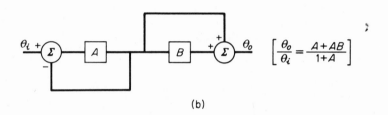

$$\left[\frac{\theta_o}{\theta_i} = \frac{A + AB}{1 + A} \right]$$

(b)

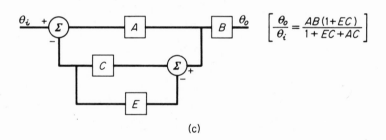

$$\left[\frac{\theta_o}{\theta_i} = \frac{AB(1 + EC)}{1 + EC + AC} \right]$$

(c)

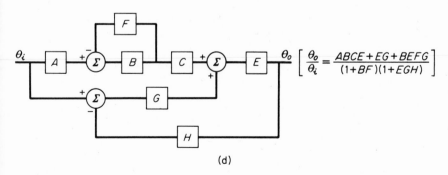

$$\left[\frac{\theta_o}{\theta_i} = \frac{ABCE + EG + BEFG}{(1 + BF)(1 + EGH)} \right]$$

(d)

Fig. 3.31

3.2 Figure 3.32 shows an automobile power steering unit. The valve block is integral with the wheel steering rod. Find the transfer function describing the primary dynamic characteristics of the unit.

Answer: $x_o/\theta_i = G/1 + T\,D$, where $T = A/k_v$ sec, and G is the gain relating θ_i and x_o.

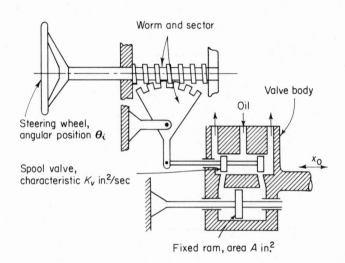

Fig. 3.32

3.3 The thermal process shown in Fig. 3.33 consists of a container of thermal capacity $C_1 = 10$ BTU °F^{-1}, in which a load of thermal capacity $C_2 = 30$ BTU °F^{-1} is to be maintained at a temperature of θ_o °F. This is achieved by passing hot gases over the container at the required rate of q BTU min^{-1}. Forty per

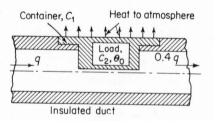

Fig. 3.33

cent of the heat in the gases passes directly into the atmosphere, 60 per cent passing into the container. In addition, the container loses heat directly to the atmosphere at the rate of $L = 300$ BTU min^{-1} per °F temperature of the container. Thermal conductivity between container and load is $K = 180$ BTU min^{-1} °F^{-1}.

Derive the process transfer function θ_o/q, and evaluate the process time constants.

Answer: $\dfrac{\theta_o}{q} = \dfrac{0.6/L}{T_1 T_2 D^2 + (T_1 + T_2 + T_3) D + 1} = \dfrac{0.002}{0.0056\, D^2 + 0.3D + 1};$

$$T_1 = \frac{C_1}{L} = \frac{1}{30} \text{ min}; \quad T_2 = \frac{C_2}{K} = \frac{1}{6} \text{ min}; \quad T_3 = \frac{C_2}{L} = \frac{1}{10} \text{ min}.$$

3.4 Derive the transfer function relating the applied torque and the angular position of the driven mass, for the rotating system shown in Fig. 3.34.

Answer: $\dfrac{\theta_o}{L_i} = \dfrac{1/k}{(I/k)\, D^2 + (c/k)\, D + 1}.$

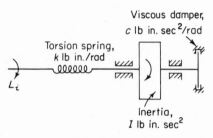

Fig. 3.34

3.5 Figure 3.35 shows an open ended U-tube containing water. Derive the transfer function relating the response head of the liquid column (h ft) and a pressure

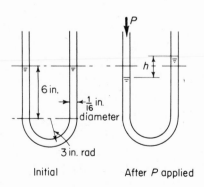

Fig. 3.35

applied to one leg of the tube P. Assume laminar motion of the water in the tube, for which

$$\Delta P = \frac{32\mu\, L\, h}{wd}$$

gives pressure loss due to fluid friction, where $\mu = 1 \times 10^{-5}$ lb sec ft^{-2} is viscosity of water; $\omega = 62.4$ lb/ft^3 is specific weight of water; L is length of liquid column; d is tube inner diameter.

Answer: $\dfrac{h}{P} = \dfrac{0.008}{1 + 0.17D + 0.0277D^2}.$

3.6 The two-tank process shown in Fig. 3.36 is controlled automatically by controlling the head in one of the tanks. The head is sensed by a float which is connected through a lever to an air flapper nozzle unit. The pressure signal gener-

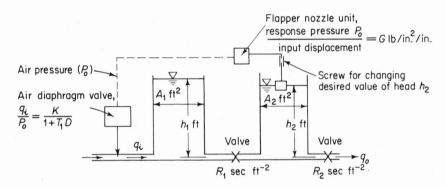

Fig. 3.36

ated at the flapper nozzle unit actuates the diaphragm valve which controls the inflow rate to the system. It is required to establish the dynamic nature of the system by relating the head h_2 in the float tank and the desired value of the head h_i.

Answer: $\dfrac{h_2}{h_1} = \dfrac{K_1}{K_2\, D^3 + K_3\, D^2 + K_4\, D + 1}$

where $\quad K_1 = \dfrac{R_2\, GK}{1 + R_2GK};\qquad K_2 = \dfrac{T_1 T_2 T_4}{1 + R_2GK};$

$$K_3 = \frac{T_1 T_2 + T_1 T_3 + T_1 T_4 + T_2 T_4}{1 + R_2GK};$$

$$K_4 = \frac{T_1 + T_2 + T_3 + T_4}{1 + R_2GK};$$

$$T_2 = A_1 R_1;\qquad T_3 = A_1 R_2;\qquad T_4 = A_2 R_2.$$

4 *The response characteristics of components and systems*

4.1 INTRODUCTION

An automatic control system is required to respond to a variety of disturbances in such a manner that the controlled variable corresponds satisfactorily to the desired value of that variable. The actual behavior of a component or system can be assessed by studying its dynamic response $[\theta_o(t)$ to defined input disturbances $[\theta_i(t)]$ which are introduced deliberately. Three common types of input disturbances, introduced in Chapter 1, are shown in Fig. 4.1. Each is readily defined mathematically and can be generated experimentally if required.

The response function $\theta_o(t)$ can be obtained by solving the differential equation governing a particular physical case. It should be kept in mind that a transfer function is this equation in an operational form. For example,

$$\frac{\theta_o}{\theta_i} = \frac{K}{K_1 D^2 + K_2 D + 1}$$

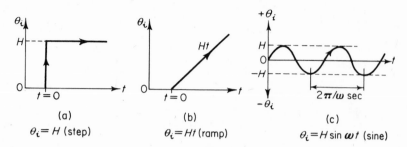

Fig. 4.1   Some common forcing functions, used as inputs.

(where K, K_1, and K_2 represent constant parameters and $D = d/dt$) can be cross-multiplied to yield

$$K_1 D^2\theta_o + K_2 D\theta_o + \theta_o = K\theta_i \quad \text{or} \quad K_1\frac{d^2\theta_o}{dt^2} + K_2\frac{d\theta_o}{dt} + \theta_o = K\theta_i$$

which is an ordinary linear differential equation in time, known as the **system equation.** If a particular input $\theta_i(t)$ is substituted into the equation, a solution can be obtained for the response $\theta_o(t)$. Whereas solutions involving initial conditions of the system variables θ_i and θ_o are readily made (see Appendix A), it is the common practice in control engineering to consider changes only in these variables from initial steady-state values, as discussed in Chapter 3. This useful and simplifying concept will be used in this chapter. Thus θ_o should be interpreted as the change in the response variable following a forcing function θ_i applied to the input variable at time $t = 0$.

Response of a system to specified forcing functions will be found using three methods:

(1) classical solution of the system equation,
(2) Laplace transform solution of the system equation,
(3) analogue computer solution of the system equation.

In addition, use of the analogue computer to simulate a real system will be discussed.

Because of their basic importance to the understanding of system dynamics, simple first- and second-order systems will be examined in detail.

4.2   CLASSICAL SOLUTION OF SYSTEM EQUATIONS

4.2.1   Introduction

The classification of ordinary linear differential equations is given in Appendix A.

Briefly, a solution obtained by the classical method contains two distinct components:

(1) **The particular solution** θ_{o1}, a solution of the same form as the input disturbance* (i.e., step, ramp, sinusoid, etc.) which satisfies the full system equation. This part of the full solution of the system equation persists in time as long as the input disturbance persists. The particular solution is often apparent from inspection of the system equation and input disturbance. Table 4.1 shows the general forms of the solution for step, ramp, and sinusoidal inputs; a and b are arbitrary constants which must be evaluated for each particular situation being analyzed.

TABLE 4.1: *Particular Solution Forms for Step, Ramp, and Sinusoidal Inputs*

Input or forcing function		Form of particular solution[a]	
$\theta_i = H$	(step)	$\theta_{o1} = a$	(step form)
$\theta_i = Ht$	(ramp)	$\theta_{o1} = at + b$	(ramp form)
$\theta_i = H \sin \omega t$	(sine)	$\theta_{o1} = a \cos \omega t + b \sin \omega t$	(sine form)

[a]Exceptions exist which require use of other forms of θ_{o1}.

(2) **The complementary solution** θ_{o2} which is the solution of the **homogeneous equation** obtained by substituting $\theta_i = 0$ in the system equation. For example, the homogeneous equation for the previous example is

$$K_1 D^2\theta_o + K_2 D\theta_o + \theta_o = 0$$

which can be put into an operational form known as the **characteristic equation** of the system,

$$K_1 D^2\theta_o + K_2 D + 1 = 0$$

by dividing throughout by θ_o.

The characteristic equation of a system is aptly named, as it is a characteristic of the system only, being independent of forcing functions (inputs). It is readily seen that the denominator of a system's transfer function, equated to zero, becomes its characteristic equation.

In general, an nth-order system equation has a characteristic equation

$$K_1 D^n + K_2 D^{n-1} + K_3 D^{n-2} + \ldots + K_n D + 1 = 0$$

*See, however, the footnote to Table 4.1.

which can be factored into n roots to give

$$(D + \alpha_1)(D + \alpha_2)\ldots(D + \alpha_n) = 0$$

where α_1, α_2, etc. are parameters composed of the equation coefficients K_1, K_2, etc.. The root values $-\alpha$ can be real, imaginary, complex, repeated, or zero. It is often difficult to extract the roots of high-order equations.

Complementary solutions of linear equations are of the form

$$\theta_{o2} = B_1 e^{-\alpha_1 t} + B_2 e^{-\alpha_2 t} + \ldots + B_n e^{-\alpha_n t} = \sum_{1}^{n} (Be^{-\alpha t})$$

where n, the number of factors $B\, e^{-\alpha t}$, is the same as the order of the equation, $-\alpha$ parameters are the root values of the characteristic equation; B coefficients are parameters composed of the system and input constants, and are evaluated by using initial conditions in the full system response function $\theta_o(t)$.

The full solution of the system equation is the sum of the particular solution and the complementary solution

$$\theta_o(t) = \theta_{o1}(t) + \theta_{o2}(t) \tag{4.1}$$

or simply

$$\theta_o = \theta_{o1} + \theta_{o2} \tag{4.1a}$$

4.2.2 The Requirement for Stable Response

Factors of the form $B\, e^{-\alpha t}$ can be of either form shown in Fig. 4.2, depending on the sign of the number α. If α is a positive number, $e^{-\alpha t}$ decays toward zero as time increases. If α is a negative number, $e^{-\alpha t}$ increases continually with time.

If the general solution $\theta_o(t)$ contains even a single factor $B\, e^{kt}$ where k is a positive number, it will continue to increase with time. This tendency

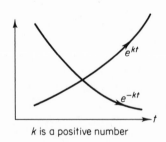

k is a positive number

Fig. 4.2 Forms of $Be^{-\alpha t}$ where B and α are constants.

is characteristic of an unstable component or system. For stability, all factors $B\ e^{-\alpha t}$ in the response solution must decay to zero with time, and hence all values of α must be positive. That is, all roots of a system's characteristic equation must be negative for stable response of the system. It is readily shown (see Chapter 6) that the imaginary parts of a conjugate pair of complex roots $(a \pm jb)$ do not affect stability, as their effects sum to zero. However, the real parts of complex roots must be negative for stable response.

Example 4.1: Investigate the stability condition of the system whose transfer function is

$$\frac{\theta_o}{\theta_i} = \frac{K}{3D^2 + 4D + 1}$$

Solution: The characteristic equation of the system is

$$3D^2 + 4D + 1 = 0$$

or

$$(3D + 1)(D + 1) = 0$$

The root values of the equation are

$$D = -\tfrac{1}{3} \quad \text{and} \quad D = -1$$

Both roots are negative and hence the system is stable, i.e.,

$$\theta_{o2} = B_1 e^{-1/3t} + B_2 e^{-t}$$

where B_1 and B_2 are evaluated by using $\theta_o = 0$ in the full solution of the system equation $3D^2\theta_o + 4D\theta_o + \theta_o = K\theta_i$. See Example 4.5 for a full solution of this type of equation.

Example 4.2: Ascertain the stability condition of the system whose transfer function is

$$\frac{\theta_o}{\theta_i} = \frac{K}{D^2 + 2D + 4}$$

Solution: The characteristic equation is

$$D^2 + 2D + 4 = 0$$

The roots of this equation are

$$D_1 = \frac{-2 + (4 - 16)^{1/2}}{2} = -1 + j \cdot 3^{1/2}$$

$$D_2 = \frac{-2 - (4 - 16)^{1/2}}{2} = -1 - j \cdot 3^{1/2}$$

where in both equations $j = -1^{1/2}$. Both roots have negative real parts (-1) and hence the system is stable in its response to input disturbances.

Example 4.3: A system has the transfer function

$$\frac{\theta_o}{\theta_i} = \frac{K}{D^3 + 3D^2 - 4D - 12}$$

Is the system stable?

Solution: The system characteristic equation is $D^3 + 3D^2 - 4D - 12 = 0$, which can be factored into the form

$$(D + 2)(D - 2)(D + 3) = 0$$

from which the root values are $D_1 = -2$, $D_2 = 2$, $D_3 = -3$.

The positive root $D = 2$ indicates immediately that the system is unstable. That is, one term of the complementary solution component of the system response to a forcing function is of the form

$$B_2 e^{2t}$$

which increases continually in time (see Fig. 4.2).

In general, only stable components and systems will be considered at present, and hence complementary function terms will all decay toward zero with increasing time. System stability will be investigated in detail in Chapter 6.

4.2.3 Comments

Because it decays in time toward zero for stable systems, the complementary solution is known as the **transient term** of the response function $\theta_o(t)$. As the transient term decays toward zero, the response approaches the particular solution value (Equation 4.1). For this reason, the particular solution is known as the **steady-state term** of the response function.

In summary, a response solution $\theta_o(t)$ contains:

(1) a steady-state term of the same form as the input; this term persists so long as the input (forcing function) is applied;
(2) a transient term containing n factors of the form $B e^{\alpha t}$, n being the order of the characteristic equation and hence of the system equation and transfer function.

Each root of the characteristic equation is a value of α. B is composed of system and forcing function constants, and is evaluated from the full response solution for $\theta_o = 0$, $\dot{\theta}_o = 0$, etc. at $t = 0$.

A system has a stable response only if all roots of its characteristic equation are negative numbers, or have negative real parts.

4.2.4 The Response of Simple First-Order Components

Consider the first-order transfer function

$$\frac{\theta_o}{\theta_i} = \frac{K}{1 + T D}$$

which can be written as the system equation

$$T D\theta_o + \theta_o = K\theta_i \tag{4.2}$$

where T and K are constants.

(a) Response to step change

If $\theta_i = H$ (a constant),

$$T D\theta_o + \theta_o = HK \tag{4.3}$$

By inspection, the particular solution is HK, i.e., $\theta_{o1} = KH$ is a solution of the system equation, being of the same form, a constant, as the input $\theta_i = H$. The homogeneous equation obtained by putting $\theta_i = 0$ in 4.2 is

$$T D\theta_o + \theta_o = 0 \quad \text{or} \quad T D + 1 = 0 \quad \text{or} \quad \left(D + \frac{1}{T}\right) = 0$$

the solution of which is $\theta_{o2} = B e^{-t/T}$, which decays in time to zero, as T must be a positive number for a real physical situation, i.e., the general solution is

$$\theta_o = \theta_{o1} + \theta_{o2} = KH + B e^{-t/T}$$

Using the initial condition that response $\theta_o = 0$ at time $t = 0$ gives $B = -KH$. Hence

$$\theta_o = KH - KHe^{-t/T} = HK(1 - e^{-t/T}) \tag{4.4}$$

is the response function.

The two component solutions θ_{o1} and θ_{o2} are illustrated in Fig. 4.3(a). These solutions can be added graphically to give the full response solution. The complete solution θ_o together with the input $\theta_i = H$ is shown in Fig. 4.3(b).

The response function, $\theta_o(t)$ (Eq. 4.4), is asymptotic to the steady-state (particular) solution HK, inferring that it will approach but never attain this condition, i.e.,

$$\theta_o = HK(1 - e^{-t/T}) \rightarrow HK \quad \text{as} \quad t \rightarrow \infty$$

While this is mathematically accurate, in fact θ_o comes indistinguishably

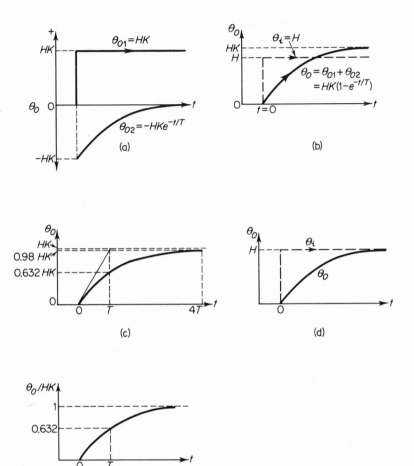

Fig. 4.3 Response of first-order system $\theta_o/\theta_i = K/(1 + TD)$ to step input $\theta_i = H$: (a) steady-state and transient components; (b) full solution; (c) useful characteristics of response; (d) for system gain constant $K = 1$; (e) in non-dimensional form θ_o/HK.

close to HK in a relatively short period of time and can be considered to have attained that value.

The response function (Eq. 4.4) has several useful practical characteristics (Fig. 4.3c):

(1) When $t = T$, $\theta_o = HK\,(1 - e^{-1}) = 0.632HK$,
  i.e., response θ_o attains 63 per cent of its final steady-state value in T sec.

(2) $d\theta_o/dt = (HK/T)\cdot e^{-t/T}$.

At $t = 0$, $e^{-t/T} = 1$ and $d\theta_o/dt = HK/T$,

which is the slope of the response curve at $t = 0$.

(3) When $t = 4T$,

$$\theta_o = HK\,(1 - e^{-4}) = 0.982HK$$

i.e., response attains 98 per cent of its final steady-state value in $4T$ sec.

For the commonly occurring case where the gain constant K equals unity, the steady-state value of the response function equals the value of the step change as illustrated in Fig. 4.3(d). Finally, the response function can be put into a general dimensionless form applicable to all simple first-order components and systems,

$$\frac{\theta_o}{HK} = 1 - e^{-t/T} \tag{4.4a}$$

which approaches unity as time increases, as shown in Fig. 4.3(e).

(b) Response to ramp input

If $\theta_i = Ht$, where H is a constant, then system equation 4.2 becomes

$$T\,D\theta_o + \theta_o = HKt \tag{4.5}$$

The steady-state solution (the particular solution) is found by assuming a solution of the same form as the input disturbance. $\theta_i = Ht$ is a straight line. Hence assume a general straight line solution $\theta_{o1} = at + b$, where a is the slope and b the intercept value of θ_{o1} when $t = 0$. It is necessary now to obtain a and b in terms of the constants K, H, and T. Using $\theta_{o1} = at + b$ for θ_o in Eq. 4.5,

$$T\,D\,(at + b) + (at + b) = Ta + at + b = HKt$$

or

$$at + b = HKt - aT$$

Equating the coefficients of like terms yields

$$a = HK, \qquad b = -aT = -HKT$$

Hence

$$\theta_{o1} = HKt - HKT$$

is the required solution, which is readily varified by substitution into Eq. 4.5.

The homogeneous equation obtained by using $\theta_i = 0$ in the system equation (Eq. 4.2) is, as for the step input,

$$T\,D\theta_o + \theta_o = 0 \quad \text{or} \quad T\,D + 1 = 0 \quad \text{or} \quad \left(D + \frac{1}{T}\right) = 0$$

the solution for which is again $\theta_{o2} = B\,e^{-t/T}$. This solution is the transient term which decays in time toward zero. The general solution of Eq. 4.5, $\theta_o = \theta_{o1} + \theta_{o2}$, is

$$\theta_o = (HKt - HKT) + Be^{-t/T}$$

Using the initial condition $\theta_o = 0$ at $t = 0$ yields $B = HKT$, and

$$\theta_o = (HKt - HKT) + HKT\,e^{-t/T} = HKT\left(e^{-t/T} + \frac{t}{T} - 1\right) \qquad (4.6)$$

which is the response function. For a particular case, in which K, H, and

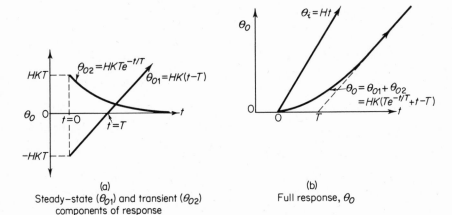

(a)
Steady–state (θ_{o1}) and transient (θ_{o2})
components of response

(b)
Full response, θ_O

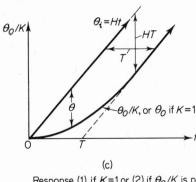

(c)
Response (1) if $K=1$ or (2) if θ_O/K is plotted
θ is error $\theta_i - \theta_O$
T is steady–state lag
HT is steady–state error

Fig. 4.4   Response of first-order system $\theta_o/\theta_i = K/(1 + TD)$ to ramp input $\theta_i = Ht$.

T are known constants, the response function can be plotted for a suitable range of time t to yield the time response $\theta_o(t)$ to the ramp input $\theta_i = Ht$.

The complementary solution coefficient B is different from that obtained for the step input, even though the characteristic equations were identical. This illustrates the vital fact that such coefficients should only be evaluated by using initial conditions in the full response equation.

Figure 4.4(a) shows the two component solutions of the response function. Figure 4.4(b) shows the general solution obtained by adding the component solutions, together with the input $\theta_i = Ht$. Figure 4.4(c) shows the solution for either the case when $K = 1$, or if θ_o/K is plotted. In both cases the response attains a steady-state condition parallel to the input.

The error between input and response at any time is given by

$$\theta = \theta_i - \theta_o = Ht - HKT \left(e^{-t/T} + \frac{t}{T} - 1 \right)$$

$$= HKT(1 - e^{-t/T}) + Ht(1 - K)$$

For $K = 1$, as time becomes large the expression approaches a constant value $\theta = HT$. This is the value of the **steady-state error** shown in Fig. 4.4(c), applying to the state when θ_o becomes parallel to θ_i due to the decay in time of the transient term $\theta_{o2} = HTe^{-t/T}$. The corresponding constant time lag between response and input is known as the **steady-state lag.** As the ratio steady-state error/steady-state lag gives the slope of the input and response ramps and the value of the slope is H, it follows that the steady-state lag is equal to the time constant T. That is, slope $= H = HT/T$.

(c) *Response to sinusoidal input*

If $\theta_i = H \sin \omega t$, where H is the constant amplitude and ω the constant angular frequency of the input, Eq. 4.2 becomes

$$T \, D\theta_o + \theta_o = KH \sin \omega t \tag{4.7}$$

The steady-state term of the solution (the particular solution) is found by assuming a generalized solution of the same form as the input. In this case try the general sine form (see Table 4.1).

$$\theta_{o1} = a \cos \omega t + b \sin \omega t$$

where a and b are arbitrary coefficients.

(NOTE: A cosine form is similar to a sine form. The addition of two sine forms of the same frequency, irrespective of phase and amplitude relationships, yields a third sine form.)

Substituting θ_{o1} for θ_o in Eq. 4.7 yields

$$-Ta\omega \sin \omega t + Tb\omega \cos \omega t + a \cos \omega t + b \sin \omega t = KH \sin \omega t$$

$$\therefore (b - Ta\omega) \sin \omega t + (a + Tb\omega) \cos \omega t = KH \sin \omega t$$

Equating the coefficients of similar terms on either side of the relationship yields,

$$b - Ta\,\omega = KH; \qquad a + Tb\,\omega = 0$$

and from these equations,

$$b = \frac{KH}{1 + \omega^2 T^2}; \quad a = -\frac{KH\,\omega T}{1 + \omega^2 T^2}$$

Substituting these coefficients in the assumed solution yields

$$\theta_{o1} = \frac{KH}{1 + \omega^2 T^2} \sin \omega t - \frac{KH\,\omega T}{1 + \omega^2 T^2} \cos \omega t$$

as the particular integral. The expression can be rearranged:

$$\theta_{o1} = \frac{KH}{(1 + \omega^2 T^2)^{1/2}} \left[\frac{1}{(1 + \omega^2 T^2)^{1/2}} \cdot \sin \omega t - \frac{\omega T}{(1 + \omega^2 T^2)^{1/2}} \cdot \cos \omega t \right]$$

Using now the standard trigonometrical relationship

$$a \cos x + b \sin x = (a^2 + b^2)^{1/2} \sin (x + \phi)$$

where $\phi = \tan^{-1} (a/b)$ yields

$$\theta_{o1} = \frac{KH}{(1 + \omega^2 T^2)^{1/2}} \cdot \sin (\omega t - \phi)$$

where $\phi = \tan^{-1} \omega T$.

The characteristic equation obtained by putting $\theta_i = 0$ in the system equation is again

$$T\,D\theta_o + \theta_o = 0 \qquad \text{or} \qquad \left(D + \frac{1}{T} \right) = 0$$

The complementary solution is again of the form $\theta_{o2} = B\,e^{-t/T}$. The general solution of Eq. 4.7, $\theta_o = \theta_{o1} + \theta_{o2}$, is therefore

$$\theta_o = \frac{KH}{(1 + \omega^2 T^2)^{1/2}} \cdot \sin (\omega t - \phi) + Be^{-t/T}$$

Using the initial condition $\theta_o = 0$ when $t = 0$,

$$\frac{KH}{(1 + \omega^2 T^2)^{1/2}} \sin (-\phi) + B = 0$$

from which

$$B = \frac{KH\,\omega T}{1 + \omega^2 T^2} \quad \text{and} \quad \theta_{o2} = \frac{KH\,\omega T}{1 + \omega^2 T^2}\cdot e^{-t/T}$$

(NOTE: $\sin(-\phi) = -\sin\phi = -\sin(\tan^{-1}\omega T) = -[\omega T/(1 + \omega^2 T^2)^{1/2}.]$)

The response function is then

$$\theta_o = \frac{HK}{(1 + \omega^2 T^2)^{1/2}} \left[\sin(\omega t - \phi) + \frac{\omega T}{(1 + \omega^2 T^2)^{1/2}}\cdot e^{-t/T} \right] \qquad (4.8)$$

Figure 4.5 shows the two component solutions θ_{o1} and θ_{o2}, together with the full solution $\theta_o = \theta_{o1} + \theta_{o2}$. The solution again consists of a steady-state term (θ_{o1}, the particular solution) plus a transient term (θ_{o2}, the

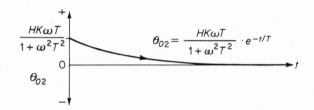

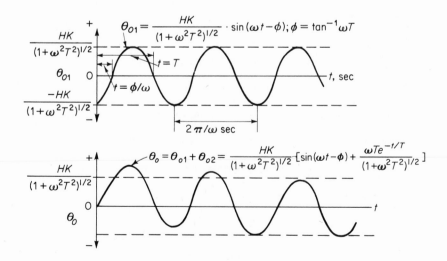

Fig. 4.5 Response of the first-order system $\theta_o/\theta_i = K/(1 + TD)$ to the sinusoidal input disturbance $\theta_i = H\sin\omega t$; H, K, ω, and T are constants.

complementary solution). The latter decays in time to zero while the former persists for as long as the input sinusoid is applied. The steady-state condition attained with time is a sinusoid of the same frequency as the input disturbance, but with a phase ϕ relative to the input. The amplitude of the steady-state response sinusoid $[KH/(1 + \omega^2 T^2)^{1/2}]$ and its phase angle relative to the input sinusoid $\phi = \tan^{-1} \omega T$ are both functions of the frequency of the input sinusoid. The well-known **frequency response method** of analysis, discussed in detail in Chapter 5, is based on describing the way in which steady-state amplitude and phase vary with input frequency ω.

Example 4.4: A hydraulic positioning device of the form discussed in Example 3.5 has the following constants associated with it:

$$a = 4 \quad \text{in.;} \quad b = 12 \quad \text{in.;} \quad A = 10 \quad \text{in.}^2; \quad k_v = 20 \quad \text{in.}^3/\text{sec/in.}$$

It is desired to study the dynamic nature of the system by plotting the response to

(1) a step input disturbance $x_i = 0.5$ in.,
(2) a ramp input disturbance $x_i = 0.25t$ in.,
(3) a sinusoidal input disturbance $x_i = \sin 2t$ in. (amplitude $H = 1$).

Solution: The system transfer function was shown in Example 3.5 to be

$$\frac{x_o}{x_i} = \frac{b/a}{1 + [(a + b)/a] \cdot (A/k_v) \cdot D}$$

which becomes

$$\frac{x_o}{x_i} = \frac{3}{1 + 2D}$$

The transfer function can be written as the system equation

$$2Dx_o + x_o = 3x_i$$

which is of the form of Eq. 4.2, where $T = 2$ sec and $K = 3$.

(1) For a step input $x_i = 0.5$ in., the system equation becomes

$$2Dx_o + x_o = 1.5$$

which is of the form of Eq. 4.3 and hence will have a solution of the form of Eq. 4.4. That is,

$$x_o = 3 \times 0.5 \, (1 - e^{-t/2}) = 1.5 \, (1 - e^{-0.5t})$$

Figure 4.6(a) shows tabulated and plotted values of t and x_o. Note that

(a) x_o reaches 63 per cent of its final steady-state value in $t = T = 2$ sec;
(b) x_o reaches 98 per cent of its final steady-state value in $t = 4T = 8$ sec;
(c) the slope of the $x_o(t)$ curve at $t = 0$ is x_o (steady-state)$/T = 1.5/2 = 0.75$.

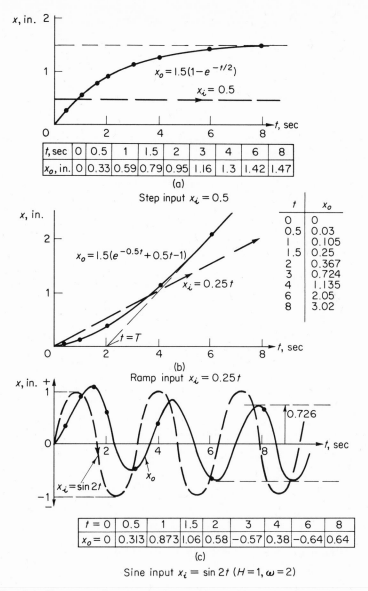

t, sec	0	0.5	1	1.5	2	3	4	6	8
x_o, in.	0	0.33	0.59	0.79	0.95	1.16	1.3	1.42	1.47

(a)

Step input $x_i = 0.5$

t	x_o
0	0
0.5	0.03
1	0.105
1.5	0.25
2	0.367
3	0.724
4	1.135
6	2.05
8	3.02

(b)

Ramp input $x_i = 0.25t$

$t = 0$	0.5	1	1.5	2	3	4	6	8
$x_o = 0$	0.313	0.873	1.06	0.58	-0.57	0.38	-0.64	0.64

(c)

Sine input $x_i = \sin 2t$ $(H = 1, \omega = 2)$

Fig. 4.6 Response of system $x_o/x_i = 3/(1 + 2D)$ to: (a) step; (b) ramp; (c) sine inputs.

(2) For a ramp input $x_i = 0.25t$, the system equation becomes

$$2Dx_o + x_o = 0.75t$$

which is of the form of Eq. 4.5 and hence will have a solution of the form of Eq. 4.6:

$$x_o = 3 \times 0.25 \times 2 \left(e^{-t/2} + \frac{t}{2} - 1 \right) = 1.5 \, (e^{-0.5t} + 0.5t - 1)$$

103

Figure 4.6(b) shows tabulated and plotted values of t and x_o. Note that for $t = T = 2$ sec, the steady-state asymptote $x_{o1} = 1.5(0.5t - 1)$ cuts the t axis.

(3) For a sinusoidal input $x_i = \sin 2t$, the system equation becomes

$$2Dx_o + x_o = 3 \sin 2t$$

which is of the form of Eq. 4.7, and hence will have a solution of the form of Eq. 4.8:

$$x_o = \frac{3 \times 1}{(1 + 2^2 \times 2^2)^{1/2}} \left[\sin (2t - \tan^{-1} 2 \times 2) + \frac{2 \times 2}{(1 + 2^2 \times 2^2)^{1/2}} \cdot e^{-t/2} \right]$$

$$= 0.726 \left[\sin (2t - \tan^{-1} 4) + 0.973 \, e^{-0.5t} \right]$$

Figure 4.6(c) shows tabulated and plotted values of t and x_o.

4.2.5 The Response of Simple Second-Order Components and Systems

Consider the second-order transfer function

$$\frac{\theta_o}{\theta_i} = \frac{K}{K_1 D^2 + K_2 D + 1} \tag{4.9a}$$

Previous Examples 3.8, 3.9, 3.10, 3.20, 3.22, 3.27, 3.28, and 3.29 in Chapter 3 all had transfer functions of this form, with parameters K, K_1 and K_2 composed of various system constants. The transfer function can be written as the system equation

$$K_1 D^2\theta_o + K_2 D\theta_o + \theta_o = K\theta_i \tag{4.9b}$$

which can be solved for $\theta_o(t)$ for specified forms of $\theta_i(t)$.

The particular solution

The particular solution (i.e., the steady-state term of the response function) is found by seeking a solution of Eq. 4.9b of the same form as the input θ_i (Table 4.1). That is,

(a) for $\theta_i = H$, a step input, try $\theta_{o1} = a$ for θ_o in Eq. 4.9b; it is readily seen that $a = KH$, and hence

$$\theta_{o1} = HK \tag{4.10a}$$

(b) for $\theta_i = Ht$, a ramp input, try $\theta_{o1} = at + b$ for θ_o in Equation 4.9; in this case, $a = HK$, $b = -HKK_2$, and hence

$$\theta_{o1} = HKt - HKK_2 = HK(t - K_2) \tag{4.10b}$$

is the required steady-state solution;

(c) for $\theta_i = H \sin \omega t$, a sine input, try $\theta_{o1} = a \cos \omega t + b \sin \omega t$ for θ_o in Equation 4.9b; for this case,

$$K_1 \frac{d^2}{dt^2}(a \cos \omega t + b \sin \omega t) + K_2 \frac{d}{dt}(a \cos \omega t + b \sin \omega t)$$
$$+ (a \cos \omega t + b \sin \omega t) = KH \sin \omega t.$$

Performing the differentiations using the identities

$$\frac{d}{dt}\sin \omega t = \omega \cos \omega t; \quad \frac{d^2}{dt^2}\sin \omega t = \frac{d}{dt}(\omega \cos \omega t) = -\omega^2 \sin \omega t$$

$$\frac{d}{dt}\cos \omega t = -\omega \sin \omega t; \quad \frac{d^2}{dt^2}\cos \omega t = \frac{d}{dt}(-\omega \sin \omega t) = -\omega^2 \cos \omega t$$

yields

$$-K_1 a\, \omega^2 \cos \omega t - K_1 b\, \omega^2 \sin \omega t - K_2 a\, \omega \sin \omega t + K_2 b\, \omega \cos \omega t$$
$$+ a \cos \omega t + b \sin \omega t = KH \sin \omega t$$

Gathering sine and cosine terms,

$$(a + K_2 b\omega - K_1 a\omega^2) \cos \omega t + (b - K_1 b\omega^2 - K_2 a\omega) \sin \omega t = KH \sin \omega t$$

Equating the coefficients of like terms on both sides of the equation,

$$a + K_2 b\omega - K_1 a\omega^2 = 0 \tag{1}$$

$$b - K_1 b\omega^2 - K_2 a\omega = KH \tag{2}$$

From (1),

$$b = \frac{K_1 a\omega^2 - a}{K_2 \omega} \tag{3}$$

which is substituted into (2) to give

$$\frac{K_1 a\omega^2 - a}{K_2 \omega} - \frac{K_1 \omega^2 (K_1 a\omega^2 - a)}{K_2 \omega} - K_2 \omega a = KH$$

from which

$$a = \frac{KHK_2\omega}{2K_1\omega^2 - K_1^2\omega^4 - 1 - K_2^2\omega^2} = \frac{-KK_2 H\omega}{(1 - K_1\omega^2)^2 + K_2^2\omega^2} \tag{4}$$

Using this expression for a in (3) yields

$$b = \frac{(K_1\omega^2 - 1)}{K_2\omega} \cdot a = \frac{(1 - K_1\omega^2) \cdot KH}{(1 - K_1\omega^2)^2 + K_2^2\omega^2} \tag{5}$$

Hence the particular solution of Eq. 4.9 for $\theta_i = H \sin \omega t$ is

$$\theta_{o1} = a \cos \omega t + b \sin \omega t$$

where a and b are given by expressions (4) and (5).
Using the common identity

$$a \cos \omega t + b \sin \omega t = (a^2 + b^2)^{1/2} \sin (\omega t + \phi)$$

where $\phi = \tan^{-1} a/b$,

$$\theta_{o1} = \frac{KH}{[(1 - K_1\omega^2)^2 + K_2^2\omega^2]^{1/2}} \cdot \sin (\omega t - \phi) \qquad (4.10c)$$

where $\phi = \tan^{-1}[K_2\omega/(1 - K_1\omega^2)]$. Equation 4.10(c) is the required steady-state solution of Eq. 4.9, for the sinusoidal forcing function $\theta_i = H \sin \omega t$.

The complementary solution

The complementary solution (i.e., the transient term of the response function) is found by solving the homogeneous equation associated with Eq. 4.9(a),

$$K_1 D^2\theta_o + K_2 D\theta_o + \theta_o = 0 \qquad (4.11)$$

The solution is of the form

$$\theta_{o2} = \sum_1^n (Be^{\alpha t}) = B_1 e^{\alpha_1 t} + B_2 e^{\alpha_2 t}$$

where $n = 2$ is the order, and α_1 and α_2 are the roots of the characteristic equation

$$K_1 D^2 + K_2 D + 1 = 0 \qquad (4.11a)$$

and coefficients B_1 and B_2 are to be evaluated using initial conditions of θ_o in the full response equation $\theta_o = \theta_{o1} + \theta_{o2}$.

The roots of Eq. 4.11(a) are

$$D = \alpha_1 = \frac{-K_2 + (K_2^2 - 4K_1)^{1/2}}{2K_1} = -\frac{K_2}{2K_1} + \frac{(K_2^2 - 4K_1)^{1/2}}{2K_1}$$

and

$$D = \alpha_2 = \frac{-K_2 - (K_2^2 - 4K_1)^{1/2}}{2K_1} = -\frac{K_2}{2K_1} - \frac{(K_2^2 - 4K_1)^{1/2}}{2K_1}$$

Assuming K_1 and K_2 to be positive numbers, it is apparent that roots α_1 and α_2 will be

(a) real and different numbers if $K_2^2 > 4K_1$,
(b) real and equal numbers if $K_2^2 = 4K_1$,
(c) a complex pair of numbers if $K_2^2 < 4K_1$,
(d) an imaginary pair of numbers if $K_2 = 0$.

The complementary solution can be written in the form

$$\theta_{o2} = B_1 e^{-(a-b)t} + B_2 e^{-(a+b)t} \qquad (4.12)$$

where $a = K_2/2K_1$; $b = (K_2^2 - 4K_1)^{1/2}/2K_1$.

In general, coefficients B_1 and B_2 are composed of system and forcing function constants.

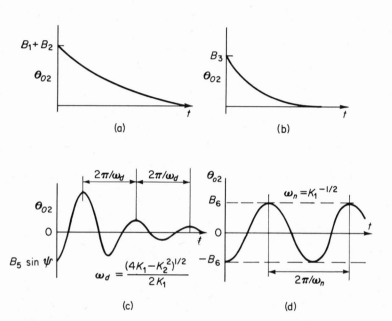

Fig. 4.7 Forms of the complementary solution (transient terms) for the system $\theta_o/\theta_i = K/(K_1 D^2 + K_2 D + 1)$ for: (a) $K_2 > 2K_1^{1/2}$; (b) $K_2 = 2K_1^{1/2}$; (c) $K_2 < 2K_1^{1/2}$; (d) $K_2 = 0$.

For Case (a): a and b are real positive numbers, and Eq. 4.12 takes the form

$$\theta_{o2} = B_1 e^{-k_1 t} + B_2 e^{-k_2 t} \tag{4.12a}$$

where $k_1 = (a - b)$ and $k_2 = a + b$ are both real positive numbers. This expression decays toward zero as time increases, as illustrated in Fig. 4.7(a).

For Case (b):

$$\alpha_1 = \alpha_2 = -\frac{K_2}{2K_1} = -a$$

For this special case of a repeated root,

$$\theta_{o2} = B_3 e^{-at} + B_4 t e^{-at} = (B_3 + B_4 t)e^{-at} \tag{4.12b}$$

where a is a positive real number.

Again, this expression experiences a simple exponential decay as time becomes large, as illustrated in Fig. 4.7(b).

For Case (c):

$$\alpha_1 = -a + j\omega_d; \qquad \alpha_2 = -a - j\omega_d$$

where $a = K_2/2K_1$; and $\omega_d = (4K_1 - K_2^2)/2K_1$; and both are real and positive,

$$\therefore \theta_{o2} = B' \exp[-(a + j\omega_d)t + B'' \exp[-(a + j\omega_d)t]$$

which can be expanded to

$$\theta_{o2} = B' \exp(-at) \cdot \exp(j\omega_d t) + B'' \exp(-at) \exp(-j\omega_d t)$$
$$= \exp(-at) [B' \exp(j\omega_d t) + B'' \exp(-j\omega_d t)]$$

Using the common identity $e^{\pm jx} = \cos x \pm j \sin x$,

$$\theta_{o2} = e^{-at} (B' \cos \omega_d t + B' \sin \omega_d t + B'' \cos \omega_d t - jB'' \sin \omega_d t)$$

$$= e^{-at} [(B' + B'') \cos \omega_d t + j (B' - B'') \sin \omega_d t]$$

Using the previously used identity $a \cos x + b \sin x = (a^2 + b^2)^{1/2} \sin (x + \tan^{-1} a/b)$,

$$\theta_{o2} = e^{-at} B_5 \sin (\omega_d t + \psi) \tag{4.12c}$$

where B_5 and ψ are both functions of B' and B''.

Thus the transient term for the case of complex roots of the characteristic equation is an exponentially decaying sinusoid, of frequency ω_d rad/sec, which will decay to zero as time t becomes large, as shown in Fig. 4.7(c). ω_d is called the **damped natural frequency** of the system.

For Case (d):

$$\alpha_1 = j\omega_n, \quad \alpha_2 = -j\omega_n,$$

where $\omega_n = K_1^{-1/2}$ is positive and real.

Hence

$$\theta_{o2} = B' \exp(j\omega_n t) + B'' \exp(-j\omega_n t)$$

For this special case of imaginary roots, B' and B'' are equal, and

$$\theta_{o2} = B[\exp(j\omega_n t) + \exp(-j\omega_n t)]$$

Using the identities $e^{jx} = \cos x + j \sin x$ and $e^{-jx} = \cos x - j \sin x$,

$$\theta_{o2} = 2B \cos \omega_n t = B_6 \cos \omega_n t \tag{4.12d}$$

Thus the transient term for the case of imaginary roots of the characteristic equation is a continuous oscillation $B_6 \cos \omega_n t$, as shown in Fig. 4.7(d). $\omega_n = K_1^{-1/2}$ is called the **undamped natural frequency** of the system. The transient neither decays nor increases in time. It is apparent that a system response containing such a transient term is the critical case between stable (decaying) and unstable (increasing in time) response. The coefficient B_6 again depends on the particular forcing function used.

The full solutions — a summary

It has been shown that

$\theta_{o1} = HK$,   for step input $\theta_i = H$

$\theta_{o1} = HK(t - K_2)$,   for ramp input $\theta_i = Ht$

$\theta_{o1} = HK[(1 - K_1\omega^2)^2 + K_2^2\omega^2]^{-1/2} \cdot \sin(\omega t - \psi)$,   for sine input $\theta_i = H \sin \omega t$

where $\psi = \tan^{-1} K_2\omega/(1 - K_1\omega^2)$

$\theta_{o2} = B_1 e^{-(a-b)t} + B_2 e^{-(a+b)t}$,   for $K_2 > 2K_1^{1/2}$

$\theta_{o2} = (B_3 + B_4 t)e^{-at}$,   for $K_2 = 2K_1^{1/2}$

$\theta_{o2} = B_5 e^{-at} \sin(\omega_d t + \psi)$,   for $K_2 < 2K_1^{1/2}$

$\theta_{o2} = B_6 \cos \omega_n t$,   for $K_2 = 0$

where $a = K_2/2K_1$; $b = (K_2^2 - 4K_1)^{1/2}/2K_1$; $\omega_d = -b$; $\omega_n = K_1^{-1/2}$

Thus, a full solution for a particular input can be made by using the appropriate form of θ_{o1} and θ_{o2} to give

$$\theta_o = \theta_{o1} + \theta_{o2}$$

Parameters B and ψ are established by using the initial conditions $\theta_o = \dot{\theta}_o = 0$ at $t = 0$, in the response function $\theta_o = \theta_{o1} + \theta_{o2}$.

The following example will demonstrate a completed solution.

Example 4.5: Obtain and plot the response expression for the system

$$\frac{\theta_o}{\theta_i} = \frac{2}{4D^2 + 3D + 1}$$

when it is subjected to the forcing function $\theta_i = 2$. θ_o is the change in the response variable due to θ_i.

Solution: The system equation is

$$4D^2\theta_o + 3D\theta_o + \theta_o = 4$$

The particular solution of this equation is

$$\theta_{o1} = 4$$

(i.e., try $\theta_{o1} = a$, a constant. Then $D^2\theta_{o1} = D\theta_{o1} = 0$, and $\theta_{o1} = 4$.) The system's characteristic equation in operational form is

$$4D^2 + 3D + 1 = 0$$

The roots of the characteristic equation are

$$D = \alpha_1 = -\frac{3}{8} + j\frac{7^{1/2}}{8} = -0.375 + j0.33$$

$$D = \alpha_2 = -\frac{3}{8} - j\frac{7^{1/2}}{8} = -0.375 - j0.33$$

The complementary solution is

$$\begin{aligned}\theta_{o2} &= B_1 e^{-(0.375+j0.33)t} + B_2 e^{-(0.375-j0.33)t} \\ &= Be^{-0.375t} \sin(0.33t + \psi)\end{aligned}$$

The full solution is

$$\theta_o = \theta_{o1} + \theta_{o2} = 4 + Be^{-0.375t} \sin(0.33t + \psi)$$

There are two unknown parameters, B and ψ, to be evaluated. Hence two initial conditions are required.

(1) $\theta_o = 0$ at $t = 0$ yields

$$0 = 4 + B \sin \psi \tag{1}$$

(2) $\dot{\theta}_o = 0$ at $t = 0$. Hence, using the identity $(d/dt)(uv) = v(du/dt) + u(dv/dt)$,

$$\dot{\theta}_o = \frac{d\theta_o}{dt} = 0 - 0.375\, Be^{-0.375t} \sin(0.33t + \psi) + Be^{-0.375t}\, 0.33 \cos(0.33t + \psi)$$

and for $\dot{\theta}_o = 0$,

$$0.375B \sin \psi = 0.33B \cos \psi$$

$$\frac{\sin \psi}{\cos \psi} = \tan \psi = \frac{0.33}{0.375} = 0.88, \quad \text{and } \psi = 41.3°$$

t, sec =	1	2	4	6	8	10	12	14	16
θ_o =	0.42	1.33	2.8	3.68	4	4.1	4.06	4.04	4.02

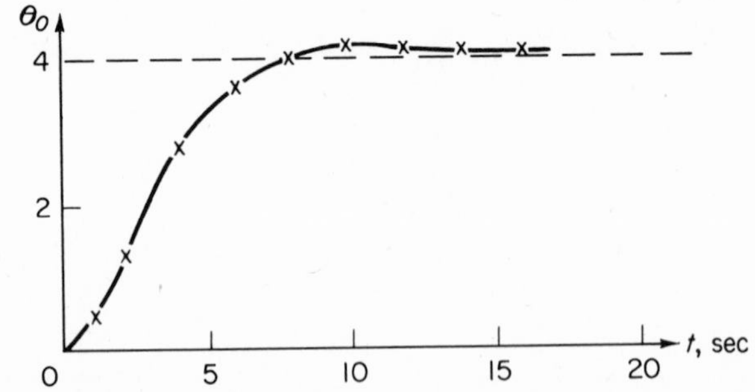

Fig. 4.8 Response of the system $\theta_o/\theta_i = 2/(4D^2 + 3D + 1)$ to step input $\theta_i = 2$.

From (1),

$$B = \frac{-4}{\sin \psi} = \frac{-4}{0.66} = -6.08$$

Hence the response function is

$$\theta_o = 4 - 6.08e^{-0.375t} \sin (0.33\, t + 41.3°)$$

Figure 4.8 shows values of θ_o for selected values of t, together with the $\theta_o(t)$ plot.

Use of parameters ω_n and ξ with quadratic factors

For system transfer functions which contain quadratic factors of the form

$$K_1 D^2 + K_2 D + 1 \tag{4.11}$$

it is common practice to use the following parameters.

(a) *Undamped natural frequency*, defined as

$$\omega_n = (K_1)^{-1/2} \quad \text{rad/sec} \tag{4.13}$$

This is the frequency associated with the solution of Eq. 4.11 for $K_2 = 0$, i.e.,

$$K_1 D^2 + 1 = 0$$

the roots of which are $\pm jK_1^{-1/2}$, and which was shown in Case (d) on p. 108 to have the transient response $B \cos K_1^{-1/2} \cdot t$. That is, the solution of $K_1 D^2 \theta_o + \theta_o = 0$ is

$$B \cos \omega_n t$$

(b) *Damping ratio*, defined as

$$\xi = \tfrac{1}{2} K_2 K_1^{-1/2} = \tfrac{1}{2} K_2 \omega_n \tag{4.14}$$

The physical significance of ξ will be illustrated shortly. It is important to see that $\xi = 0$ for $K_2 = 0$, and $\xi = 1$ for $K_2 = 2K_1^{1/2}$, or for $K_2^2 - 4K_1 = 0$.

The simple second-order transfer function, Eq. 4.9, can be written in terms of ω_n and ξ:

$$\frac{\theta_o}{\theta_i} = \frac{K}{(1/\omega_n^2)D^2 + (2\xi/\omega_n)D + 1} \tag{4.15}$$

(c) *Quadratic time constants:* Noting that angular velocity ω has units $\sec^{-1}$, a quadratic time constant T can be defined by

$$T = \omega_n^{-1} \quad \text{sec} \tag{4.13a}$$

in which case the simple second-order transfer function can be written

$$\frac{\theta_o}{\theta_i} = \frac{K}{T^2 D^2 + 2\xi T D + 1} \tag{4.16}$$

In terms of ω_n and ξ, the particular solutions 4.10(a), (b), and (c) can be written

$$\text{(step)} \quad \theta_{o1} = HK \tag{4.17a}$$

$$\text{(ramp)} \quad \theta_{o1} = HK \left(t - \frac{2\xi}{\omega_n} \right) \tag{4.17b}$$

$$\text{(sine)} \quad \theta_{o1} = HK\omega_n^2 \left[(\omega_n^2 - \omega^2)^2 + 4\xi^2\omega_n^2\omega^2 \right]^{-1/2} \cdot \sin{(\omega t - \psi)} \tag{4.17c}$$

where $\psi = \tan^{-1}\left[2\xi\omega_n\omega/(\omega_n^2 - \omega^2)\right]$.

The characteristic equation becomes

$$\frac{1}{\omega_n^2} \cdot D^2 + \frac{2\xi}{\omega_n} \cdot D + 1 = 0$$

the roots of which are

$$D = -\xi\omega_n \pm \omega_n(\xi^2 - 1)^{1/2}$$

These roots will be

(a) real and different if $\xi > 1$,
(b) real and equal if $\xi = 1$,
(c) a complex pair if $\xi < 1$,
(d) an imaginary pair if $\xi = 0$.

The general complementary function, Eq. 4.12, becomes

$$\theta_{o2} = B_1 e^{-[\xi-(\xi^2-1)^{1/2}]\omega_n t} + B_2 e^{-[\xi+(\xi^2-1)^{1/2}]\omega_n t} \tag{4.18}$$

which reduces to

$$\theta_{o2} = (B_3 + B_4 t)e^{-\xi\omega_n t}, \qquad \text{for } \xi = 1 \tag{4.18a}$$

$$\theta_{o2} = B_5 e^{-\xi\omega_n t} \sin{(\omega_d t + \psi)}, \qquad \text{for } \xi < 1 \tag{4.18b}$$

(where $\omega_d = (1 - \xi^2)^{1/2} \cdot \omega_n$);

$$\theta_{o2} = B_6 \cos{\omega_n t}, \qquad \text{for } \xi = 0 \tag{4.18c}$$

As discussed previously, parameters B and ψ have to be established for the particular input forcing function used, using the zero initial conditions. The technique was demonstrated in Example 4.5. Further evaluations of B and ψ parameters will be made in Section 4.3, which deals with Laplace transform solutions of system equations. However, the effects of damping ratio ξ on system response can best be seen in Fig. 4.10 (on p. 125), which shows the responses of a second-order system to step input for various values of ξ. It can be seen that increasing ξ causes a decreasing tendency of the response to overshoot and oscillate about its final steady-state value. Thus a system with low damping ratio is said to be lightly damped, whereas a system with high damping ratio (say > 1) is said to be heavily damped. Hence heavy damping causes a slow, nonoscillatory response, whereas light damping causes a rapid but oscillatory response. Many real systems are designed at a compromise value of $\xi \doteq 0.65$, which gives a reasonably fast response with an acceptable degree of overshoot and oscillation.

The foregoing expressions for θ_{o1} and θ_{o2} are readily converted to use $T = 1/\omega_n$ instead of ω_n.

4.3 LAPLACE TRANSFORM SOLUTION OF SYSTEM EQUATIONS

4.3.1 Introduction

It is apparent from Section 4.2 that classical solutions of high-order system equations become very tedious to obtain. Special analysis techniques (frequency response, root locus, etc.) have been highly developed to circumvent the necessity to make full response solutions of system equations in order to understand the nature of a system. However, these techniques do not completely remove the necessity to study the full dynamic response of a system to specified input disturbances. For this reason, the Laplace transform method for solving differential equations has been closely associated with control system analysis. In essence, the differential equation to be solved can be transformed to an equivalent algebraic expression. The manipulations necessary for solution become algebraic. On completion of these manipulations, the resulting algebraic function can be retransformed to yield the solution in the original domain. The method is applicable to any constant coefficient linear differential equation. Initial conditions can be included directly in the transform process, eliminating the tedious problem of applying them to the general solution to evaluate coefficients, as is necessary in classical solution methods. The complete solution is obtained, i.e., the particular and complementary solutions combined.

The application of the Laplace transform method is made easy by the availability of tabulated Laplace transforms of normally occurring functions. Solution of low-order equations requires little more than the ability to recognize appropriate solutions from a table.

Particularly useful for dynamic system analysis is the fact that the Laplace transform method can be directly associated with the system's transfer function. It will be shown that subject to the conditions (discussed in Sections 1.2 and 3.3),

(1) the system is in equilibrium at the instant $t = 0$ when the input disturbance is introduced, and
(2) changes in the response and input variables after $t = 0$ are related, rather than their absolute values;

then the operator $D = d/dt$ and the Laplace transform operator s are directly interchangeable in transfer functions. Hence a transfer function in the D (time) domain can be converted to the Laplace transform domain simply by substituting s for D. The transfer function can then be solved for a particular input disturbance by the Laplace transform method. Conditions (1) and (2) above simply mean that all initial conditions are zero.

4.3.2 The Laplace Transformation of Functions of Time

The Laplace transform of a function of time is defined by

$$L[f(t)] = F(s) = \int_0^\infty f(t) \cdot e^{-st} \, dt, \qquad \text{where } t > 0$$

where $f(t)$ is the function of time being transformed; s is a complex variable called the Laplace operator; $F(s)$ is the Laplace transform of $f(t)$; $L\,[\quad]$ denotes the Laplace transform of the enclosed function.

Examples:

(*a*) Find the Laplace transform of the constant H:

$$L[H] = \int_0^\infty H e^{-st} \, dt = H\left[\frac{e^{-st}}{-s}\right]_0^\infty = \frac{H}{s}$$

i.e., $F(s) = H/s$ for $f(t) = H$

(*b*) Find the Laplace transform of the ramp function Ht:

$$L[Ht] = \int_0^\infty Ht e^{-st} \, dt = H\int_0^\infty t \cdot e^{-st} \cdot dt$$

Using the integration by parts identity $\int u \, dv = uv - \int v \, du$, let $u = t$ and $dv = e^{-st} \, dt$. Then, $du/dt = 1$ or $du = dt$; $v = \int dv = e^{-st}/-s$.
Hence,

$$L[Ht] = H\left[\left[\frac{te^{-st}}{-s}\right]_0^\infty - \int_0^\infty \frac{e^{-st}}{-s} \, dt\right]$$

$$= H\left[\frac{te^{-st}}{-s} - \frac{e^{-st}}{s^2}\right]_0^\infty = H\left[-0 + 0 - 0 + \frac{1}{s^2}\right] = \frac{H}{s^2}$$

i.e., $F(s) = H/s^2$ for $f(t) = Ht$.

(*c*) Find the Laplace Transform of the sine function $H \sin \omega t$:

$$L\,[H \sin \omega t] = H\int_0^\infty \sin \omega t \cdot e^{-st} \, dt$$

Again, integration by parts can be made. However, use of a table of standard integrals shows that

$$\int_0^\infty \sin \omega t \cdot e^{-st}\, dt = \frac{\omega}{s^2 + \omega^2}$$

Hence,

$$F(s) = \frac{H\omega}{s^2 + \omega^2}, \quad \text{for } f(t) = H \sin \omega t$$

In this manner, "pairs" of $F(s)$ and $f(t)$ functions have been compiled. Table 4.2 shows some of the simpler pairs which occur in system analysis. Extensive tables of Laplace transform pairs are widely available.

(d) It was shown in Section 4.2.4 that the response of the first order system

$$\frac{\theta_o}{\theta_i} = \frac{K}{1 + T\,D}$$

to step input $\theta_i = H$ is

$$\theta_o(t) = HK\,(1 - e^{-t/T}) \tag{4.4}$$

Consider now the Laplace transform of $\theta_o = HK\,(1 - e^{-t/T})$:

$$L[\theta_o(t)] = \theta_o(s) = \int_0^\infty HK(1 - e^{-t/T}) \cdot e^{-st}\, dt = KH \int_0^\infty (1 - e^{t/T}) \cdot e^{-st}\, dt$$

For integration by parts, let $u = 1 - e^{-t/T}$, and $dv = e^{-st}\, dt$.
Hence

$$v = \int dv = \frac{e^{-st}}{-s}$$

and

$$du = \frac{du}{dt} \cdot dt = \frac{d}{dt}\,(1 - e^{-t/T}) \cdot dt = -\frac{1}{T}\, e^{-t/T} \cdot dt$$

Using $\int u\, dv = uv - \int v\, du$,

$$\theta_o(s) = HK\left[(1 - e^{-t/T}) \cdot \frac{e^{-st}}{-s} - \int \frac{e^{-st}}{-s} \cdot \frac{e^{-t/T}}{-T}\, dt \right]_0^\infty$$

$$= HK\left[e^{-st}\left(\frac{e^{-t/T}}{s} - \frac{1}{s}\right) - \frac{1}{Ts} \cdot \int e^{-[s+(1/T)]t}\, dt \right]_0^\infty$$

$$= HK\left[e^{-st}\left(\frac{e^{-t/T}}{s} - \frac{1}{s}\right) - \frac{1}{Ts} \cdot \frac{e^{-[s+(1/T)]t}}{-(s + 1/T)} \right]_0^\infty$$

$$= HK\left[e^{-st}\left(\frac{e^{-t/T}}{s} - \frac{1}{s} + \frac{e^{-t/T}}{s(Ts + 1)}\right) \right]_0^\infty$$

and applying the limits,

$$\theta_o(s) = HK\left[1\left(\frac{1}{s} - \frac{1}{s} + \frac{1}{s(1 + Ts)} - 0\right) \right] = \frac{HK}{s(1 + Ts)}$$

Thus, $HK/s(1 + Ts)$ is the Laplace transform of the expression $HK(1 - e^{t/T})$.

TABLE 4.2: *Laplace Transform Pairs Associated with the Factors* $\dfrac{\theta_o}{\theta_i} = \dfrac{K}{1+Ts}$ *and* $\dfrac{\theta_o}{\theta_i} = \dfrac{K}{K_1 s^2 + K_2 s + 1}$ *Subjected to Free Response, Step, Ramp, and Sine Inputs*

No.	$F(s)$	$f(t)$	Comment
1	$\dfrac{H}{s}$	H	Step
2	$\dfrac{H}{s^2}$	Ht	Ramp
3	$\dfrac{H}{\omega + s^2/\omega}$	$H\sin\omega t$	Sine
4	$\dfrac{K}{1+Ts}$	$\dfrac{K}{T}\cdot e^{-t/T}$	Free response of first-order system
5	$\dfrac{K}{(1+T_1 s)(1+T_2 s)}$	$\dfrac{K}{T_1-T_2}(e^{-t/T_1} - e^{-t/T_2})$	Free response of second-order system, $\xi > 1$
6	$\dfrac{K}{(1+Ts)^2}$	$\dfrac{Kt}{T^2}\cdot e^{-t/T}$	As for 5, with $\xi = 1$
7	$\dfrac{K}{s^2/\omega_n^2 + (2\xi/\omega_n)s + 1}$	$\dfrac{K\omega_n}{(1-\xi^2)^{1/2}}\cdot e^{-\xi\omega_n t}\cdot\sin\omega_d t$	As for 5, with $\xi < 1$
8	$\dfrac{HK}{s(1+Ts)}$	$HK(1-e^{-t/T})$	First-order system, response to step input
9	$\dfrac{HK}{s^2(1+Ts)}$	$HKT\left(e^{-t/T} + \dfrac{t}{T} - 1\right)$	First-order system, response to ramp input
10	$\dfrac{HK}{(\omega + s^2/\omega)(1+Ts)}$	$\dfrac{HK}{(1+\omega^2 T^2)^{1/2}}\left[\sin(\omega t - \phi) + \dfrac{\omega T}{(1+\omega^2 T^2)^{1/2}}\cdot e^{-t/T}\right]$ where $\phi = \tan^{-1}\omega T$	First-order system, response to sine input
11	$\dfrac{HK}{s(1+T_1 s)(1+T_2 s)}$	$HK\left[1 + \dfrac{1}{T_2 - T_1}(T_1 e^{-t/T_1} - T_2 e^{-t/T_2})\right]$	Second-order system, response to step input when $\xi > 1$
12	$\dfrac{HK}{s(1+Ts)^2}$	$HK\left[1 - \dfrac{T+t}{T}e^{-t/T}\right]$	Second-order system, response to step input when $\xi = 1$

No.	$F(s)$	$f(t)$	Comment
13	$\dfrac{HK}{s[s^2/\omega_n^2 + (2\xi/\omega_n)s + 1]}$	$HK[1 + (1-\xi^2)^{-1/2}e^{-\xi\omega_n t}\sin(\omega_d t - \psi)]$ where $\psi = \tan^{-1}(1-\xi^2)^{1/2}/-\xi$	Second-order system, response to step input when $\xi < 1$
14	$\dfrac{HK}{s^2(1+T_1 s)(1+T_2 s)}$	$HK\left[t - T_1 - T_2 - \dfrac{1}{T_1 - T_2}(T_2^2 e^{-t/T_2} - T_1^2 e^{-t/T_1})\right]$	Second-order system, $\xi > 1$, response to ramp input
15	$\dfrac{HK}{s^2(1+Ts)^2}$	$HK[t - 2T + (t + 2T)e^{-t/T}]$	Second-order system, $\xi = 1$, response to ramp input
16	$\dfrac{HK}{s^2(s^2/\omega_n^2 + (2\xi/\omega_n)s + 1)}$	$HK[t - 2\xi/\omega_n + (e^{-\xi\omega_n t}/\omega_d)\cdot\sin(\omega_d t - \psi)]$ where $\psi = 2\tan^{-1}(1-\xi^2)^{1/2}/(-\xi)$	Second-order system, $\xi < 1$, response to ramp input
17	$\dfrac{HK}{(\omega + s^2/\omega)(1+T_1 s)(1+T_2 s)}$	$HK\left[\dfrac{T_1^2\omega e^{-t/T_1}}{(T_1-T_2)(1+T_1^2\omega^2)} + \dfrac{T_2^2\omega e^{-t/T_2}}{(T_2-T_1)(1+T_2^2\omega^2)} + \dfrac{\sin(\omega t - \phi)}{[(1+T_1^2\omega^2)(1+T_2^2\omega^2)]^{1/2}}\right]$ where $\phi = \tan^{-1}\omega T_1 + \tan^{-1}\omega T_2$	Second-order system, $\xi > 1$, response to sine input
18	$\dfrac{HK}{(\omega + s^2/\omega)(1+Ts)^2}$	$\dfrac{HK}{1+T^2\omega^2}\left[\sin(\omega t - \phi) + \dfrac{\omega t + 2T\omega}{1+T^2\omega^2}e^{-t/T}\right]$ where $\phi = 2\tan^{-1}\omega T$	Second-order system, $\xi = 1$, response to sine input
19	$\dfrac{HK}{(\omega + s^2/\omega)[s^2/\omega_n^2 + (2\xi/\omega_n)s + 1]}$	$\dfrac{HK}{[(1-\omega^2/\omega_n^2)^2 + (2\xi\omega/\omega_n)^2]^{1/2}}$ $\cdot\left[\sin(\omega t - \phi) + \dfrac{\omega}{\omega_d}\cdot e^{-\xi\omega_n t}\sin(\omega_d t - \psi)\right]$ where $\phi = \tan^{-1}\dfrac{2\xi\omega/\omega_n}{1-\omega^2/\omega_n^2}$; $\psi = \tan^{-1}\dfrac{-2\xi(1 - \xi^2)^{1/2}}{\omega^2/\omega_n^2 - (1 - 2\xi^2)}$	Second-order system, $\xi < 1$, response to sine input

$\xi = \frac{1}{2}K_2 K_1^{-1/2}$ is the damping ratio

$\omega_n = K_1^{-1/2}$ is the undamped natural frequency

$\omega_d = \omega_n(1 - \xi^2)^{1/2}$ is the damped natural frequency

associated with the quadratic

$$K_1 D^2 + K_2 D + 1 = \frac{D^2}{\omega_n^2} + \frac{2\xi}{\omega_n}D + 1 \equiv \frac{s^2}{\omega_n^2} + \frac{2\xi}{\omega_n}s + 1$$

Note that gain constants do not affect the forms of Laplace transformations, i.e.,

$$L[Kf(t)] = KL[f(t)] = KF(s)$$

It is important to note that integration constants were neglected. This is justified only where initial conditions of the variables θ_o and θ_i are zero, as described by conditions (1) and (2) in Section 4.3.1. The association of these conditions with the application of Laplace transform techniques to transfer functions will be discussed more completely in Section 4.3.4.

4.3.3 The Procedure for Getting System Response

Consider the following procedure for obtaining the response of the system discussed in the previous example:

$$\frac{\theta_o}{\theta_i} = \frac{K}{1 + T\,D} \quad \text{in the time domain}$$

Substitute s for D to convert to the Laplace domain:

$$\frac{L[\theta_o]}{L[\theta_i]} = \frac{K}{1 + Ts}$$

from which

$$L[\theta_o] = \frac{K \cdot L[\theta_i]}{1 + Ts}$$

For step input $\theta_i = H$,

$$L[\theta_i] = \frac{H}{s} \quad \text{(previous Example)}$$

$$\theta_o(s) = L[\theta_o] = \frac{HK}{s(1 + Ts)}$$

As shown in the previous example, the function of time corresponding to the above $F(s)$ is

$$\theta_o = HK(1 - e^{-t/T})$$

Note that $\theta_o(t)$ above could have been taken directly from Table 4.2 (Function 8) by recognizing the corresponding $F(s)$.

The reader can consolidate this idea by seeking the system response to ramp and sinusoid inputs.

4.3.4 The Relationship between Operators D and s

Consider the expression

$$\frac{dx}{dt} = Dx$$

where $x = x(t)$; $x = x_o$ at $t = 0$.

Then,

$$L[Dx] = \int_0^\infty Dx \cdot e^{-st}\, dt$$

For integration by parts, choose $u = e^{-st}$ and $dv = Dx \cdot dt$, i.e.,

$$v = \int dv = \int \frac{dx}{dt}\, dt = x$$

and

$$du = \frac{du}{dt} \cdot dt = \frac{d}{dt} e^{-st} \cdot dt = -se^{-st} \cdot dt$$

Then $\int u\, dv = uv - \int v\, du$ yields

$$\left[e^{-st} \cdot x - \int x \cdot - se^{-st}\, dt \right]_0^\infty$$

and

$$L[Dx] = -x_o + s\, L[x] = sL[x] - x_o$$

The procedure can be used for higher order differentiations to yield

$$L[D^2x] = L\left[\frac{d^2x}{dt^2}\right] = s^2\, L[x] - sx_o - \dot{x}_o$$

$$L[D^3x] = s^3\, L[x] - s^2x_o - s\dot{x}_o - \ddot{x}_o$$

and more generally,

$$L[D^n x] = s^n L[x] - s^{n-1}x_o - s^{n-2}\dot{x}_o - s^{n-3}\ddot{x}_o \ldots$$

If all initial conditions were zero, then $x_o = \dot{x}_o = \ddot{x}_o$, etc. $= 0$, and

$$L[D^n x] = s^n\, L[x]$$

Consider now the dynamic relationship

$$D^3x = y, \quad \text{or} \quad x \underline{\hspace{2cm}} \boxed{D^3} \underline{\hspace{2cm}} y$$

$$L[D^3x] = L[y]$$

and for all initial conditions zero, $L\,[D^3x] = s^3L[x]$, and $s^3L\,[x] = L\,[y]$

$$\text{or} \quad L[x] \underline{\hspace{2cm}} \boxed{s^3} \underline{\hspace{2cm}} L[y]$$

In transfer function form, these expressions are

$$\frac{y}{x} = D^3 \quad \text{and} \quad \frac{L[y]}{L[x]} = s^3$$

which shows how a relationship in the D (time) domain can be converted into a corresponding relationship in the s (Laplace) domain simply by putting $L[\theta]$ for θ and s for D. For example, a system has the system equation

$$A \, D^2\theta_o + B \, D\theta_o + \theta_o = K\theta_i$$

This equation can be written as the D domain transfer function

$$\frac{\theta_o}{\theta_i} = \frac{K}{A \, D^2 + B \, D + 1}$$

Taking the Laplace transform of the system equation, with all initial conditions zero, yields

$$As^2 \, L[\theta_o] + Bs \, L[\theta_o] + L[\theta_o] = K \, L[\theta_i]$$

which can be written

$$(As^2 + Bs + 1) \, L[\theta_o] = K \, L[\theta_i]$$

or

$$\frac{L[\theta_o]}{L[\theta_i]} = \frac{K}{As^2 + Bs + 1}$$

Many authors adapt this interchangeability of D and s under conditions of zero initial conditions to the extent of writing all system equations and block diagrams in the Laplace transform domain. Thus it is common to see

$$\frac{\theta_o}{\theta_i} = \frac{K}{As^2 + Bs + 1}$$

in which $L[\ ]$ symbols have been dropped from θ_o and θ_i for convenience. The fact that the transfer function involves s instead of D immediately indicates that the author means $L[\theta]$ for θ. Figure 4.9 shows the block

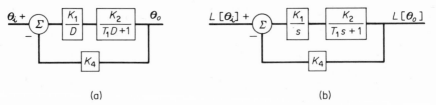

(a)   (b)

Fig. 4.9 Block diagram of a system in: (a) D (time) domain form; (b) Laplace transform form.

diagram of the present system in (a) time domain, and (b) Laplace transform domain.

4.3.5 Inverse Transformation

To get the response of a system to a particular input disturbance by the Laplace transform method,

(a) put the system transfer function $\theta_o/\theta_i = F(D)$ into the Laplace transform domain:

$$\frac{L[\theta_o]}{L[\theta_i]} = F(s)$$

(b) cross-multiply to get the response function:

$$L[\theta_o] = L[\theta_i] \cdot F(s)$$

(c) transform $\theta_i(t)$ to $F_i(s)$ to yield

$$L[\theta_o] = F_i(s) \cdot F(s) = F_o(s)$$

(d) retransform $F_o(s)$ back to the time domain to get the appropriate response function.

This final reconversion is called **inverse transformation**, and is carried out by the use of pair tables such as Table 4.2. Inverse transformation is denoted by

$$L^{-1}[F(s)] = f(t)$$

For example, the previous example produced a transfer function in the Laplace transform domain,

$$\frac{L[\theta_o]}{L[\theta_i]} = \frac{K}{As^2 + Bs + 1}$$

For $\theta_i = Ht$, a ramp function, $L[\theta_i] = (H/s^2)$

$$L[\theta_o] = \frac{L[\theta_i]K}{As^2 + Bs + 1} = \frac{HK}{s^2(As^2 + Bs + 1)} = F_o(s)$$

which is the response function in the Laplace transform domain. $F_o(s)$ is recognizable in Table 4.2 as one of Functions 14, 15, or 16. If the quadratic $As^2 + Bs + 1$ has two real and distinct roots $(1 + T_1 D)$ and $(1 + T_2 D)$, Function 14 is the appropriate form, and the corresponding time function is

$$L^{-1}\left[F_o(s)\right] = \theta_o(t) = HK\left[t - T_1 - T_2 - \frac{1}{T_1 - T_2}(T_2^2 e^{-t/T_2} - T_1^2 e^{-t/T_1})\right]$$

which is the time response of the system to ramp input. Observe that the response expression contains both the particular solution (steady-state term) $HK[t - (T_1 + T_2)]$, and the complementary solution (transient term) $(T_2^2 e^{-t/T_2} - T_1^2 e^{-t/T_1})(T_1 - T_2)$. Note also that the transient term's coefficients are fully evaluated. The response solution can be compared with the corresponding forms developed by classical methods in Section 4.2.5 (i.e., Eq. 4.10b plus Eq. 4.12a).

4.3.6 Use of Partial Fractions

The Laplace transform of the sum of two functions equals the sum of the separate Laplace transforms of the functions, i.e.,

$$L[x + y] = L[x] + L[y] = F_x(s) + F_y(s) = F(s)$$

This very useful linear characteristic enables a complicated $F(s)$ to be broken down by partial fractioning into simpler components which can be recognized in a Laplace transform pair table.

Example:

$$\theta_o(s) = \frac{s + 3}{s^2 + 3s + 2} = \frac{s + 3}{(s + 2)(s + 1)}$$

Let

$$\frac{s + 3}{(s + 2)(s + 1)} = \frac{A}{s + 2} + \frac{B}{s + 1}$$

where A and B are constants. Multiplying both sides by $(s + 2)(s + 1)$ yields

$$s + 3 = A(s + 1) + B(s + 2) = (A + B)s + (A + 2B)$$

Equating like coefficients yields

$$A + B = 1 \quad \text{(the coefficient of } s \text{ on the lefthand side)}$$
$$A + 2B = 3$$

Solving simultaneously yields

$$A = -1; \quad B = 2$$

$$\therefore \theta_o(s) = \frac{s + 3}{s^2 + 3s + 2} = \frac{-1}{s + 2} + \frac{2}{s + 1} = \frac{-\frac{1}{2}}{\frac{1}{2}s + 1} + \frac{2}{s + 1}$$

From Table 4.2, Function 4, the corresponding time function is

$$\theta_o(t) = -e^{-2t} + 2e^{-t}$$

In general, partial fraction expansion can be denoted by

$$F(s) = \frac{Kf_1(s)}{f_2(s)} \quad \text{(where } f_1(s) \text{ and } f_2(s) \text{ are polynomials in } s\text{)}$$

$$= \frac{A_1}{(s + a)} + \frac{A_2}{(s + a)^2} + \cdots + \frac{A_n}{(s + a)^n} + \frac{B_1}{(s + b)} + \frac{B_2}{(s + b)^2}$$

$$+ \cdots + \frac{B_m}{(s + b)^m} + \cdots$$

where $(s + a)$, $(s + b)$, etc. are the distinct root factors of the denominator polynomial $f_2(s)$. The terms

$$\frac{A_2}{(s + a)^2} + \cdots + \frac{A_n}{(s + a)^n} + \cdots + \frac{B_m}{(s + b)^m}$$

appear only where the root factor is repeated.

Example:

$$\theta_o(s) = \frac{10}{(s + 4)(s + 2)^3}$$

Let

$$\frac{10}{(s + 4)(s + 2)^3} = \frac{A}{(s + 2)} + \frac{B}{(s + 2)^2} + \frac{C}{(s + 2)^3} + \frac{D}{s + 4}$$

Multiply both sides by $(s + 4)(s + 2)^3$ to yield

$$10 = A(s + 4)(s + 2)^2 + B(s + 4)(s + 2) + C(s + 4) + D(s + 2)^3$$

Expand and gather terms to yield

$$10 = (A + D)s^3 + (8A + B + 6D)s^2 + (20A + 6B + C + 12D)s$$
$$+ (16A + 8B + 4C + 8D)$$

All coefficients of s terms on the left are zero, and equating coefficients yields

$$A + D = 0; \qquad 8A + B + 6D = 0;$$

$$20A + 6B + C + 12D = 0; \qquad 16A + 8B + 4C + 8D = 10$$

Solving these four simultaneous equations yields

$$A = \tfrac{5}{4}; \quad B = -\tfrac{5}{2}; \quad C = 5; \quad D = -\tfrac{5}{4}.$$

Hence

$$\frac{10}{(s + 4)(s + 2)^3} = \frac{\tfrac{5}{4}}{s + 2} - \frac{\tfrac{5}{2}}{(s + 2)^2} + \frac{5}{(s + 2)^3} - \frac{\tfrac{5}{4}}{s + 4}$$

from which the corresponding $f(t)$ is readily found.

4.3.7 The Response of Second-Order Systems

The response of simple second-order systems to step, ramp, and sine forcing functions was discussed in Section 4.2. The B coefficients associated with the transient terms of the responses were not generally evaluated. Consider the transfer function

$$\frac{\theta_o}{\theta_i} = \frac{K}{D^2/\omega_n^2 + 2\xi/\omega_n\, D + 1}$$

For all initial conditions equal to zero, in the Laplace transform domain,

$$\frac{\theta_o}{\theta_i}(s) = \frac{L[\theta_o]}{L[\theta_i]} = \frac{K}{s^2/\omega_n^2 + 2\xi/\omega_n\, s + 1}$$

and

$$\theta_o(s) = \frac{\theta_i(s)\, K}{s^2/\omega_n^2 + 2\xi/\omega_n\, s + 1}$$

(a) *For* $\theta_i = H$, *step input:* $\theta_i(s) = H/s$ (Table 4.2), and

$$\theta_o(s) = \frac{HK}{s(s^2/\omega_n^2 + 2\xi/\omega_n s + 1)}$$

From Table 4.2, the corresponding $\theta_o(t)$ is

$$\theta_o = HK[1 + (1 - \xi^2)^{1/2}\cdot\exp(-\xi\omega_n t)\cdot\sin\,(\omega_d t - \psi)] \qquad (4.19)$$

where $\omega_d = (1 - \xi^2)^{1/2}\omega_n$ is called the damped natural frequency; $\psi = \tan^{-1}$ $[(1 - \xi^2)^{1/2}/-\xi]$

It should be apparent that HK is the steady-state term of the solution, which is similar to Eq. 4.10(a) obtained by classical solution. The remainder of the expression is the transient term, containing $\exp(-\xi\omega_n t)$ which causes the term to decay in time to 0.

Equation 4.19 is the general response function for the simple second-order system subjected to step input, and is appropriate for all values of damping ratio ξ. However, the expression can be simplified if $\xi \geq 1$. Functions 11 and 12 in Table 4.2 show separately the corresponding $F_o(s)$ and $f_o(t)$ for the cases $\xi = 1$ and $\xi > 1$. The reader can compare the transient parts of Functions 11, 12, and 13 with Eqs. 4.18 and 4.18(a)–(c), which were developed by the classical method.

Figure 4.10(a) shows the response of a second-order system to step input, for various values of damping ratio ξ. The diagram illustrates the real meaning of ξ. For low values of ξ (low damping), the response is fast, has large overshoot, and is highly oscillatory, before it reaches its equilibrium value. For high values of ξ (heavy damping), the response has no overshoot and no oscillation, and is slow to reach its equilibrium value; $\xi = 1$ is the critical case where there is just no overshoot and oscillation. For this case, the response is as rapid as possible without overshoot. Thus damping ratio ξ describes the nature of the response of a second-order system. Figure 4.10(b) shows the degree of overshoot associated with various values of ξ, and Fig. 4.10(c) shows the effect of ξ on ω_d.

The meaning of undamped natural frequency (ω_n) is also shown in Fig. 4.10. For $\xi = 0$, the system experiences a continuous sinusoidal response of frequency ω_n radian/sec. Also it can be seen from Eq. 4.19 that the frequency of the decaying response oscillation is

$$\omega_d = (1 - \xi^2)^{1/2}\,\omega_n$$

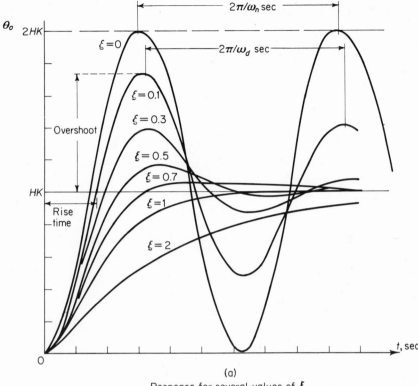

(a)

Response for several values of ξ

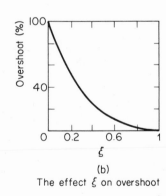

(b)

The effect ξ on overshoot

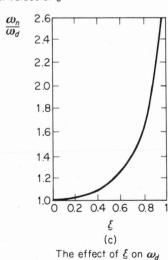

(c)

The effect of ξ on ω_d

Fig. 4.10   Response of the system

$$\frac{\theta_o}{\theta_i} = \frac{K}{D^2/\omega_n^2 + 2\xi D/\omega_n + 1} \text{ to step input } \theta_i = H.$$

which decreases as ξ increases, and disappears when $\xi = 1$.

(b) *For $\theta_i = Ht$, ramp input:* $\theta_i(s) = H/s^2$ (Table 4.2), and

$$\theta_o(s) = \frac{HK}{s^2[s^2/\omega_n^2 + (2\xi/\omega_n)s + 1]}$$

From Table 4.2,

$$\theta_o(t) = HK\left(t - \frac{2\xi}{\omega_n} + \frac{e^{-\xi\omega_n t}}{\omega_d} \sin\,(\omega_d t - \psi)\right) \tag{4.20}$$

where $\omega_d = (1 - \xi^2)^{1/2}\omega_n$; $\psi = 2\,\tan^{-1}\,[(1 - \xi^2)^{1/2}/-\xi]$
Again, for $\xi \geq 1$, the above response expression reduces to the simple forms shown as Functions 14 and 15, Table 4.2.

Figure 4.11(a) shows the effect of ξ on the response of the second-order system to ramp input. Again, the transient region of the response is in-

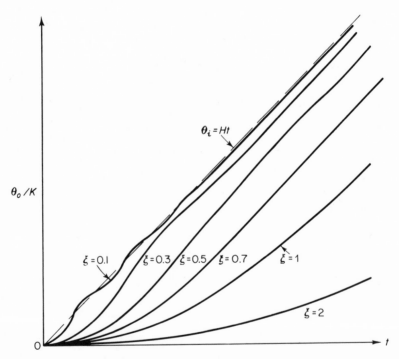

Fig. 4.11   Response of the system

$$\frac{\theta_o}{\theta_i} = \frac{K}{D^2/\omega_n^2 + 2\xi D/\omega_n + 1}$$

to ramp input $\theta_i = Ht$ for various values of damping ratio ξ.

creasingly oscillatory for decreasing values of ξ, and is increasingly sluggish for increasing values of ξ.

(c) *For $\theta_i = H \sin \omega t$, sine input:* $\theta_i(s) = \omega H/(\omega^2 + s^2)$ and

$$\theta_o(s) = \frac{\omega HK}{(\omega^2 + s^2)[s^2/\omega_n^2 + (2\xi/\omega_n)s + 1]}$$

for which (from Table 4.2),

$$\theta_o(t) = \frac{HK\omega_n^2}{[(\omega_n^2 - \omega^2)^2 + (2\xi\omega_n\omega)^2]^{1/2}}$$

$$\cdot \left[\sin(\omega t - \phi) + \frac{\omega}{\omega_d} e^{-\xi\omega_n t} \sin(\omega_d t - \psi) \right] \quad (4.21)$$

where $\omega_d = \omega_n(1 - \xi^2)^{1/2}$;

$$\phi = \tan^{-1}\left[\frac{2\xi\omega_n\omega}{\omega_n^2 - \omega^2} \right]; \quad \psi = \tan^{-1}\left[\frac{-2\xi\omega_n\omega_d}{\omega^2 - \omega_n^2(1 - 2\xi^2)} \right]$$

The value of $\omega_d = \omega_n(1 - \xi^2)^{1/2}$ affects the nature of the response, and it is again apparent that low damping causes the transient region of the response to be magnified and oscillatory.

4.3.8 The Response of High-Order Systems

The response to specified inputs of systems having high-order transfer functions is readily found using Laplace transform methods. If the particular response function $\theta_o(s)$ is not recognizable in available tables of transforms it can be expanded by partial fractioning to the sum of several lower order forms $\theta_o(s)_1 + \theta_o(s)_2 + \cdots$, which are recognizable. The following example demonstrates the complete technique for getting a response solution.

Example 4.6: A system has the transfer function

$$\frac{\theta_o}{\theta_i} = \frac{5(\frac{1}{2}D + 1)}{(3D + 1)(2D^2 + 4D + 1)}$$

It is required to study the nature of the system by examining its response to a step input disturbance $\theta_i = 2$.

Solution: Assume that all initial conditions of θ_o and θ_i are zero. Then, the transfer function can be put into the Laplace transform form

$$\frac{\theta_o}{\theta_i}(s)^* = \frac{5(\frac{1}{2}s + 1)}{(3s + 1)(2s^2 + 4s + 1)}$$

*It is usual to drop the L[ ] or (s) sign and write simply $\dfrac{\theta_o}{\theta_i}$.

Let

$$\frac{5(\frac{1}{2}s + 1)}{(3s + 1)(2s^2 + 4s + 1)} = \frac{A}{(3s + 1)} + \frac{Bs}{(2s^2 + 4s + 1)} + \frac{C}{(2s^2 + 4s + 1)}$$

For $s = 0$,

$$A + C = 5 \qquad (1)$$

Multiply both sides of the expression by $(3s + 1)$:

$$\frac{5(\frac{1}{2}s + 1)}{2s^2 + 4s + 1} = A + \frac{Bs(3s + 1)}{(2s^2 + 4s + 1)} + \frac{C(3s + 1)}{2s^2 + 4s + 1} \qquad (2)$$

for $3s = -1$, or $s = -\frac{1}{3}$ (i.e., force B and C terms to become zero),

$$\frac{5(-\frac{1}{6} + 1)}{\frac{2}{9} - \frac{4}{3} + 1} = A$$

from which $A = -37.5$.   From Expression (1),

$$C = 5 - A = 42.5$$

Using $A = 37.5$, $C = 42.5$, and $s = 1$ (an arbitrary choice) in Expression (2),

$$1.07 = -37.5 + 4B + 24.3$$

$$B = 25$$

$$\therefore \frac{\theta_o}{\theta_i}(s) = \frac{-37.5}{3s + 1} + \frac{25s}{2s^2 + 4s + 1} + \frac{42.5}{2s^2 + 4s + 1}$$

Now, for $\theta_i(t) = 2$, $\theta_i(s) = 2/s$, and

$$\theta_o(s) = \frac{-75}{s(3s + 1)} + \frac{50}{2s^2 + 4s + 1} + \frac{85}{s(2s^2 + 4s + 1)}$$

each term of which is recognizable in Table 4.2.   The quadratic $2s^2 + 4s + 1$ has real factors $(0.585s + 1)(3.4s + 1)$,

$$\therefore \theta_o(t) = -75(1 - e^{-t/3}) + \frac{50}{3.4 - 0.59}(e^{-t/3.4} - e^{-t/0.59})$$

$$+ 85\left[1 + \frac{1}{3.4 - 0.59}(0.59e^{-t/0.59} - 3.4e^{-t/3.4})\right]$$

$$= 10 + 75e^{-t/3} - 85e^{-t/3.4}$$

4.3.9 Summary

The Laplace transform method of solving linear differential equations is readily applied to control system transfer functions to yield response solutions for specified inputs to a system.

If all initial conditions of the system response and input variables are assumed zero, the system transfer function can be put into Laplace transform form by substituting s for D, and reading $\theta(s)$ for θ.

The solutions of most common system response functions have been made and are available in tables of Laplace transform pairs.

If necessary, a complicated system response function $\theta_o(s)$ can be reduced by partial fractioning to the sum of several simple $f(s)$, each of which is recognizable in a table of Laplace transforms. It is a property of linearity that

$$\theta_o(s) = f_1(s) + f_2(s) \cdots$$

has a corresponding

$$\theta_o(t) = f_1(t) + f_2(t) + \cdots$$

4.4 RESPONSE BY ANALOGUE COMPUTER

4.4.1 Introduction

Analog computers are used extensively in the analysis of dynamic systems. They are used

(a) to obtain the response of a system for specified input forcing functions, by solving the appropriate system equation;
(b) to simulate a system, component for component, so that the effect on response of varying one or more system parameters can be studied. Parameter variations can be made on the computer by very simple adjustments.

In effect, the dynamic system to be studied is represented by a dynamically equivalent electrical model on the computer. The real system variables are represented on the computer by voltages of corresponding magnitudes.

The systems of Examples 3.1 through 3.7 had the same form of transfer function, and hence have the same dynamic nature. Hence the electrical circuit of Example 3.2 could be used as an analog of any of the other systems, so long as provision was made that the steady-state relationship between input and response, i.e., the system gain constant, could be other than unity. The system's input and response variables θ_i and θ_o would be represented by the voltages E_i and E_o.

Similarly, the systems of Examples 3.8 through 3.10 could be represented analogously by an electrical system of the form of Example 3.9.

A system which has been represented by a dynamically equivalent voltage circuit on the analog computer can be examined by applying a forcing voltage E_i corresponding to the desired input disturbance θ_i. The response voltage E_o is displayed on an oscilloscope, chart recorder, or voltmeter, and yields the full time response characteristic of the system to the specified disturbance.

Analog computers become increasingly useful as analytical solutions of system equations become difficult or tedious. These conditions can arise when

(a) the system equations are of high order,
(b) a large number of variables are involved,
(c) it is desired to study the effects of parameter variations,
(d) it is desired to optimize system performance, and
(e) nonlinearities are present.

An analog computer contains facilities for selecting and connecting electrical components and circuits which represent actual system quantities, and which are capable of performing the mathematical operations necessary to solving system equations.

While the analog computer is especially suited to solving nonlinear situations, the following work will be confined to linear analysis.

4.4.2 Mathematical Requirements

The solution of a differential equation is essentially an integration process, in which the equation is progressively reduced in order until it yields an algebraic response function $\theta_o(t)$. Thus the ability to integrate is a primary function of the computer. Multiplication and addition are also primary requirements.

The principle mathematical requirements and the symbols used to represent them are now introduced. A more complete discussion is given in following Section 4.4.4.

(a) Multiplication by a constant

Multiplication by a constant is achieved in two ways:

(1) The amplifier-multiplier, represented in Fig. 4.12(a), where

$$e_o = -ne_i \qquad [\text{see } (e) \text{ below.}]$$

and where e_o is response; e_i is input; n is a constant. On the computer, only a limited choice of n is available, possibly $n = 1, 2, 5, 10, 20, 50, 100$. Note that for $n = 1$, the unit only reverses the sign of the input voltage.

(2) The potentiometer-multiplier, represented in Fig. 4.12(b), where

$$e_o = Ke_i, \quad 1 > K > 0$$

K is normally continually variable between 0 and 1.

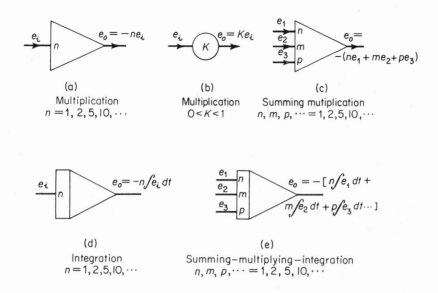

Fig. 4.12 Basic operations and their symbols, associated with analogue computing.

(b) *Summing and summing-multiplying*

The summing-multiplier is represented in Fig. 4.12(c), where

$$e_o = -[ne_1 + me_2 + pe_3 + \ldots] \text{ [see (e) below]}$$

and n, m, and $p = 1, 2, 5, 10, 20 \ldots$, or a similar set of numbers. Note that for $n = m = p = 1$, the unit is a simple adder, with sign reversal.

(c) *Integration*

Integration is represented in Fig. 4.12(d), where

$$e_o = -n \int e_i \, dt \quad \text{[see (e), below]}$$

and again there is a restricted choice of numbers for n. For $n = 1$, the output is minus the time integral of the input.

(d) *Summing-multiplying integration*

Summing-multiplying integration is represented in Fig. 4.12(e), where

$$e_o = -\left[n \int e_1 \, dt + m \int e_2 \, dt + p \int e_3 \, dt + \ldots \right] \quad \text{[see (e), below]}$$

and there is a restricted choice of numbers for n, m, p, etc. For $n = m = p = 1$, the response is minus the sum of the time integrals of the inputs.

(e) *Sign inversion*

The output voltage from the computer units used to produce addition, multiplication by numbers > 1, and integration, is of opposite sign to the input voltage. The origins of this characteristic are revealed in Section 4.4.4. It is often necessary to reverse the sign of the voltage output of a computer unit. Passing the voltage through a unity multiplier (Fig. 4.12a, with $n = 1$) achieves sign reversal. This process is known as sign inversion.

(f) *Function generation*

Forcing functions must be generated before system responses can be obtained. Function generators with voltage outputs are widely available. Steps, ramps, and sinusoids are among the common functions used with analog computer analysis.

Additional requirements for more advanced use of the computer include: multiplication by time varying coefficients of the form $n(t)$; generation of nonlinear operations such as e_i^n, $\exp(e_i t)$, etc.

4.4.3 The Approach for a Computer Solution

The basic approach used to solve a differential equation will be demonstrated with an example:

Consider the system

$$\frac{\theta_o}{\theta_i} = \frac{K}{1 + TD} \qquad \text{or} \qquad T\,D\theta_o + \theta_o = K\theta_i$$

(a) Reduce the coefficient of the highest-order derivative term to unity:

$$D\theta_o + \frac{1}{T}\theta_o = \frac{K}{T}\theta_i$$

(b) Equate the highest-order derivative term to the sum of the remaining terms:

$$D\theta_o = \frac{K}{T}\theta_i - \frac{1}{T}\theta_o$$

(c) Represent this expression symbolically (Fig. 4.13a). It is not usually necessary to compensate for the sign inversion due to the adder at this stage.

(d) Perform the integration(s) necessary to produce the required output or response (Fig. 4.13b). Note that the integrator has reinverted the sign so that $+\theta_o$ is obtained.

(e) Feed back the appropriate variables to the original first adder (Fig. 4.13c). In this case, a sign inverter must be used in the .feedback line to produce $-\theta_o$ from $+\theta_o$.

Thus the computer diagram has been formed.

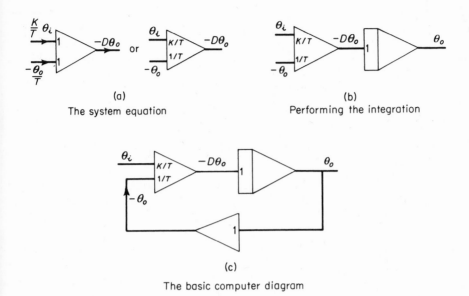

(a)

The system equation

(b)

Performing the integration

(c)

The basic computer diagram

(d)

Alternative forms for (a)

Fig. 4.13 Formation of an analogue computer diagram for response of the system $\theta_o/\theta_i = K/(1 + TD)$.

(f) Connect adders and integrators on the analog computer to complete a circuit similar to the computer diagram.

(g) Generate a suitable voltage $\theta_i(t)$, i.e., step, ramp, sine, etc., and obtain the appropriate response $\theta_o(t)$ from the computer's display device.

Note that several alternatives exist for arranging the computer diagram. In addition to the forms shown in Fig. 4.13(a), the region in the vicinity of the first adder could be represented by either form of Fig. 4.13(d).

The latter form is the most general. On a computer, only a limited choice of α and β values are available. In selecting α and β values, it must be remembered that potentiometer multipliers cannot have values greater than unity. Thus the numbers $K/\alpha T$ and $1/\beta T$ must be less than unity if the latter arrangement is used.

4.4.4 Basic Computer Components

The electrical circuits required to produce the mathematical operations discussed in Section 4.4.2 and used in Section 4.4.3 will now be examined.

The high-gain direct-coupled amplifier

This high input impedance (high-resistance) device is shown symbolically in Fig. 4.14(a). The device's mathematical characteristic is

$$e_o = -Ke_i \quad \text{or} \quad \frac{e_o}{e_i} = -K$$

where e_i and e_o are the input and output voltages respectively, and K is the gain of the amplifier. The negative sign of K shows that the amplifier output is of the opposite sign to the voltage applied to it. For analog computer circuits, gain K is a very high number (of the order 10^5). The high input impedance of the amplifier indicates that only a very small current is required to flow through it to accommodate a substantial amplification in voltage.

The operational amplifier

(a) *With single input:* Consider the resistance-amplifier circuit of Fig. 4.14(b). If the input impedance of the amplifier is much greater than the resistance R_f, then $i_A \doteq 0$, and $i_i \doteq i_f$ (Kirchhoff's law). Then, applying Ohm's law across the resistors,

$$e_i - e = R_i i_i; \quad e - e_o = R_f i_f \doteq R_f i_i$$

$$\therefore i_i = \frac{e_i - e}{R_i} = \frac{e - e_o}{R_f}$$

Using the amplifier relationship $e_o/e = -K$,

$$\frac{e_i + e_o/K}{R_i} = \frac{-e_o/K - e_o}{R_f}$$

and if K is a very large number making $e_i \gg e_o/K$ and $e_o \gg e_o/K$,

$$\frac{e_i}{R_i} = -\frac{e_o}{R_f}$$

or

$$\frac{e_o}{e_i} = -\frac{R_f}{R_i}$$

If $R_f = R_i$, then $e_o = -e_i$ and the circuit provides sign inversion only. If $R_f \neq R_i$, the circuit provides multiplication of the input voltage by a constant, with sign inversion.

No.	Circuit	Operation	Symbol
a	———	Amplifier $$\frac{e_o}{e_i} = -K$$	
b	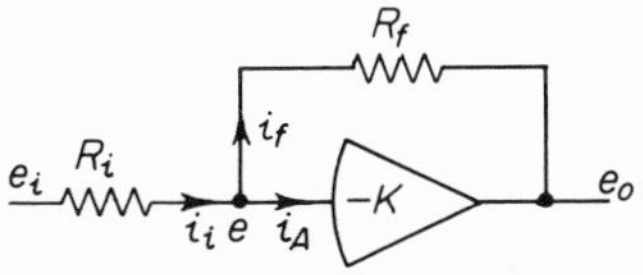	Multiplier $$\frac{e_o}{e_i} = \frac{R_f}{R_i}$$	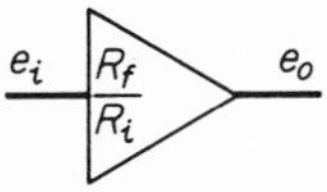
c	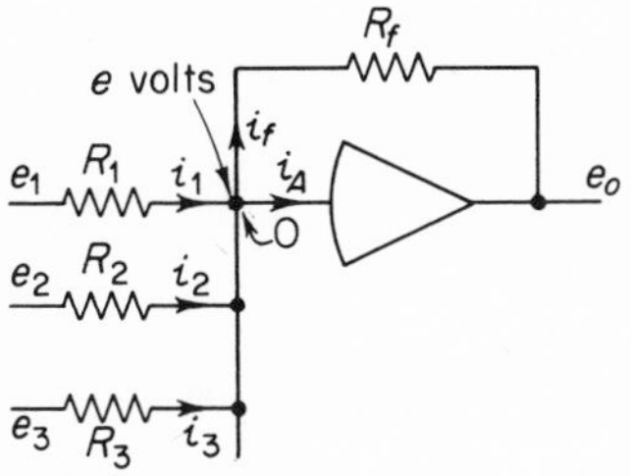	Summing–multiplier $$e_o = -R_f\left[\frac{e_1}{R_1} + \frac{e_2}{R_2} + \frac{e_3}{R_3}\right]$$	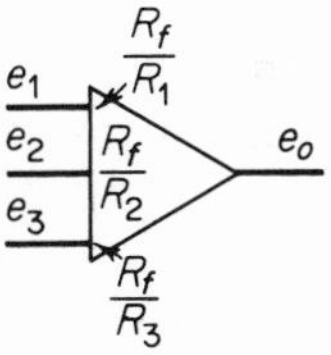
d	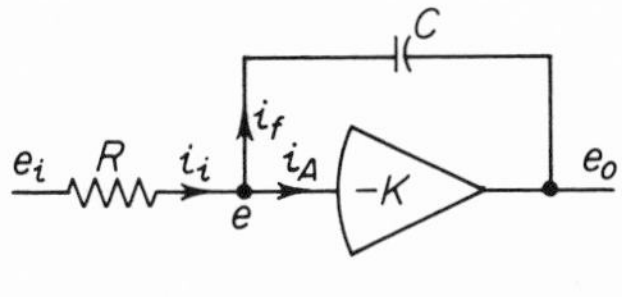	Integrator $$\frac{e_o}{e_i} = -\frac{e_i}{RCD}$$	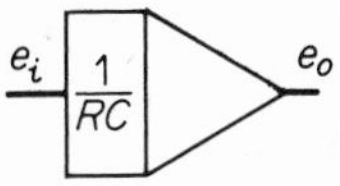
e	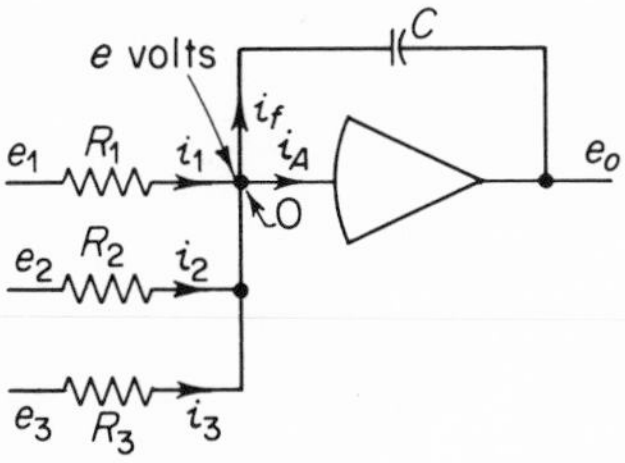	Summing–multiplier–integrator $$e_o = -\left[\frac{e_1}{R_1 CD} + \frac{e_2}{R_2 CD} + \frac{e_3}{R_3 CD}\right]$$	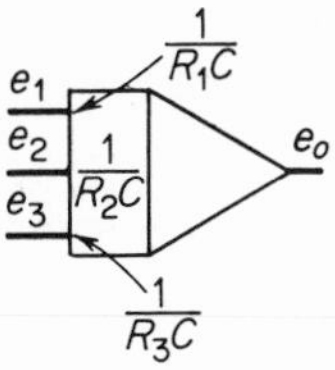
f	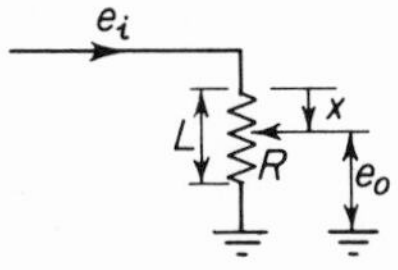	Multiplier $$\frac{e_o}{e_i} = 1 - \frac{x}{L} = K$$	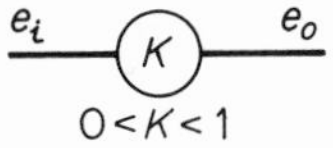 $$0 < K < 1$$

Fig. 4.14 Analogue computer circuits, operations, symbols.

(b) *With multiple inputs:* Consider the resistance-amplifier circuit of Fig. 4.14(c). At the junction 0, $\sum i_o = 0$ (Kirchhoff) yields

$$i_1 + i_2 + i_3 = i_f + i_A \doteq i_f \quad \text{if } i_A \text{ is negligible}$$

Using Ohm's law,

$$\frac{e_1 - e}{R_1} + \frac{e_2 - e}{R_2} + \frac{e_3 - e}{R_e} = \frac{e - e_o}{R_f}$$

Using $e = -e_o/K$,

$$\frac{e_1 + e_o/K}{R_1} + \frac{e_2 + e_o/K}{R_2} + \frac{e_3 + e_o/K}{R_3} = \frac{-e_o/K - e_o}{R_f}$$

If K is sufficiently large to make $e_o/K \ll e_1, e_2, e_3$, and e_o,

$$\frac{e_1}{R_1} + \frac{e_2}{R_2} + \frac{e_3}{R_3} = -\frac{e_o}{R_f}$$

or

$$e_o = -\left(\frac{R_f}{R_1} e_1 + \frac{R_f}{R_2} e_2 + \frac{R_f}{R_3} e_3\right)$$

If $R_1 = R_2 = R_3 = R_f$,

$$e_o = -(e_1 + e_2 + e_3)$$

Thus if $R_1 = R_2 = R_3 = R_f$, the circuit of Fig. 4.14(c) provides a direct summing of the input voltages e_1, e_2, e_3, with sign inversion. If $R_1 \neq R_f$, $R_2 \neq R_f$, and $R_3 \neq R_f$, the circuit provides an addition of proportions of the input voltages, again with sign inversion.

In general, the circuit operation can be written

$$e_o = -\sum_1^n \left(\frac{R_f}{R_i} e_i\right) = -R_f \sum_1^n \frac{e_i}{R_i}$$

where there are n input voltages e_i being applied simultaneously through n input resistors R_i. The circuit provides a multiplying-summing unit.

The integrating amplifier

(a) *With single input:* Consider the resistance-capacitance-amplifier circuit of Fig. 4.14(d):

$$i_i = \frac{e_i - e}{R} \quad \text{(Ohm)}; \quad e - e_o = \frac{1}{C} \int i_f \, dt \quad \text{(Faraday)}$$

$$\therefore i_f = C \frac{d}{dt} (e - e_o)$$

If $i_A \doteq 0$, $i_f \doteq i_i$ and

$$\frac{e_i - e}{R} = C \, D(e - e_o)$$

Using $eK = -e_o$ or $e = -e_o/K$,

$$\frac{e_i + e_o/K}{R} = C\,D(-e_o/K - e_o)$$

which, if K is very large, becomes

$$e_i/R = -C\,De_o$$

or

$$e_o = -\frac{e_i}{RC\,D} = -\frac{1}{RC}\int e_i\,dt$$

That is, the output voltage e_o is a constant $1/RC$ multiplied by the time integral of the input voltage, with sign inversion. If $RC = 1$

$$e_o = -\int e_i\,dt$$

so that output voltage e_o is minus the time integral of the input voltage.

(b) *With multiple inputs:* Consider the circuit of Fig. 4.14(e). $\sum i = 0$ applied to the junction 0 yields

$$i_1 + i_2 + i_3 = i_f + i_A \doteq i_f \quad \text{as } i_A \text{ is negligible}$$

$$\frac{e_1 - e}{R_1} + \frac{e_2 - e}{R_2} + \frac{e_3 - e}{R_3} = -C\,D(e - e_o)$$

and eliminating e as before,

$$\frac{e_1}{R_1} + \frac{e_2}{R_2} + \frac{e_3}{R_3} = -C\,De_o$$

$$e_o = -\left(\frac{e_1}{R_1C\,D} + \frac{e_2}{R_2C\,D} + \frac{e_3}{R_3C\,D}\right)$$

$$= -\left(\frac{1}{R_1C}\int e_1\,dt + \frac{1}{R_2C}\int e_2\,dt + \frac{1}{R_3C}\int e_3\,dt\right)$$

That is, the circuit acts as a summing integrator, with sign inversion. The integrated voltages are multiplied by a constant $1/RC$. If $R_1 = R_2 = R_3 = R$, and $RC = 1$, then

$$e_o = -\int (e_1 + e_2 + e_3)\,dt$$

In gneral, the circuit performance can be expressed

$$e_o = -\sum_1^n \frac{e_i}{R_iC\,D} = -\frac{1}{C\,D}\sum_1^n \frac{e_i}{R_i} = -\frac{1}{C}\int \sum_1^n \frac{e_i}{R_i}\,dt$$

The potentiometer

Consider the linear potentiometer illustrated in Fig. 4.14(f). If the wiper is at the top end of the resistor, such that $x = 0$, then the output voltage e_o is the same as the input voltage e_i. If the wiper is at the lower end of the resistor, the output voltage is zero, as the voltage has been fully dissipated in the resistance. If the wiper is part of the way down the resistor, the output voltage lies between e_i and 0. For a linear potentiometer,

$$e_o = e_i \left(1 - \frac{x}{L} \right)$$

where L is the total length of the resistor and x is the displacement of the wiper.

The expression can be written

$$e_o = K e_i \quad \text{or} \quad \frac{e_o}{e_i} = K$$

where K can be varied between 0 and 1.

Thus a potentiometer provides a means for multiplying voltages by constants in the range 0–1. As demonstrated in the example of Section 4.3.3, a potentiometer can be used in conjunction with amplifier multipliers to give a required multiplication. Note that there is no sign inversion. For example, a required multiplication constant of 5.5 can be achieved by using 0.55 on a potentiometer and feeding the output into a "10 times" multiplier on a summing unit.

4.4.5 Some Examples

Example 4.7: Construct an analog computer diagram for obtaining the response of the damped-spring-mass system of Example 3.8, whose transfer function is

$$\frac{x}{F_i} = \frac{1/k}{(W/gk) \cdot D^2 + (c/k)\, D + 1}$$

Assume all initial conditions are zero.

Solution: The system differential equation is

$$\frac{W}{gk}\, D^2 x + \frac{c}{k}\, Dx + x = \frac{1}{k} F_i$$

Making the coefficient of the d^2x/dt^2 term unity, and equating this term to the remaining terms,

$$D^2 x = \frac{g}{W} \cdot F_i - \frac{cg}{W}\, Dx - \frac{kg}{W} x$$

Represent this equation symbolically, as shown in Fig. 4.15(a).

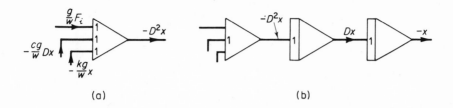

(a)   (b)

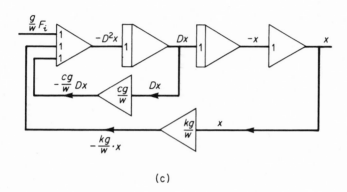

(c)

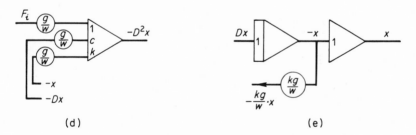

(d)   (e)

Fig. 4.15   Formation of computer diagram for the system

$$\frac{x}{F_i} = \frac{1/k}{WD^2/gk + cD/k + 1}$$

It is apparent that two integrations of D^2x are necessary to get x, the desired response. These integrations are shown in Fig. 4.15(b): $-x$ can be put through a unit summing unit to give sign inversion to $+x$ (Fig. 4.15c); Dx can be fed back through a "(cg/W) times" multiplier to give the $(-cg/W) \cdot Dx$ required at the first summing unit; x can be fed back through a (kg/W) times multiplier to give the $-kg/W \cdot x$ term required at the first summing unit.

Figure 4.15(c) is a suitable basic computer diagram. It can now be modified

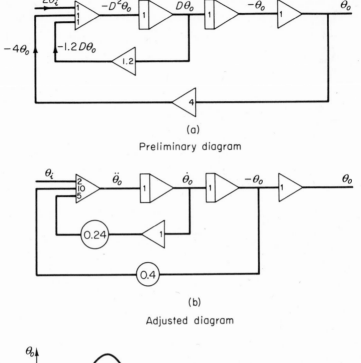

(a)

Preliminary diagram

(b)

Adjusted diagram

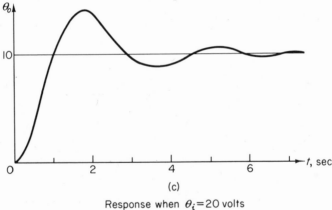

(c)

Response when $\theta_i = 20$ volts

Fig. 4.16 Solution of the equation $2\ddot{\theta}_o + 2.4\dot{\theta}_o + 8\theta_o = 4\theta_i$ for $\theta_i = 20$.

depending on the values of the numbers g/W, cg/W, and kg/W. For example, if $g/W < 1$, the initial summing unit could be connected in the form shown in Fig. 4.15(d). Or, if $kg/W < 1$, then $-x$ could have been fed back through a potentiometer as shown in Fig. 4.15(e). There are several other possible combinations and connections.

Having obtained a suitable computer diagram, generate the input voltage representing F_i and study the response voltage representing $x(t)$ generated and displayed by the computer.

Example 4.8: Solve the differential equation

$$2\ddot{\theta}_o + 2.4\dot{\theta}_o + 8\theta_o = 4\theta_i$$

where all initial conditions are zero; θ_i is the forcing function; θ_o is the response variable. The summing units of the computer are capable of multiplications by 1, 2, 5, 10, and 20 only.

Solution: The equation can be written

$$D^2\theta_o = 2\theta_i - 1.2D\theta_o - 4\theta_o$$

Figure 4.16(a) shows the initial computer diagram formed from the equation. The diagram will now be matched to the computer.

(a) θ_i can be fed directly into a "2 times" multiplier on the first summing unit (Fig. 4.16b).
(b) $D\theta_o$ can be fed back through a sign inverter (i.e., a unity amplifier multiplier or summer), then through a potentiometer set at $K = 0.24$, and then into a "5 times" multiplier on the summing unit.
(c) $-\theta_o$ can be fed back instead of θ_o. $-\theta_o$ can be fed back through a potentiometer set at 0.4, and then into the "10 times" multiplier on the summing unit.

The resulting diagram, Fig. 4.16(b), is by no means the only possible form. Time and magnitude scaling of the diagram, to be discussed in Section 4.4.6, affects the best final form of the computer diagram.

Figure 4.16(c) shows the response of the computer when step change $\theta_i = 20$ volts is applied to it. As no scaling was attempted, 1 volt represents 1 unit of θ_i, and 1 volt represents 1 unit of θ_o.

4.4.6 Applying Initial Conditions

Commonly, the response variable and/or its derivations can have initial values at the time $t = 0$ when the forcing function is applied. Such initial conditions are readily included in computer solutions, by applying biasing voltages representing the initial values at the appropriate points on the computer. Most commonly the initial condition of a variable is included by applying the voltage representing it across the capacitor of the integrator the output of which is the variable being considered. Figure 4.17(a) shows the arrangement, with the initial value being applied across the integrator the output of which is x. In operation, the switch in the initial condition circuit is closed, maintaining the biasing voltage across the capacitor. At time $t = 0$ when the forcing function is applied and the solution begins, the switch is automatically opened to allow the bias voltage to drain into

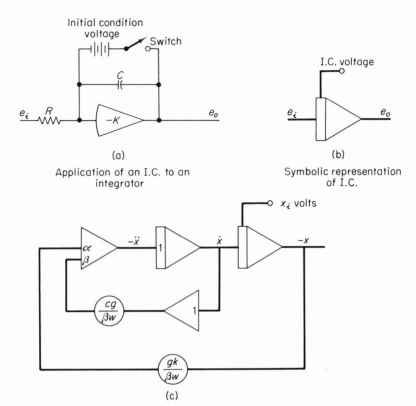

(a)

Application of an I.C. to an integrator

(b)

Symbolic representation of I.C.

(c)

Using the I.C. $x = x_i$ at $t = 0$,
to examine the transient nature of the system

$$\frac{w}{gk} D^2 x + \frac{c}{k} Dx + x = 0$$

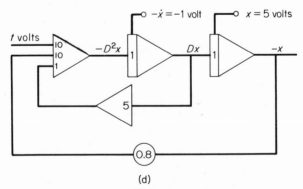

(d)

Computer diagram for solving,
$D^2 x + 5Dx + 8x = 10t$ where $x = 5$ and $\dot{x} = 1$ at $t = 0$

Fig. 4.17 Applying initial conditions.

the circuit as the initial condition. Figure 4.17(b) shows the computer diagram symbol for an initial condition.

The sign and magnitude of an initial condition voltage are governed by the following rules:

(1) If the sign of the real initial condition is negative, the signs of the initial condition voltage and the associated integrator output must be the same. That is, both are negative or both are positive. If the sign of the real initial condition is positive, the signs of the initial condition voltage and the integrator output must be opposite. That is, if the integrator output is negative the initial condition voltage must be positive, and vice versa.
(2) The magnitude of the initial condition voltage must be multiplied by any coefficient appearing with the output variable. That is, if the output from an integrator is $2\dot{x}$, any initial condition of $\dot{x}$ must be multiplied by 2.

When it is desired to study the free (transient) response of a system without applying a forcing function, a suitable initial condition can be applied to generate the response. The damped-spring-mass system (Example 3.8) could be examined in this manner by displacing the mass a distance x_i and then releasing it. The following example demonstrates this point.

Example 4.9: Construct an analog computer diagram for studying the free response of the damped-spring-mass unit of Example 3.8.

Solution: Consider the system to be in equilibrium when the mass is displaced downwards by x_i and released.

The system equation is then

$$\frac{W}{gk} D^2x + \frac{c}{k} Dx + x = 0, \quad \text{as } F_i = 0$$

with initial conditions $x = x_i$ at $t = 0$, $\dot{x} = 0$ at $t = 0$.

$$\therefore D^2x = \frac{cg}{W} Dx - \frac{gk}{W}x$$

The basic computer diagram is shown in Fig. 4.17(c). The initial condition $x = x_i$ at $t = 0$ is shown as a voltage $+x_i$ volts applied to the integrator whose output is $-x$.

Actuation of the switch in the initial condition circuit corresponds to physical displacement and release of the mass. The resulting response $x(t)$ volts on the computer corresponds to the physical motion of the mass after release.

Example 4.10: Construct an analog computer diagram for solving the equation

$$D^2x + 5Dx + 8x = 10t$$

where $x = 5$ and $\dot{x} = 1$ at $t = 0$.

$$D^2x = -5Dx - 8x + 10t$$

Figure 4.17(d) shows the computer diagram, with the initial conditions applied.

4.4.7 Time and Magnitude Scaling

So far, no attempt has been made to scale the computer diagram relative to the real system being represented. One volt has been used to represent one unit of the real system variable. Real time has been used on the computer.

Magnitude scaling is often necessary

(a) to limit the voltages representing the variables of a system to the maximum allowed on the computer; commonly, analog computers can accept voltages up to 100 volts; hence a system variable which has a maximum value of 500 real units must be scaled down by a factor of less than 0.2 to fit onto the computer;

(b) to increase very small voltages, representing very small values of a system variable, to levels where computer noise and error are minimized. For example, a 0–100 volt computer cannot be expected to operate very accurately on a signal of 2 volts. It would be necessary to scale this low voltage up by a factor of 10 or 20.

Computer diagrams need to be magnitude scaled only in regions of problem voltages. For example, in Fig. 4.17 the injection of a 1-volt initial condition for $\dot{x}$ on a 100-volt computer would lead to inaccurate results. The voltages in the region of $\dot{x}$ could be multiplied by 10, and the computer diagram suitably compensated, as shown in Fig. 4.18.

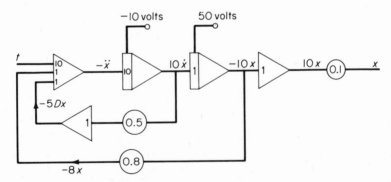

Fig. 4.18 The magnitude of Fig. 4.17(d), scaled 10 times in the region of the integrators.

The normal limit of scaling is that the output from any summing or integrating unit should not exceed the rated maximum voltage of the computer.

Time scaling is necessary if

(a) a solution in real time would be so fast that the computer output display unit could not respond adequately,
(b) a solution in real time would be very slow. That is, if the real system had a very slow response.

In the former case it is necessary to slow down the computer solution so that the computer time is a multiple of the real time unit (seconds). In the latter case, it is convenient to speed up the computer operation so that it reacts faster than the real system.

Let

$$t = aT$$

where t is the real time unit; T is the computer time unit; a is a constant. Then,

$$\frac{dx}{dt} = \frac{dx}{d(aT)} = \frac{1}{a}\frac{dx}{dT}$$

and

$$\frac{d^2x}{dt^2} = \frac{d^2x}{d(a^2T^2)} = \frac{1}{a^2}\frac{d^2x}{dT^2}$$

and generally,

$$\frac{d^nx}{dt^n} = \frac{1}{a^n}\frac{d^nx}{dT^n}$$

To time scale an equation,

(a) decide the scaling factor a, noting
   (1) for slowing down a solution, $T > t$ and $a < 1$,
   (2) for speeding up a solution, $T < t$ and $a > 1$;
(b) put T for t in the equation to be solved;
(c) multiply each derivative term by its appropriate a^{-n};
(d) program the equation obtained.

Example 4.11: A system response equation is

$$\frac{d^3x}{dt^3} + K_1\frac{d^2x}{dt^2} + K_2\frac{dx}{dt} + K_3x = H \sin \omega t$$

It is required to solve the equation for $x(t)$ on an analog computer. It is required to slow down the solution to 5 times real time. Obtain the equation to be put onto the computer.

Solution:

$$t = 0.2T \quad \text{or} \quad a = 0.2$$

Hence,

$$\frac{1}{0.2^3}\frac{d^3x}{dT^3} + \frac{K_1}{0.2^2}\frac{d^2x}{dT^2} + \frac{K_2}{0.2}\frac{dx}{dT} + K_3x = H \sin 0.2\,\omega T$$

is the equation to be set up on the computer.

The time scale of a computer response can be changed to read real time by multiplying it by a.

4.4.8 Simulation

So far this chapter has been concerned only with the solution of system equations to yield the systems response to specified input disturbances. It will now be shown that a system can be directly simulated, component by component, on the computer. A simulation computer diagram can be drawn directly from the block diagram of the system.

Figure 4.19(a) shows the block diagram of the damped-spring-mass

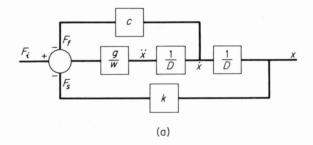

(a)

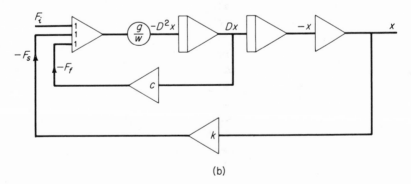

(b)

Fig. 4.19 (a) Block diagram; (b) basic computer diagram simulating the damped-spring-mass system.

system of Example 3.8 (see also Example 3.14). Figure 4.19(b) shows the computer diagram for direct simulation. It should be apparent that the diagram can have a number of minor variations, depending on the range of values of the system constants. The similarity between Fig. 4.19(b) and Fig. 4.15(c) is apparent. In general, the computer diagram for direct simulation is only a more detailed extension of the diagram for simple solution. The simulation diagram can be treated for initial conditions, time and magnitude scaling. Simulation allows study of the effects on system respones of direct variation of system parameters.

4.5 GENERAL SUMMARY

The nature of a dynamic engineering system can be revealed by effecting a time solution of the system equation (or transfer function), using specified forcing functions to simulate system input disturbances.

The time history (i.e., the response) of the system to specified inputs reflects the following characteristics of the system:

(a) stability, if it reaches a steady-state condition of the same form as the input disturbance;
(b) instability, if it does not reach in time an appropriate steady-state condition;
(c) possible oscillatory nature;
(d) rapidity of response, or its sluggishness of response;
(e) steady-state error for the particular input used.

Three methods for obtaining a system's time response were investigated:

(a) Classical solution of the system equation

The classical solution of the system equation contains two distinct components. The particular solution is of the same form as the applied disturbance. The complementary solution is of exponential form, and decays toward zero with time for a stable system, but increases continually with time for an unstable system. The particular solution is called the steady-state term of the full response function, and the complementary solution is called the transient term. The full response solution is the algebraic sum of the steady-state and transient terms. For a stable system, the response approaches the steady-state term as time increases. The stability of the system is associated only with the transient response term. The roots of the characteristic equation, which is the equation whose solution yields the complementary function, must be negative for the system to be stable.

Classical solution of differential equations is increasingly tedious as the order of the equation increases. However, a study of the classical solutions of first- and second-order systems gives an understanding of the nature of time response exceeding the understanding to be gained from the following two alternative methods of solution.

(b) Laplace transform solution of the system equation

A linear differential equation in the time domain can be transformed to an equivalent algebraic equation in the Laplace operator domain. Solution of this algebraic equation is readily made, using tables of Laplace transform pairs. The Laplace operator domain solution is then retransformed to the time domain to give the required time solution. The technique is quickly learned and quickly applied. The solution obtained combines the steady-state and transient terms, and includes evaluation of the response coefficients.

Subject to the condition that the input and response variables, and all of their time derivatives, are zero at the instant the forcing function is introduced, a transfer function can be converted from the time domain ($D = d/dt$) to the Laplace transform domain by substituting the Laplace operator s for D.

High-order transfer functions can be reduced to the sum of several simpler transfer function components, the forms of which are available in Laplace transform pair tables, by use of partial fractioning.

(c) Analog computer solution of the system equation

The engineering system can be simulated on an analog computer, with the system variables being represented by voltage signals. With a little practice, solutions of linear differential equations are quickly effected. Normally the solution is displayed as a response-time curve on a voltage sensitive meter such as an oscilloscope or a chart recorder. Equations can be scaled, regarding both magnitude and time, to fit the available computer voltages. Initial conditions of the system variables are readily applied.

Direct simulation of the system, component for component, on the computer allows a rapid study of the effect on system response of variations in selected system parameters.

Analog computer methods are especially suited to the solution of nonlinear system equations.

It should be recognized that system equations can also be solved on a digital computer. However, at the present level of work, it is unlikely that any further understanding of system dynamics would be gained from studying this method.

PROBLEMS

4.1 A system has the transfer function

$$\frac{\theta_o}{\theta_i} = \frac{1.33}{1 + 7.45D}$$

Use the classical method to obtain and plot the response of the system $\theta_o(t)$, to a ramp forcing function $\theta_i = 6t$.

Answer: $x_o = 59.5\,(e^{-0.135t} + 0.135t - 1)$

4.2 A system has the transfer function

$$\frac{h_o}{P_i} = \frac{0.016}{1 + 0.17D + 0.0277D^2}$$

Use the classical method to obtain and plot the response of the system $h_o(t)$, to a step input disturbance $P_i = 20$.

Answer: $h_o = 0.32[1 + 1.16\,e^{-3t}\sin{(5.2t - 1.04)}]$

4.3 Solve Problem 4.1 using Laplace transforms.

4.4 Solve Problem 4.2 using Laplace transforms.

4.5 Use partial fractions and Table 4.2 to get the time responses associated with the following transformed response functions:

(a) $\theta_o(s) = \dfrac{2(s + 6)}{s(s + 2)(s + 4)}$ (b) $\theta_o(s) = \dfrac{20}{s^2(1 + 2s)(1 + 3s + 2s^2)}$

4.6 The system of Problem 3.3 had the transfer function (converted to seconds units from minutes),

$$\frac{\theta_o}{q} = \frac{0.12}{20D^2 + 18D + 1}$$

Obtain the response function $\theta_o(t)$ if the system is subjected to a sine input $q = 50 \sin 0.1\,t$.

Answer: $\theta_o = 6[0.475e^{-0.06t} - 0.0092e^{-0.84t} + 0.51 \sin{(0.1 - 1.155)}]$

4.7 Construct the analogue computer diagram for solving Problem 4.6.

4.8 (a) Solve the equation $K_1 D^2\theta_o + \theta_o = 0$, where $\theta_o = 0$ and $\dot{\theta}_o = K_2$ at $t = 0$.
(b) Construct an analogue computer diagram for generating the sinusoid $40 \sin 2t$.

Answer: (a) $K_2 K^{1/2} \sin K^{-1/2}t = \dfrac{k_2}{\omega_n} \sin \omega_n t$, where $\omega_n = K_1^{-1/2}$

4.9 Construct the analog computer diagram for the system whose system equation is

$$D^3\theta_o + 2D^2\theta_o + 5D\theta_o + 10\theta_o = f(t)$$

where $\theta_o = 5$, $\dot{\theta}_o = 0$, and $\ddot{\theta}_o = 10$ at $t = 0$.
Maximum expected values are $\theta_{om} = 10$, $\theta_{om} = 20$, $\theta_{om} = 50$, $\theta_{om} = 100$, and $f(t) = 25$, where all units are consistent.
It is required to slow down the solution to 20 per cent of real time. Maximum computer voltage is 10 volts.

4.10 Draw a computer diagram suitable for complete simulation of the pneumatic servomechanism of Example 3.23.

5 *Frequency response analysis*

5.1 INTRODUCTION

The response of components and systems to several types of input disturbance was investigated in Chapter 4. It was established that the response function $\theta_o = f(t)$ contained two complementary terms — a transient term (the complementary solution) and a steady-state term (the particular solution) — obtained by solution of the system equation or transfer function for the particular disturbance introduced. Only stable systems, in which the transient term decays in time to zero, are being considered at this stage. Further, it was established that the steady-state term for persisting input disturbances (steps, ramps, sinusoids, etc.) is of the same form as the disturbance, and that the response function is asymptotic to its steady-state term as the transient term decays in time.

Analysis using sinusoidal input signals has been highly developed, as sinusoids are

(a) readily generated for experimental analysis in most physical dimensions (voltage, pressure, displacement, force, etc.), and readily varied in amplitude and frequency as required;

(b) continuous in time, but limited in magnitude (amplitude);
(c) readily expressed mathematically.

In particular, analysis involving only the steady-state term of the response to sinusoidal input has been developed to the point where it provides a comprehensive description of the dynamic behavior of a linear system. Analysis via the steady-state term of the response due to sinusoidal input is known as **steady-state frequency response analysis,** or simply as **frequency response.**

5.2 THE FREQUENCY RESPONSE CHARACTERISTIC

5.2.1 Classical Approach

In general, a physical component or system whose transfer function is $\theta_o/\theta_i = f(D)$ will respond to a sinusoidal input disturbance $\theta_i = H \sin \omega t$ as follows:

$$\frac{\theta_o}{\theta_i} = f(D)$$

$$\therefore f(D)^{-1} \cdot \theta_o = \theta_i$$

and for $\theta_i = H \sin \omega t$,

$$\theta_o = f(t) = \theta_{o1} + \theta_{o2}$$

where $\theta_{o2} = f_2(t)$ is the complementary solution which yields an exponentially decaying transient term of the form $f(\omega, e^{-\alpha t})$ for a stable situation; $\theta_{o1} = f_1(t)$ is the particular solution which yields a steady-state term of the form $B \sin (\omega t + \phi)$, where B and ϕ are constants for a particular input frequency ω.

As θ_{o2} decays toward zero with time, the response θ_o becomes asymptotic to θ_{o1}. After full decay of θ_{o2}, $\theta_o = \theta_{o1}$. This situation is illustrated in Fig. 5.1.

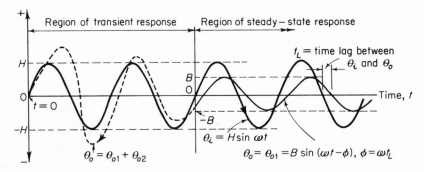

Fig. 5.1 Typical system response to sinusoidal input: θ_{o2} is transient term of response; θ_{o1} is steady-state term of response.

It was shown in Chapter 4 that the steady-state response sinusoid

(a) has the same frequency as the input sinusoid;
(b) has an amplitude which is a function of the input frequency;
(c) has a phase relative to the input sinusoid, and that the phase is a function of the input frequency.

Thus, for $\theta_i = H \sin \omega t$,

$$\theta_{o1} = B \sin (\omega t + \phi)$$

where $B = f_1(\omega)$, $\phi = f_2(\omega)$.

Consider the first-order transfer function $\theta_o/\theta_i = K/(1 + T D)$ analyzed in detail in Chapter 4. For $\theta_i = H \sin \omega t$, the steady-state response is

$$\theta_{o1} = \frac{KH}{(1 + \omega^2 T^2)^{1/2}} \cdot \sin (\omega t + \phi)$$

where $\phi = -\tan^{-1} \omega T$. Thus, B is the amplitude,

$$B = f_1(\omega) = \frac{KH}{(1 + \omega^2 T^2)^{1/2}}$$

and ϕ is the phase relative to the input sinusoid of the response,

$$\phi = f_2(\omega) = -\tan^{-1} \omega T$$

For a particular case, K, H, and T are constants and B and ϕ can be evaluated for various values of ω.

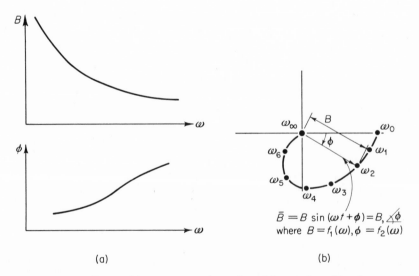

Fig. 5.2 Types of frequency-response plots: (a) cartesian; (b) polar.

The frequency response characteristic of a component or system is essentially a plot against input frequency of its steady-state response amplitude $[B = f_1(\omega)]$ and phase $[\phi = f_2(\omega)]$, for a sinusoidal input disturbance $(\theta_i = H \sin \omega t)$ whose amplitude (H) is maintained constant and whose frequency (ω) is varied over an adequate range.

The frequency response characteristic can be plotted as two curves in Cartesian form, as shown in Fig. 5.2(a).

The response sinusoid for a particular input frequency can be represented by the phasor $\bar{B} = B \sin (\omega t + \phi)$ shown in Fig. 5.2(b). The phasor can be described in polar notation by $B,\ \angle \phi$. Phasors can be drawn to represent the response sinusoid for a full range of frequency ω, and the locus of the heads of the phasors is the frequency response characteristic in polar form. Figure 5.2(b) shows a polar frequency response locus representing amplitude B and phase ϕ for a range of values of frequency ω. The single polar curve contains the same information as the two Cartesian curves of Fig. 5.2(a).

Example 5.1: Plot the frequency response locus of the system whose transfer function is

$$\frac{\theta_o}{\theta_i} = \frac{3}{1 + 2D}$$

for an input sinusoid $\theta_i = 2 \sin \omega t$.

Solution: The steady-state solution of this problem is

$$\theta_{o1} = \frac{6}{(1 + 4\omega^2)^{1/2}} \cdot \sin (\omega t - \phi)$$

where $\phi = \tan^{-1} 2\omega$; i.e., amplitude of response is

$$B = \frac{6}{(1 + 4\omega^2)^{1/2}}$$

and phase of response is

$$\phi = -\tan^{-1} 2\omega$$

The $B\text{–}\omega$, $\phi\text{–}\omega$ relationships can be evaluated and plotted in either Cartesian or polar form as shown in Fig. 5.3.

Higher-order transfer functions can be treated similarly to yield the response amplitude-frequency, and the response phase-frequency characteristics.

5.2.2 Nondimensional Presentation of Response Data

It is common practice to generalize frequency response characteristics by presenting the response amplitude, and if possible the frequency, in

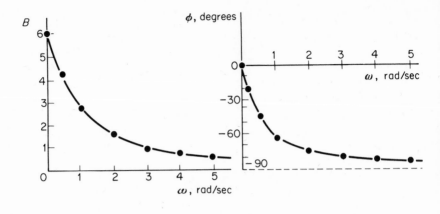

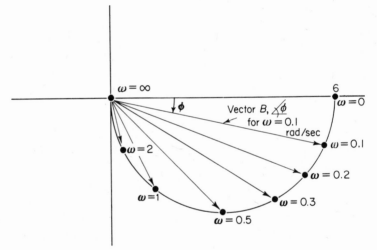

Polar plot

ω, rad/sec =	0	0.1	0.2	0.3	0.4	0.5	1	2	3	4	5	10	∞
B =	6	5.9	5.55	5.12	4.7	4.25	2.68	1.45	0.98	0.75	0.595	0.3	0
ϕ, degrees =	0	$-11\frac{1}{4}$	$-21\frac{3}{4}$	-31	$-38\frac{1}{2}$	-45	$-63\frac{1}{2}$	-76	$-80\frac{1}{2}$	-83	$-84\frac{1}{4}$	-87	-90

Fig. 5.3 Frequency response characteristics of the system $\theta_o/\theta_i = 3/(1 + 2D)$ for $\theta_i = 2 \sin \omega t$.

nondimensional form. Response amplitude can be represented by the **nondimensional magnitude ratio:**

$$G^* = \frac{B}{KH} \tag{5.1}$$

where B is the amplitude of the response sinusoid $[B = f_1(\omega)]$; H is the amplitude of the input sinusoid (constant); and K is the system gain constant relating the static equilibrium values of θ_o and θ_i (K is often unity). Frequency ω can be nondimensionalized by using ωT to represent ω, T being a convenient time constant.

Example 5.2: For the first-order transfer function $\theta_o/\theta_i = K/(1 + T D)$, and $\theta_i = H \sin \omega t$,

$$B = \frac{KH}{(1 + \omega^2 T^2)^{1/2}}; \qquad \phi = -\tan^{-1} \omega T; \qquad G^* = \frac{B}{KH} = \frac{1}{(1 + \omega^2 T^2)^{1/2}}$$

$$(5.2)$$

which are evaluated and plotted in Fig. 5.4. The plots of Fig. 5.4 are applicable to all components and systems whose transfer function is of the form $\theta_o/\theta_i = K/1 + T D$. The amplitude of the response sinusoid, represented by the magnitude ratio G^*, attenuates continually as frequency is increased from zero. The response sinusoid lags the input sinusoid by an increasing phase angle as frequency increases, and is asymptotic to $\phi = -90°$ at high frequencies. The polar frequency response characteristic is a semicircle in the fourth quadrant, which is apparent from the form of the $B = f_1(\omega)$ relationship for the first-order case.

It may be preferred to define the **magnitude ratio** as $G = B/H$. In this case, the frequency response characteristic plot starts from $G = K$ for $\omega = 0$, which will be unity only if $K = 1$, and which will be dimensionless only if K is dimensionless.

5.2.3 The Complex Number Approach

The properties of a complex number are reviewed in Appendix B (pp. 411–415).

A complex number $(a + jb)$ can be represented on the complex plane by the phasor shown in Fig. 5.5(a), the magnitude of which is $(a^2 + b^2)^{1/2}$, and the position of which relative to the positive real axis is $\phi = \tan^{-1} b/a$.

Complex number phasors and products of complex number phasors can be presented in polar notation using the following common procedures (Fig. 5.5b):

$$\bar{P} = P, \phi_p; \qquad \bar{Q} = Q, \phi_Q$$

$$\bar{P} \cdot \bar{Q} = PQ, (\phi_p + \phi_Q)$$

$$\frac{\bar{P}}{\bar{Q}} = \frac{P}{Q}, (\phi_p - \phi_Q)$$

$$\frac{\bar{P}}{\bar{Q} \cdot \bar{R}} = \frac{P}{Q \cdot R}, (\phi_p - \phi_Q - \phi_R), \quad \text{etc.}$$

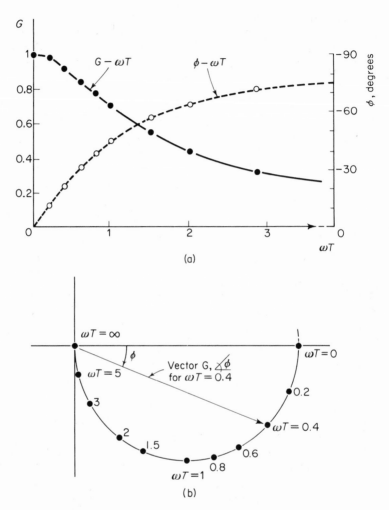

$\omega T =$	0	0.2	0.4	0.6	0.8	1	1.5	2	3	5	10	∞
$G =$	1	0.98	0.925	0.855	0.78	0.71	0.55	0.45	0.32	0.20	0.10	
ϕ, degrees $=$	0	−11.3	−21.8	−31	−38.7	−45	−56.3	−63.4	−71.6	−78.7	−84.3	−90

Fig. 5.4 General frequency response characteristics of $1/(1 + TD)$ in: (a) linear cartesian form; (b) polar form.

The magnitude of the phasor or phasor combination is obtained by treating it as a scalar quantity, i.e.,

$$\left| \frac{\bar{P}}{\bar{Q} \cdot \bar{R}} \right| = \frac{P}{Q \cdot R}$$

where P, Q, R are magnitude of $\bar{P}$, $\bar{Q}$, $\bar{R}$ respectively. The angular position of the phasor combination is the algebraic sum of the individual phasor angles, in the sense that numerator phasors have positive angles and denominator phasors have negative angles associated with them respectively.

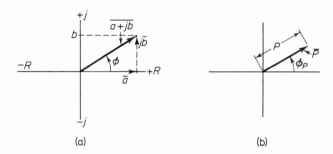

Fig. 5.5 Phasor representations.

Consider now the result of substituting $j\omega$ for D in a transfer function. The first order transfer function

$$\frac{\theta_o}{\theta_i} = \frac{K}{1 + T D} \quad \text{or} \quad \frac{\theta_o}{K\theta_i} = \frac{1}{1 + T D}$$

becomes

$$\left(\frac{\theta_o}{K\theta_i}\right)_{j\omega} = \frac{1}{1 + T j\omega} = \frac{1}{1 + j\omega T}$$

which can be recognized as a phasor combination of the form

$$\frac{\bar{P}}{\bar{Q}}$$

where $\bar{P} = 1$, which in polar notation becomes 1, $\not{\angle}0$; $\bar{Q} = 1 + j\omega T$, which in polar notation becomes $(1^2 + \omega^2 T^2)^{1/2}$, $\tan^{-1}(\omega T/1) = (1 + \omega^2 T^2)^{1/2}$, $\tan^{-1} \omega T$;

$$\therefore \left(\frac{\theta_o}{K\theta_i}\right)_{j\omega} = \frac{1}{(1 + \omega^2 T^2)^{1/2}}, \ -\tan^{-1} \omega T = G^*, \ \phi$$

which is identical with the relationships obtained in Section 5.2.2 and plotted in Fig. 5.4 for magnitude ratio G^* and phase ϕ for the steady-state sinusoidal response of the first-order transfer function.

Higher-order and more complicated transfer functions can be evaluated similarly for the frequency response magnitude ratio and phase functions. By substituting $j\omega$ for D and treating the resulting function as a combination of complex number phasors, $G = f_1(\omega)$ and $\phi = f_2(\omega)$ can be obtained. This method for obtaining frequency response data is much simpler than the classical approach, which requires evaluation of the particular solution of the system equation.

Significance of substituting $j\omega$ for D

By definition,

$$e^{j\omega t} = \cos \omega t + j \sin \omega t$$

which is a complex number with $\cos \omega t$ as the real part and $\sin \omega t$ as the imaginary part. Hence an input sinusoid can be represented as

$$\theta_i = H \sin \omega t = I(He^{j\omega t})$$

where I indicates use of the imaginary part of $He^{j\omega t}$ only.

Consider a transfer function and its corresponding response function,

$$\frac{\theta_o}{\theta_i} = f(D); \qquad \theta_o = f(D) \cdot \theta_i$$

Using $\theta_i = I\,(He^{j\omega t})$ for $\theta_i = H \sin \omega t,$

$$\theta_o = f(D) \cdot I(He^{j\omega t})$$

Now, $De^{j\omega t} = (d/dt)e^{j\omega t} = j\omega \cdot e^{j\omega t}$; $D^2e^{j\omega t} = (j\omega)^2 \cdot e^{j\omega t}$, etc., i.e.,

$$f(D) \cdot I(He^{j\omega t}) = f(j\omega) \cdot I(He^{j\omega t})$$

which indicates that $j\omega$ and D are interchangeable operators when considering steady-state response to sinusoidal inputs. Hence

$$\theta_o = f(j\omega) \cdot I(He^{j\omega t}) \quad \text{and} \quad \frac{\theta_o}{\theta_i} = f(j\omega)$$

for frequency response analysis.

5.3 THE FREQUENCY RESPONSE OF SECOND-ORDER SYSTEMS

Consider the simple second-order transfer function,

$$\frac{\theta_o}{\theta_i} = \frac{K}{1 + K_2\,D + K_1\,D^2}$$

where K, K_1, and K_2 are system constants. The steady-state response of the system to a sinusoidal input disturbance $\theta_i = H \sin \omega t$ (i.e., the response after the transient term has died away) was shown in Section 4.2 to be

$$\theta_o = \theta_{o1} = B \sin (\omega t + \phi) \tag{5.3}$$

where amplitude $B = KH/[(1 - K_1\omega^2)^2 + K_2^2\omega^2]^{1/2}$ and phase of response relative to input $\phi = -\tan^{-1} K_2\omega/(1 - K_1\omega^2)$. For a particular system and input sinusoid, K, K_1, K_2, and H would be known and the B–ω and ϕ–ω relationships could be plotted to give the frequency response characteristics of the system.

The response amplitude B can be divided by the constant input amplitude H to give the magnitude ratio

$$G = \frac{B}{H} = \frac{K}{[(1 - K_1\omega^2)^2 + (K_2\omega)^2]^{1/2}} \tag{5.4}$$

If preferred, the magnitude ratio can be unified by dividing it by the system gain constant K, to give

$$G^* = \frac{G}{K} = \frac{B}{HK} = \frac{1}{[(1 - K_1\omega^2)^2 + (K_2\omega)^2]^{1/2}} \tag{5.4a}$$

It is usual to plot G or G^* against ω to represent the response amplitude B.

Alternatively, the transfer function can be written in terms of the parameters damping ratio $\xi = K_2/2K_1^{1/2}$ and time constant $T = 1/\omega_n = K_1^{1/2}$ discussed in Section 4.2.5 to give

$$\frac{\theta_o}{\theta_i} = \frac{K}{1 + 2\xi T\,D + T^2\,D^2}$$

In this form, the response amplitude and phase are

$$B = \frac{HK}{[(1 - T^2\omega^2)^2 + (2\xi T\omega)^2]^{1/2}} \quad \text{and} \quad \phi = -\tan^{-1}\frac{2\xi T\omega}{1 - T^2\omega^2} \tag{5.5}$$

while the magnitude ratio becomes

$$G = \frac{K}{[(1 - T^2\omega^2)^2 + (2\xi T\omega)^2]^{1/2}}$$

or

$$G^* = \frac{G}{K} = \frac{1}{[(1 - T^2\omega^2)^2 + (2\xi T\omega)^2]^{1/2}} \tag{5.6}$$

For a particular system K, ξ, and T would be known and the G–ω and ϕ–ω relationships can be plotted.

Alternatively, the complex number method of substituting $j\omega$ for D in the transfer function can be used to give

$$\left(\frac{\theta_o}{\theta_i}\right)_{j\omega} = \frac{K}{1 + K_2 \cdot j\omega + K_1(j\omega)^2} = \frac{K}{(1 - K_1\omega^2) + j \cdot K_2\omega}$$

as $j^2 = -1$. This relationship is a complex number phasor of the form $\bar{P}/\bar{Q}$, where

$$\bar{P} = K + j \cdot 0, \qquad \bar{Q} = (1 - K_1\omega^2) + j \cdot K_2\omega$$

i.e., K is the real part and 0 the imaginary part of $\bar{P}$, and $(1 - K_1\omega^2)$ is the real part and $K_2\omega$ the imaginary part of $\bar{Q}$.

$$\therefore G = \frac{P}{Q} = \frac{K}{[(1 - K_1\omega^2)^2 + (K_2\omega)^2]^{1/2}}$$

and $\quad \phi = \phi_P - \phi_Q = 0 - \tan^{-1}\frac{K_2\omega}{1 - K_1\omega^2} = -\tan^{-1}\frac{K_2\omega}{1 - K_1\omega^2}$

where

$$\phi_P = \tan^{-1}\frac{\text{imaginary part}}{\text{real part}} \text{ of } \bar{P} = \tan^{-1}\frac{0}{K} = \tan^{-1}0 = 0°$$

$$\phi_Q = \tan^{-1}\frac{\text{imaginary part}}{\text{real part}} \text{ of } \bar{Q} = \tan^{-1}\frac{K_2\omega}{1 - K_1\omega^2}$$

Hence for a particular system, the G–ω and ϕ–ω relationships can be plotted; G and ϕ are readily expressed in terms of ξ and $T = 1/\omega_n$ instead of K_1 and K_2, and magnitude ratio is readily expressed as $G^* = G/K$, if desired.

The phase expression

$$\phi = -\tan^{-1}\frac{K_2\omega}{1 - K_1\omega^2} = -\tan^{-1}\frac{2\xi T\omega}{1 - T^2\omega^2}$$

is completely independent of the system gain constant K. Also, for $\omega = 1/T = \omega_n$ rad/sec, $T\omega = 1$ and

$$\phi = -\tan^{-1}\frac{2\xi}{0} = -\tan^{-1}\infty = -90°$$

Hence, the response lags the input by 90° for the input frequency $\omega = \omega_n = 1/T$ (where ω_n is the undamped natural frequency of the system, discussed in Section 4.2).

Example 5.3: Draw the frequency response characteristics of the system whose transfer function is

$$\frac{\theta_o}{\theta_i} = \frac{1}{1 + 0.7D + 0.1D^2}$$

(Note: Comparing the transfer function with the previous forms, $K = 1$ and $G = G^*$; $K_2 = 0.7$, $K_1 = 0.1$; or $\xi = 1.11$, $T = 0.316$, $\omega_n = 1/T = 3.16$ rad/sec.)

Solution: Putting $j\omega$ for D for steady-state frequency response,

$$\left(\frac{\theta_o}{\theta_i}\right)_{j\omega} = \frac{1}{(1 - 0.1\omega^2) + j \cdot 0.7\omega}$$

hence

$$G = \frac{1}{[(1 - 0.1\omega^2)^2 + (0.7\omega)^2]^{1/2}} = \left(\frac{1}{1 + 0.29\omega^2 + 0.01\omega^4}\right)^{1/2}$$

$$\phi = 0 - \tan^{-1}\frac{0.7\omega}{1 - 0.1\omega^2} = -\tan^{-1}\frac{0.7\omega}{1 - 0.1\omega^2}$$

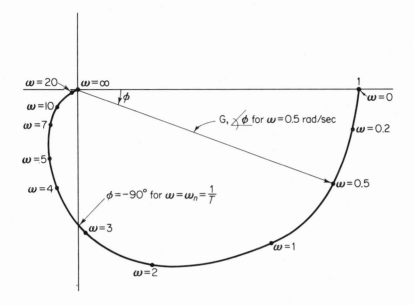

ω, rad/sec	0	0.2	0.5	1	2	3	4	5	7	10	20	100	∞
G	1	0.994	0.96	0.87	0.65	0.49	0.35	0.26	0.16	0.09	0.024	$\sim$0	0
ϕ, degrees	0	-8	-19.5	-38	-67	-87	-102	-113	-128	-142	-160	-176	-180

Fig. 5.6 Frequency response of the system $\theta_o/\theta_i = 1/(1 + 0.7D + 0.1D^2)$

The G–ω and ϕ–ω relationships are shown evaluated and plotted in Fig. 5.6. The useful frequency range was established by evaluating $\omega = \omega_n = 1/T = 3.16$ rad/sec and taking values of ω about this frequency. Note that $\phi = -90°$ for $\omega = \omega_n = 1/T$.

Sample calculation: For $\omega = 3$

$$G = \frac{1}{[(1 - 0.1 \times 9)^2 + (0.7 \times 3)^2]^{1/2}} = \frac{1}{[0.1^2 + 2.1^2]^{1/2}} = 0.49$$

$$\phi = -\tan^{-1} \frac{0.7 \times 3}{1 - 0.1 \times 9} = -\tan^{-1} \frac{2.1}{0.1} = -\tan^{-1} 21 = -87°$$

General second-order response characteristics

The response relationships

$$G^* = \frac{1}{[(1 - T^2\omega^2)^2 + (2\xi T\omega)^2]^{1/2}}; \quad \phi = -\tan^{-1} \frac{2\xi T\omega}{1 - T^2\omega^2} \qquad (5.7)$$

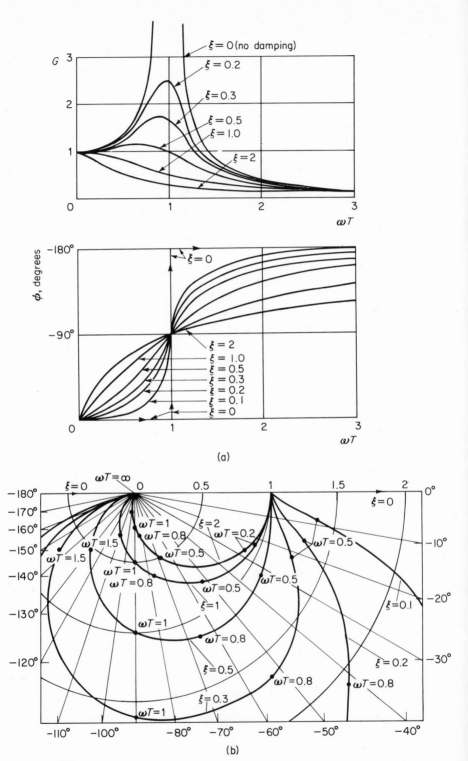

(a)

(b)

can be used to obtain a family of response curves applicable to all second-order systems of the form under discussion. $T\omega$ is used to represent frequency ω, and curves are plotted for different values of damping ratio ξ.

Figure 5.7 shows the G^*–ωT and ϕ–ωT relationships for various values of ξ, in both Cartesian and polar forms.

To use the general curves of Fig. 5.7 for a particular example, put the particular value of the system gain constant K at the starting point $\omega T = 0$ of the G^*–ωT locus. This converts the G^*–ωT relationship to G–ωT, and fixes the correct scale of the diagram. Next, the curves are adjusted to read ω instead of ωT by dividing the present values of ωT by the particular time constant T.

Figure 5.7 clearly illustrates the effect of damping on the response of a second-order system. For values of $\xi < 0.707$ the amplitude of the response sinusoid is magnified as ω is increased from $\omega = 0$, reaches a maximum value at a frequency less than $\omega = \omega_n = 1/T$ rad/sec, and then attenuates toward $G^* = 0$ for large ω. The smaller ξ, the larger the initial magnification effect, as indicated by a higher peaking of the G^*–ωT loci. For the theoretical case where $\xi = 0$ (i.e., zero damping) the peak value of G is ∞ at $\omega = \omega_n = 1/T$. The peaking effect of the G–ω relationship at low values of ξ is known as resonance, and the frequency at which G^* reaches a maximum is the resonant frequency ω_c. Peak resonance does not occur at $\omega = \omega_n = 1/T$ rad/sec. This can be illustrated by considering the maximum value of G^*, which occurs when the slope of the G^*–ω curve is zero, i.e., for

$$G^* = \frac{1}{[(1 - T^2\omega^2)^2 + (2\xi T\omega)^2]^{1/2}}$$

the slope is given by

$$\frac{dG^*}{d\omega} = \frac{-4\omega T^2(1 - \omega^2 T^2) + 8\xi^2\omega T^2}{(1 - \omega^2 T^2)^2 + 4\xi^2\omega^2 T^2}$$

Then

$$\frac{dG^*}{d\omega} = 0$$

for $G^* = G^*_{\max}$, when $\omega = \omega_c$ rad/sec. Cross-multiplication eliminates the denominator, leaving

$$-4\omega_c T^2(1 - \omega_c{}^2 T^2) + 8\xi^2\omega_c T^2 = 0$$

which reduces to

$$\omega_c = \frac{1}{T}(1 - 2\xi^2)^{1/2} \tag{5.8}$$

Equation 5.8 shows that $\omega_c < (\omega_n = 1/T)$, for all positive values of ξ, and

---

Fig. 5.7 Frequency response characteristics of $(1 + 2\xi T\,D + T^2\,D^2)^{-1}$, where $T = 1/\omega_n$, in: (a) linear cartesian form; (b) polar form.

that $\omega_c = \omega_n = 1/T$ only for $\xi = 0$ (no damping). Figure 5.8(a) shows $\omega_c T$ plotted against ξ, illustrating the effect of damping on resonant frequency.

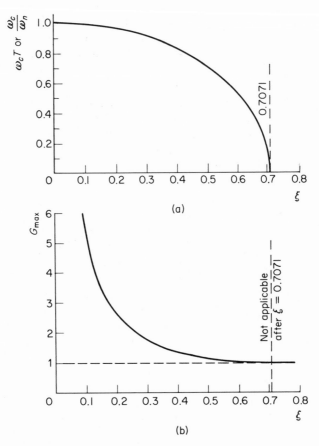

Fig. 5.8 The effect of damping ratio on: (a) resonant frequency; (b) maximum magnitude ratio.

Using Eq. 5.8 in Eq. 5.6, yields the $G^*_{\max}$–ξ relationship

$$G^*_{\max} = \frac{1}{2\xi(1 - \xi^2)^{1/2}} \tag{5.9}$$

Figure 5.8(b) shows $G^*_{\max}$ plotted against ξ to illustrate the effect of damping on resonant magnitude ratio. It is apparent that peaking of the G^*–ω

curve will occur only if G^*_{max} is greater than 1, which occurs only if ξ is less than 0.707.

For values of $\xi > 0.707$, the response amplitude attenuates continually as ω is increased from zero. The larger ξ becomes, the more rapid the attenuation.

Ideally, a system would respond such that $G^* = 1$ for all frequencies. Hence it is common to design second-order systems with a damping ratio $\xi \doteq 0.65$, which gives a maximum applied frequency range with minimum deviation from the $G^* = 1$ ideal. For all values of ξ, the response amplitude is asymptotic to $G^* = 0$ as ωT becomes large, indicating that the system will not respond to sinusoidal inputs of high frequency.

The $\phi - \omega T$ relationship of Fig. 5.7 illustrates that phase lag at any frequency below $\omega T = 1$ (i.e., $\phi = -90°$) increases as ξ increases. Ideally, phase lag would be zero for all frequencies. Thus a larger phase lag at a given frequency indicates a more sluggish response. Hence increasing ξ (i.e., increasing the damping present) causes a more sluggish response of the system.

Figure 5.7 can be compared with Fig. 4.10(a) which showed the response of simple second-order systems to a step input disturbance, for a range of damping ratio ξ. In both cases, small values of ξ are associated with overshoot or amplification of the response. However, it should be noted that the critical value of ξ for no overshoot to step input is 1, while for no amplification of the frequency response characteristic, the critical value of ξ is 0.707 ($2^{-1/2}$). Also, the damped natural frequency following step input $[\omega_d = (1/T)(1 - \xi^2)^{1/2}$, Eq. 4.18(b)] does not correspond with resonant frequency (Eq. 5.8).

5.4 THE EFFECT OF NUMERATOR FACTORS

The polar frequency response plot of the simple first-order transfer function of Fig. 5.4 lies fully within the fourth quadrant, with a phase lag approaching 90° as input frequency becomes large. The plot of the simple second-order transfer function of Fig. 5.7(b) occupies the third and fourth quadrants, with phase lag approaching 180° as frequency becomes large. The frequency response locus of the simple third-order transfer function

$$\frac{\theta_o}{K\theta_i} = \frac{1}{(1 + T_1 D)(1 + T_2 D)(1 + T_3 D)}$$

or

$$\frac{1}{(1 + T_1 D)(1 + 2\xi T_2 D + T_2 D^2)}$$

would occupy the second, third, and fourth quadrants with a phase lag approaching 270° as frequency becomes large, as illustrated in Fig. 5.9(a).

That is, each $(1 + T\,D)$ factor in the denominator of a transfer function contributes a phase lag which approaches $90°$ as frequency becomes large, causing the locus to occupy an additional quadrant in the negative sense of rotation (clockwise rotation).

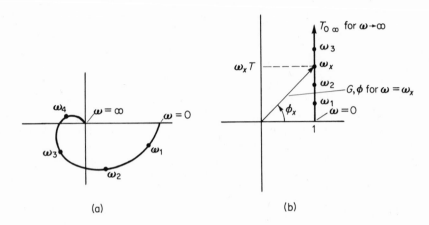

Fig. 5.9 Polar frequency response plots of: (a) $1/(1 + T_1\,D)(1 + T_2\,D)$ $\cdot(1 + T_3\,D)$; (b) $1 + TD$.

It was established previously that a numerator factor expressed in polar form has a positive phase angle associated with it. For example,

$$\frac{\theta_o}{\theta_i} = 1 + T\,D; \qquad \left(\frac{\theta_o}{\theta_i}\right)_{j\omega} = 1 + j\omega T$$

has the magnitude ratio and phase relationships

$$G = (1 + \omega^2 T^2)^{1/2}; \qquad \phi = \tan^{-1} wT$$

and its frequency response characteristic would occupy the first quadrant of a polar plot as shown in Fig. 5.9(b).

The positive phase of such a factor is called **phase lead,** and it approaches $90°$ as frequency becomes large.

The addition of a phase lead factor $(1 + T\,D)$ to a transfer function containing denominator factors affects the transfer function magnitude ratio and, more significantly, the phase. The positive phase of a numerator factor acts to decrease the phase lag due to the denominator factors. This action can be illustrated by considering the transfer function

$$\frac{\theta_o}{K\theta_i} = \frac{(1 + T_1\,D)}{(1 + T_2\,D)(1 + T_3\,D)}$$

If the numerator factor $(1 + T_1\,D)$ were not present, the frequency response locus would occupy the third and fourth quadrants as indicated in Fig. 5.7(b). The addition of $(1 + T_1 D)$ in the numerator changes magnitude ratio G^*, and *reduces* phase ϕ for a particular frequency ω according to

$$\phi = \phi_1 - \phi_2 - \phi_3$$

That is, the numerator factor tends to restrict the locus to the fourth quadrant only. The relative values of T_1, T_2, and T_3 dictate whether the locus is fully confined to the fourth quadrant, or if it extends into the first and/or third quadrants. In the limiting case when $T_1 = T_2$ or T_3, the transfer function reduces to the form

$$\frac{\theta_o}{K\theta_i} = \frac{1}{1 + T D}$$

which occupies only the fourth quadrant, as shown in Fig. 5.4.

Each factor $(1 + T D)$ in the numerator of a transfer function acts to offset a similar factor in the denominator, and hence acts to restrict the polar frequency response locus to one less quadrant than is indicated by the denominator factors.

Example 5.4: A system has the transfer function

$$\frac{\theta_o}{\theta_i} = \frac{K(1 + T_1 D)}{(1 + T_2 D)(1 + T_3 D)}$$

where $K = 20$; $T_1 = 0.1$ sec; $T_2 = 0.2$ sec; $T_3 = 0.04$ sec. Establish the frequency response characteristic of the system. Make both Cartesian and polar plots of the data.

Solution:

$$\frac{\theta_o}{\theta_i} = \frac{20(1 + T_1 D)}{(1 + T_2 D)(1 + T_3 D)}$$

For steady-state frequency response analysis, $j\omega$ can be substituted for D to give

$$\left(\frac{\theta_o}{K\theta_i}\right) = \frac{1 + j\omega T_1}{(1 + j\omega T_2)(1 + j\omega T_3)}$$

which is a complex number phasor relationship of the form $\bar{P}/\bar{Q}\cdot\bar{R}$, where $\bar{P} = (1 + j\omega T_1)$; $\bar{Q} = (1 + j\omega T_2)$; $\bar{R} = (1 + j\omega T_3)$.

In polar notation, the magnitude and angle of each phasor can be written

$$\bar{P} = (1 + \omega^2 T_1^2)^{1/2}, \tan^{-1} \omega T_1$$

$$\bar{Q} = (1 + \omega^2 T_2^2)^{1/2}, \tan^{-1} \omega T_2$$

$$\bar{R} = (1 + \omega^2 T_y^2)^{1/2}, \tan^{-1} \omega T_3$$

and magnitude ratio is

$$G = \frac{20(1 + \omega^2 T_1^2)^{1/2}}{(1 + \omega_2^2 T_2)^{1/2}(1 + \omega^2 T_3^2)^{1/2}} \quad \text{or} \quad \left[\frac{1 + \omega^2 T_1^2}{(1 + \omega^2 T_2^2)(1 + \omega^2 T_3)}\right]^{1/2} \times 20$$

and phase $\phi = \tan^{-1} \omega T_1 - \tan^{-1} \omega T_2 - \tan^{-1} \omega T_3$.

Substituting the known values of T_1, T_2, and T_3,

$$G = \frac{20(1 + 0.01\omega^2)^{1/2}}{(1 + 0.04\omega^2)^{1/2}(1 + 0.0016\omega^2)^{1/2}} \quad \text{or} \quad \left[\frac{1 + 0.01\omega^2}{1 + 0.0416\omega^2 + 0.000064\omega^4}\right]^{1/2} \times 20$$

$$\phi = \tan^{-1} 0.1\omega - \tan^{-1} 0.2\omega - \tan^{-1} 0.04\omega$$

and G and ϕ can be evaluated for various values of ω (rad/sec), as shown in the tabulation.

$\omega =$	0	1	2	5	10	15	20	30	40	50	100	∞
$G =$	20	19.7	18.4	15.6	11.6	9.75	8.6	6.7	5.42	4.54	2.4	0
$\phi° =$	0	−8.2	−15.2	−30	−40	−46	−51	−59.5	−65	−69	−76	−90

Figure 5.10 shows both Cartesian and polar plots of G, ϕ against ω.

Points to note

(1) The plots of Fig. 5.10 are readily converted to read $G^* = \theta_o/K\theta_i$ instead of $G = \theta_o/\theta_i$, by altering the G scale, i.e., for $G = 20$ at $\omega = 0$, write $G^* = 20/20 = 1$ for $\omega = 0$.

(2) The transfer function can be expanded to contain a single complex number in the denominator, i.e.,

$$\frac{\theta_o}{K\theta_i} = \frac{1 + T_1 D}{1 + (T_2 + T_3) D + T_2 T_3 D^2}$$

$$\left(\frac{\theta_o}{K\theta_i}\right)_{j\omega} = \frac{1 + j\omega T_1}{1 + j\omega(T_2 + T_3) + j^2\omega^2 T_2 T_3}$$

$$= \frac{1 + j\omega T_1}{(1 - \omega^2 T_2 T_3) + j\omega(T_2 + T_3)}, \quad \text{as } j^2 = -1$$

Thus $(1 - \omega^2 T_2 T_3)$ is the real part, and $\omega(T_2 + T_3)$ the imaginary part of the denominator complex number.

Then,

$$G^* = \left[\frac{1 + \omega^2 T_1^2}{(1 - \omega^2 T_2 T_3)^2 + \omega^2(T_2 + T_3)^2}\right]^{1/2}$$

and

$$\phi = \tan^{-1} \omega T_1 - \tan^{-1} \frac{\omega(T_2 + T_3)}{1 - \omega^2 T_2 T_3}$$

(3) It may be preferable to calculate the magnitude and phase of each individual $(1 + T D)$ factor for the full range of ω, before combining them to get G and ϕ for the system.

(4) When seeking the values of frequency to use in the G and ϕ relationships, start with $\omega = 0$ and finish with $\omega = \infty$. The order of the frequencies most

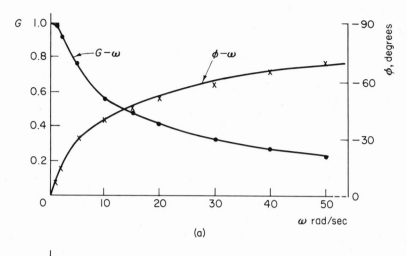

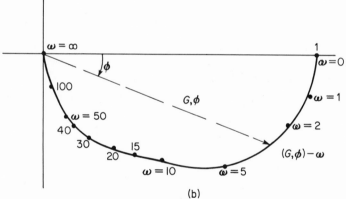

Fig. 5.10 Frequency-response characteristics of the system

$$\frac{\theta_o}{\theta_i} = \frac{20(1 + 0.1D)}{(1 + 0.2D)(1 + 0.04D)}$$

in: (a) linear cartesian form; and (b) polar form.

suitable is indicated by the inverse of the system time constants. For the present case, the appropriate values of ω are $1/T_1 = 10$, $1/T_2 = 5$, $1/T_3 = 25$ rad/sec.

5.5 THE EFFECT OF ZERO FACTORS IN A TRANSFER FUNCTION

A transfer function can contain factors of the forms

$$\frac{1}{T\,D}, \qquad \frac{1}{T^2\,D^2}, \quad \text{etc.;} \quad T\,D, \; T^2\,D^2, \quad \text{etc.}$$

Such factors will appear frequently in future stability studies. They can be thought of as being of the forms

$$\frac{1}{(0 + T\,D)}, \qquad \frac{1}{(0 + T\,D)^2}, \quad \text{etc.;} \quad (0 + T\,D), \quad (0 + T\,D)^2, \quad \text{etc.}$$

and are called zero factors.

Consider the factor

$$\frac{\theta_o}{K\theta_i} = \frac{1}{T\,D} = \frac{1}{0 + T\,D}$$

For frequency response analysis,

$$\left(\frac{\theta_o}{K\theta_i}\right)_{j\omega} = \frac{1}{0 + j\omega T}$$

from which

$$G^* = \frac{1}{(0^2 + \omega^2 T^2)^{1/2}} = \frac{1}{\omega T}; \quad \phi = 0 - \tan^{-1}\frac{\omega T}{0} = -\tan^{-1}\infty = -90°$$

That is, phase lag ϕ is 90° for all values of ω, and hence the polar frequency response locus lies on the 270° = $-90°$ axis.

For $\omega = 0$, $G = \infty$; and for $\omega = \infty$, $G = 0$. The locus is shown in Fig. 5.11(a). It can be shown similarly that the factor $1/T^2\,D^2$ has a polar frequency response locus which starts at ∞ for $\omega = 0$ on the 180° = $-180°$ axis, and progresses along this axis towards the origin as ω is increased, reaching the origin for $\omega = \infty$ (Fig. 5.11b).

The numerator factor $\theta_o/K\theta_i = T\,D = 0 + T\,D$ becomes

$$\left(\frac{\theta_o}{K\theta_i}\right)_{j\omega} = (0 + j\omega T)$$

for frequency response analysis.

(This is a complex number phasor, whose real part is zero, and hence it would lie along the imaginary axis if plotted on the complex plane.)

$$G^* = \omega T \quad \text{and} \quad \phi = \tan^{-1}\frac{\omega T}{0} = 90°$$

for all values of ω. For $\omega = 0$, $G = 0$; for $\omega = \infty$, $G = \infty$. Hence the frequency response locus is as shown in Fig. 5.11(c), starting from the origin for $\omega = 0$ and progressing along the 90° axis as ω increases, to approach ∞ as ω becomes large.

Example 5.5: A system has the transfer function

$$\frac{\theta_o}{\theta_i} = \frac{K}{T_1\,D(1 + T_2\,D)}$$

Obtain the magnitude ratio and phase relationships from which the frequency response characteristics can be plotted, for the case when $K = 1$, $T_1 = 0.1$ sec, $T_2 = 0.3$ sec.

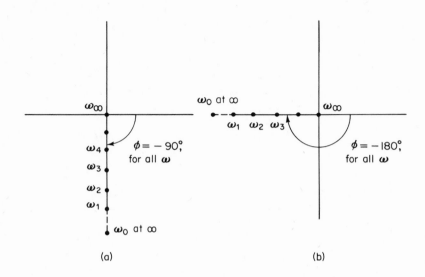

(a)   (b)

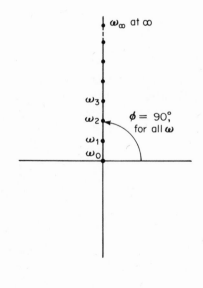

(c)

Fig. 5.11   The polar frequency-response characteristics of some zero factors: (a) $1/T\,D$; (b) $1/T^2\,D^2$; (c) $T\,D$.

Solution: For steady-state response to sinusoidal input substitute $j\omega$ for D,

$$\left(\frac{\theta_o}{\theta_i}\right)_{j\omega} = \frac{K}{T_1 j\omega(1 + T_2 j\omega)}$$

which is a complex phasor combination of the form $\bar{P}/\bar{Q} \cdot \bar{R}$, where $\bar{P} = K,\ \angle 0$; $\bar{Q} = \omega T_1,\ \angle 90°$; $\bar{R} = [1 + (\omega T_2)^2]^{1/2},\ \angle \tan^{-1} \omega T_2$.

magnitude ratio $G = \dfrac{K}{\omega T_1[1 + (\omega T_2)^2]^{1/2}} = \dfrac{K}{(T_1^2 \omega^2 + T_1^2 T_2^2 \omega^4)^{1/2}}$

phase $\phi = 0 - 90° - \tan^{-1} \omega T_2 = -90^2 - \tan^{-1} \omega T_2$

For the given values of K, T_1, and T_2,

$$G = \left(\frac{1}{0.01\omega^2 + 0.0009\omega^4}\right)^{1/2}$$

$$\phi = -90° - \tan^{-1} 0.3\omega$$

which can be evaluated for values of ω and plotted.

5.6 LOGARITHMIC REPRESENTATION— THE BODE DIAGRAM

5.6.1 Introduction

Logarithmic plotting of frequency response data is a widely used alternative to the linear Cartesian and polar forms of plot used in the preceding work. Magnitude ratio-frequency and phase-frequency data can be calculated in the same manner. Use of suitable logarithmic graph paper minimizes the necessity to take logarithms of the data. One method is to plot frequency logarithmically, with magnitude ratio and phase shown linearly. This semi-log technique is demonstrated in Figure 5.12(a), which shows the frequency response data of Example 5.3 (Figure 5.6, p. 161).

The **Bode diagram** is a particularly descriptive form of logarithmic plot widely used to represent frequency response data. It consists of the magnitude ratio expressed in **decibels** plotted against $\log_{10}$ frequency with phase-$\log_{10}$ frequency superimposed or shown separately.

Note: N expressed in decibels [denoted in this text by $(N,\ \text{db})$] = $20 \log_{10} N$, where N is any number.

Figure 5.12(b) shows the response data of Example 5.3 in Bode diagram form.

Logarithmic plotting of data has the advantages that

(a) a wide range of the plotted variables can be represented, without obscuring the effects at each end of the range;
(b) multiplications of quantities can be made additive;
(c) curved relationships can often be represented linearly.

In particular, the Bode diagram permits a magnitude ratio-frequency

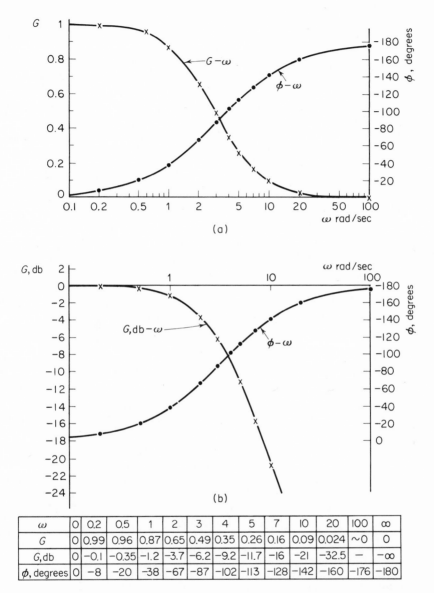

ω	0	0.2	0.5	1	2	3	4	5	7	10	20	100	∞
G	0	0.99	0.96	0.87	0.65	0.49	0.35	0.26	0.16	0.09	0.024	~0	0
G,db	0	−0.1	−0.35	−1.2	−3.7	−6.2	−9.2	−11.7	−16	−21	−32.5	−	−∞
ϕ, degrees	0	−8	−20	−38	−67	−87	−102	−113	−128	−142	−160	−176	−180

Fig. 5.12 Frequency-response plots of $1/(1 + 0.7D + 0.1D^2)$ in: (a) semilog form; (b) Bode form (see Fig. 5.6 for polar plot).

locus to be approximated by a series of straight lines to which the actual G–ω curve is asymptotic. It will be shown that this straight line approximation can be drawn from inspection of a transfer function without any evaluations of magnitude ratio.

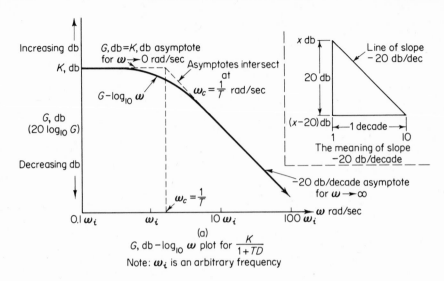

(a)

G, db $-\log_{10} \omega$ plot for $\dfrac{K}{1+TD}$

Note: ω_i is an arbitrary frequency

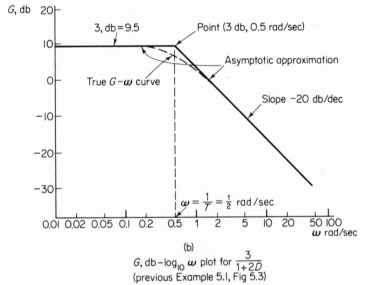

(b)

G, db $-\log_{10} \omega$ plot for $\dfrac{3}{1+2D}$

(previous Example 5.1, Fig 5.3)

Fig. 5.13 Magnitude ratio–frequency plots in Bode form, of first-order transfer function $K/(1 + TD)$.

5.6.2 Bode Diagram of Simple First-Order System

Consider the first-order transfer function

$$\frac{\theta_o}{\theta_i} = \frac{K}{1 + T\,D}$$

For steady-state response to sinusoidal input,

$$\left(\frac{\theta_o}{\theta_i}\right)_{j\omega} = \frac{K}{1 + j\omega T} \quad \text{and} \quad G = K(1 + \omega^2 T^2)^{-1/2}, \quad \phi = -\tan^{-1} \omega T$$

Then, expressed in decibels, G, db $= 20 \log_{10} [K(1 + \omega^2 T^2)^{-1/2}]$, i.e.,

$$G, \text{db} = 20 \log_{10} K + 20 \log_{10} (1 + \omega^2 T^2)^{-1/2}$$
$$= K, \text{db} - 10 \log_{10} (1 + \omega^2 T^2) \qquad (a)$$

As ω approaches zero, $\log_{10} (1 + \omega^2 T^2)$ approaches $\log_{10} 1$, which is 0, i.e.,

$$G, \text{db} = K, \text{db} \quad \text{for} \quad \omega = 0 \qquad (b)$$

As ω increases from zero, (G, db) decreases from K, db by the amount $10 \log_{10} (1 + \omega^2 T^2)$, which increases with ω. That is, the (G, db)–$(\log_{10} \omega)$ curve is asymptotic to the horizontal line K, db at low frequencies, as shown on the low-frequency range of Fig. 5.13(a).

Now, as frequency ω becomes large, $\omega^2 T^2$ becomes much larger than 1 and Eq. (a) can be written

$$G, \text{db} \doteq K, \text{db} - 10 \log_{10} \omega^2 T^2 \quad \text{for} \quad \omega \gg 1$$

That is,

$$G, \text{db} = K, \text{db} - 10 \log_{10} \omega^2 - 10 \log_{10} T^2$$
$$= K, \text{db} - 20 \log_{10} \omega - 20 \log_{10} T$$
$$= (K - T), \text{db} - 20 \log_{10} \omega \qquad (c)$$

Equation (c) is of the form $y = mx + n$, a straight line, if G, db is considered as y and $\log_{10} \omega$ is considered as x. The slope of the line is -20. That is, the $(G, \text{db}) = \log_{10} \omega$ curve is asymptotic to a straight line of slope -20 db/decade as ω becomes large, as illustrated in Fig. 5.13(a).

The -20 db/dec asymptote described by Eq. (c) can be located on the Bode diagram by considering the point on it G, db $= K$, db, which is its intercept point with the line G, db $= K$, db of Eq. (b).

That is, Eq. (c) becomes

$$K, \text{db} = K, \text{db} - T, \text{db} - 20 \log_{10} \omega_c$$

where ω_c is the frequency at which $G = K$ or G, db $= K$, db in Eq. (c), i.e., $20 \log_{10} T + 20 \log_{10} \omega_c = 0$, or $\log_{10} \omega_c T = 0$, from which

$$\omega_c T = 1 \quad \text{or} \quad \omega_c = \frac{1}{T}$$

That is, the asymptote G, db $= K$, db for $\omega \to 0$ intersects the asymptote of slope -20 db/dec for $\omega \to \infty$ at the point

$$\left(G, \text{db} = K, \text{db}; \quad \omega_c = \frac{1}{T}\right)$$

as illustrated in Fig. 5.13(a).

Thus a straight line approximation of the magnitude ratio-frequency characteristic of a first-order system can be obtained without calculation by

(1) drawing the horizontal line G, db $= K$, db;
(2) locating on this line the point $\omega_c = 1/T$ rad/sec;
(3) drawing from this point a line of slope -20 db/dec.

Example 5.6: Consider the numerical Example 5.1 (Fig. 5.3, p. 154).

$$\frac{\theta_o}{\theta_i} = \frac{3}{1 + 2D}; \qquad \theta_i = 2 \sin \omega t$$

That is,

$$K = 3; \qquad T = 2$$

To obtain the Bode diagram asymptotic approximation to the magnitude ratio-frequency relationship (Fig. 5.13b),

(1) draw the horizontal line 3, db $= 20 \log_{10} 3 = 9 \cdot 54$;
(2) locate on it the point $\omega = 1/T = \frac{1}{2}$ rad/sec;
(3) draw a line from this point at a slope of -20 db/dec.

Figure 5.13(b) shows the asymptotic approximation together with the accurate response plots obtained from the data of Example 5.1 (Fig. 5.3).

General Bode diagram for first-order systems

Consider

$$\frac{\theta_o}{\theta_i} = \frac{K}{1 + T D}$$

If $K = 1$, or $\theta_o/K\theta_i = 1/(1 + T D)$ is plotted,

$$G = (1 + \omega^2 T^2)^{-1/2}; \quad \phi = -\tan^{-1} \omega T$$

Equation (a) becomes

$$G, \text{db} = -10 \log_{10} (1 + \omega^2 T^2) \qquad \text{(d)}$$

For the general case, ω can be represented by ωT. For ωT approaching 0,

$$G, \text{db} = 0 \qquad \text{(e)}$$

For ωT becoming large, $\omega^2 T^2 \gg 1$, and

$$G, \text{db} = -10 \log_{10} \omega^2 T^2 = -20 \log_{10} \omega T \qquad \text{(f)}$$

As for Eq. (c), Eq. (f) describes a straight line on the Bode diagram, of slope -20 db/dec, which intercepts the low frequency asymptote (G, db $= 0$ in this case) at the frequency $\omega_c T = 1$. Thus the general frequency response characteristic of a first-order system can be approximated by

(1) drawing the horizontal line G, db $= 0$;
(2) locating on it the point $\omega_c T = 1$;
(3) drawing from this point a straight line of slope -20 db/dec, as shown
    in Fig. 5.14(a);
(4) adding the calculated phase-frequency data.

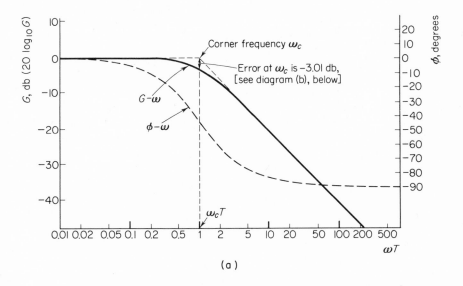

(a)

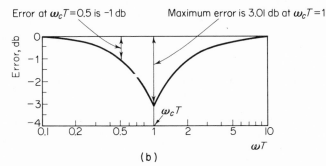

(b)

Fig. 5.14 (a) Bode diagram for $1/(1 + T D)$; (b) error between asymptotic
approximation and true magnitude ratio–frequency curves.

Note that the ϕ–ω characteristic of Fig. 5.14(a) experiences inflection
at $\omega T = 1$, i.e., at the same frequency at which the G, db–ω asymptotes
intersect.

Figures 5.14(a) and 5.4 (p. 156) are directly comparable.

Error between asymptotic approximation and true locus

The error between the asymptotic approximation and the true response curve is readily found by calculating the difference between the two curves at given frequencies.

Sample calculation: For $\omega T = 1$,

(a) $(G, \mathrm{db}) = 0$ according to the asymptotic approximation;
(b) $G = 1/(1 + 1^2)^{1/2} = 1/2^{1/2} = 0.707$, which expressed in decibels is $(G, \mathrm{db}) = 20 \log_{10} 0.707 = -3.01$.

This is the accurate value of G for $\omega T = 1$, i.e., the error is -3.01 db at $\omega T = 1$.

This procedure can be extended to yield the error curve of Fig. 5.14(b). This curve can be used to obtain the correct magnitude ratio curve from its asymptotic approximation. It is apparent that the error relationship of Fig. 5.14(b) is applicable to the numerical Example 5.6 (Fig. 5.13b).

5.6.3 Bode Diagram for Simple Second-Order System

Consider the simple second-order transfer function

$$\frac{\theta_o}{\theta_i} = \frac{K}{1 + K_2 D + K_1 D^2}$$

It was shown in Section 5.3 that the magnitude ratio and the phase relationship could be written

$$G = K[(1 - K_1\omega^2)^2 + (K_2\omega)^2]^{-1/2}; \qquad \varphi = -\tan^{-1} \frac{K_2\omega}{1 - K_1\omega^2}$$

Expressing the magnitude ratio in decibels,

$$\begin{aligned}
G, \mathrm{db} &= 20 \log_{10} K[(1 - K_1\omega^2)^2 + (K_2\omega)^2]^{-1/2} \\
&= 20 \log_{10} K + 20 \log_{10} [(1 - K_1\omega^2)^2 + (K_2\omega)^2]^{-1/2} \\
&= K, \mathrm{db} - 10 \log_{10} [(1 - K_1\omega^2)^2 + (K_2\omega)^2] \\
&= K, \mathrm{db} - 10 \log_{10} [1 + (K_2^2 - 2K_1)\omega^2 + K_1^2\omega^4] \qquad \text{(a)}
\end{aligned}$$

When ω approaches 0 the second term of Expression (a) approaches $10 \log_{10} 1$, which is zero. Hence,

$$G, \mathrm{db} \rightarrow K, \mathrm{db} \qquad \text{as } \omega \rightarrow 0 \qquad\qquad \text{(b)}$$

which indicates that the magnitude ratio is asymptotic to the horizontal line K, db on the Bode diagram as frequency ω is reduced to zero. This characteristic is indicated in Fig. 5.15, and is also apparent in Fig. 5.12(b) ($K = 1; K$, db $= 0$).

As ω is increased from zero rad/sec, the G locus will deviate from the K, db line. The deviation can be initially in the positive db direction or

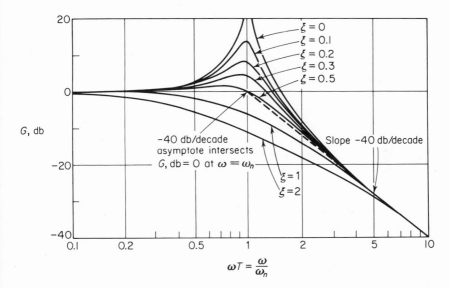

Fig. 5.15 Magnitude ratio–frequency relationship in Bode form, of the second-order transfer function $1/(1 + 2\xi T D + T^2 D^2)$; phase–frequency relationships are as in Fig. 5.7(a).

in the negative db direction, depending on the sign of the second term of Eq. (a). The sign of the expression is initially dependent on the damping ratio $\xi = K_2/2K^{1/2}$. It is readily shown that for $\xi < 0.707$, the G locus will increase initially in magnitude as ω is increased from zero, while for $\xi > 0.707$, G decreases continually from its initial value as illustrated in Fig. 5.12(b). These characteristics are directly associated with the curves of Figs. 5.7 and 5.8.

When ω becomes large, $K_1^2\omega^4$ dominates the second term of Expression (a), which becomes

$$G, \text{db} \doteq K, \text{db} - 10 \log_{10} K_1^2\omega^4 = K, \text{db} - 20 \log_{10} K_1 - 40 \log_{10} \omega$$

$$= (K - K_1), \text{db} - 40 \log_{10} \omega \tag{c}$$

On a G, db–$\log_{10} \omega$ plot this relationship is a straight line of the form $y = mx + n$, where y corresponds with G, db; m corresponds with -40, and is the slope -40 db/dec; x corresponds with $\log_{10} \omega$, with 1 decade as the unit; n corresponds with $(K - K_1)$, db, a constant. Hence the G–ω relationship becomes asymptotic to a line of slope -40 db/dec as ω becomes large, as indicated in Fig. 5.15.

It remains now to locate the point of intersection of the asymptotes described by Expressions (b) and (c). Equating Expressions (b) and (c) yields

$$K, \text{db} = (K - K_1), \text{db} - 40 \log_{10} \omega_c \qquad \text{(d)}$$

where ω_c is the frequency at which the intersection occurs, i.e.,

$$-K_1, \text{db} - 40 \log_{10} \omega_c = 0 \quad \text{or} \quad -20 \log_{10} K_1 - 40 \log_{10} \omega_c = 0$$

$$\log_{10} K_1 + 2 \log_{10} \omega_c = 0 \quad \text{or} \quad K_1 \omega_c^2 = 1$$

$$\omega_c = K_1^{-1/2}$$

Thus the -40 db/dec asymptote is located by locating the point $\omega_c = K_1^{-1/2}$ on the horizontal K, db asymptote, as illustrated in Fig. 5.15. Note that $K_1^{-1/2}$ is the natural undamped frequency of the system (see Section 5.3). Hence the intersection or corner frequency is given by

$$\omega_c = \omega_n = \frac{1}{T} \text{ rad/sec}$$

For example, with the problem of Fig. 5.12(b), $K = 1$ and hence K, db $= 20 \log_{10} 1 = 0$ to give the horizontal asymptote; $K_1 = 0.1$, and $\omega_n = K_1^{-1/2} = 0.1^{-1/2} = 3.15$ rad/sec to give the corner or intersection point. Draw the asymptote of slope -40 db/dec from this point.

Figure 5.15 shows the general magnitude ratio-frequency relationships for the simple second-order transfer function, for several values of damping ratio ξ. The curves are directly comparable with Figs. 5.7(a) and (b). The phase-frequency data is not reproduced, as it is identical with that of Fig. 5.7(a). It is apparent that the G–ω relationship cannot be closely approximated by the low- and high-frequency asymptotes, except for values of ξ around about 0.7. However, the locating of these asymptotes is of assistance in the construction or interpretation of second-order response relationships.

5.6.4 Bode Diagram of Numerator Factors

Consider the transfer function

$$\frac{\theta_o}{\theta_i} = 1 + T D$$

It was shown in Section 5.4 that the frequency response expressions are

$$G = (1 + \omega^2 T^2)^{1/2}; \quad \phi = \tan^{-1} \omega T$$

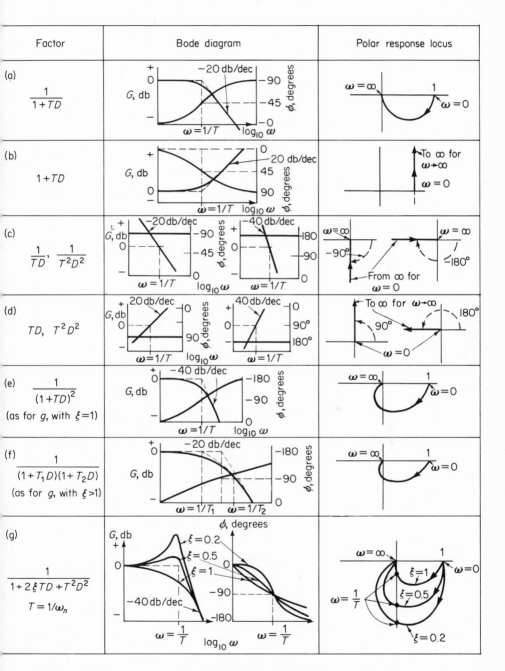

Fig. 5.16 Frequency response characteristics of the factors which commonly appear in or as transfer functions: Bode and polar forms.

and that G increases continually with ω, and ϕ is a positive angle (phase lead).

With the technique used in Section 5.6.2 it is readily shown that the Bode magnitude ratio locus is asymptotic to

(a) the line $(G, \text{db}) = 0$ for low values of ω, i.e., for $\omega \to 0$;
(b) a line of slope 20 db/dec which cuts the G, db $= 0$ line at $\omega = 1/T$ rad/sec, for high frequencies, i.e., for $\omega \to \infty$.

Figure 5.16(b) shows the asymptotic approximation, and illustrates that the (G, db) locus breaks upwards for the $(1 + T\,D)$ factor. It is readily established that the error between the true locus and its asymptotic approximation is similar in magnitude to that of Fig. 5.14(b), but of positive sign.

The Bode diagrams of higher order numerator factors can be similarly ascertained.

5.6.5 Bode Diagram of Zero Factors

(a) *Consider the transfer function*

$$\frac{\theta_o}{\theta_i} = \frac{1}{T\,D}$$

It was shown in Section 5.5 that the frequency response expressions are

$$G = \frac{1}{\omega T}; \quad \phi = -90°$$

i.e., that G decreases continually with ω, and ϕ is constant at $-90°$ for all ω.

$$G, \text{db} = 20 \log_{10} G = 20 \log_{10} (\omega T)^{-1} = -20 \log_{10} \omega - 20 \log_{10} T$$

From previous discussion, the expression is recognizable as a line of slope -20 db/dec, which cuts the G, db $= 0$ line at the frequency $\omega_c = 1/T$ or $\omega_c T = 1$. This situation is illustrated in Fig. 5.16(c).

(b) *Consider the transfer function*

$$\frac{\theta_o}{\theta_i} = T\,D$$

$G = \omega T$, and $\phi = 90°$ for all ω.

Thus G, db $= 20 \log_{10} \omega T = 20 \log_{10} \omega + 20 \log_{10} T$, which is recognizable as a straight line of slope 20 db/dec, which cuts the G, db $= 0$ line at $\omega = 1/T$ or $\omega T = 1$. Figure 5.16(d) shows this situation.

Higher-order zero factors ($1/T^2 D^2$, $T^2 D^2$, etc.) are readily shown to have straight line magnitude characteristics on the Bode diagram, the slopes of which are dictated by the order of the factor (i.e., -40 db/dec for $1/T^2 D^2$, -60 db/dec for $1/T^3 D^3$, etc.). Figures 5.16(c) and (d) shows several such factors.

It is apparent that zero factors in the denominator of a system transfer function lead to unstable response, as G approaches infinity when ω approaches 0. That is, such a system has a large response for zero disturbance. Zero factors in the numerator do not produce this instability, as G approaches 0 when ω approaches 0.

5.6.6 Bode Diagrams for Multiple Factors

Figure 5.16 shows magnitude ratio-frequency characteristics of the common transfer function factors discussed so far, in both Bode diagram and polar forms.

Logarithmic representation of a transfer function permits evaluation of multiple factors by simple addition and subtraction of the component factors.

For example, consider the transfer function

$$\frac{\theta_o}{\theta_i} = \frac{K(1 + T_2 D)}{(1 + T_1 D)(1 + T_2 D)}; \quad G^* = \left(\frac{\theta_o}{K\theta_i}\right)_{j\omega} = \frac{(1 + j\omega T_2)}{(1 + j\omega T_1)(1 + j\omega T_3)}$$

$$G^*, \text{db} = 20 \log_{10} G^* = 20 \log_{10} (1 + \omega^2 T_2^2)^{1/2} + 20 \log_{10} (1 + \omega^2 T_1^2)^{-1/2}$$

$$+ 20 \log_{10} (1 + \omega^2 T_3^2)^{-1/2}$$

Assuming for this example that $T_2 < T_1$ and $T_3 < T_2$, these three components of G^*, db can be constructed as shown in Figs. 5.17(a), (b), and (c). The component Bode diagrams can be directly added to give the complete G^*, db–ω locus. It is particularly valuable that the asymptotic approximation of each component can be drawn from inspection of the transfer function. Thus the asymptotic approximation for the full transfer function is easily obtained. The technique for obtaining the asymptotic approximation to the G, db–ω locus for such transfer functions can be simplified to the following:

(a) Locate the critical or corner frequencies $\omega_1 = 1/T_1$, $\omega_2 = 1/T_2$, $\omega_3 = 1/T_3$, etc.

(b) Draw the asymptote(s) associated with the lowest corner frequency (i.e., draw Fig. 5.17a for the present example).

(c) Where the asymptote cuts the next corner frequency, apply the break condition associated with this frequency, i.e., in Fig. 5.17(d) $\omega_2 = 1/T_2$ is associated with a break up of 20 db/dec. Hence at $\omega_2 = 1/T_2$, the -20 db/dec asymptote associated with the $\omega_1 = 1/T_1$ factor experiences a change in slope of $+20$ db/dec, producing a horizontal asymptote.

(d) Where the new asymptote cuts the next corner frequency, apply the slope break associated with this frequency. That is, in Fig. 5.17(d), the asymptotic approximation experiences a change in slope of -20

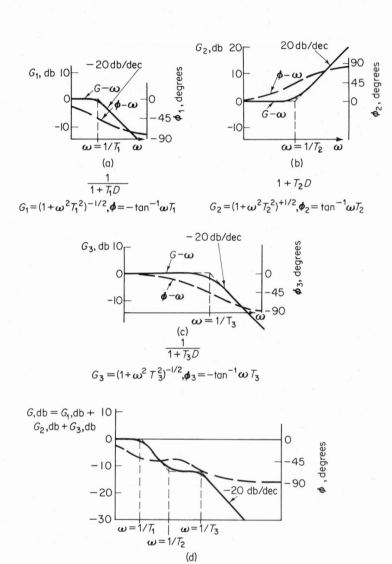

$$\frac{1}{1+T_1D}$$

$$G_1=(1+\omega^2T_1^2)^{-1/2},\phi=-\tan^{-1}\omega T_1 \qquad G_2=(1+\omega^2T_2^2)^{+1/2},\phi_2=\tan^{-1}\omega T_2$$

$$\frac{1}{1+T_3D}$$

$$G_3=(1+\omega^2 T_3^2)^{-1/2},\phi_3=-\tan^{-1}\omega T_3$$

Fig. 5.17 Component factors and full transfer function Bode diagrams for the transfer function

$$\frac{\theta_o}{K\theta_i} = \frac{1+T_2\,D}{(1+T_1\,D)(1+T_3\,D)}$$

where $T_2 < T_1$ and $T_3 < T_2$.

db/dec at $\omega_3 = (1/T_3)$ rad/sec, giving the full G, db–ω relationship shown.

Zero and higher-order factors in a transfer function can be handled similarly. Thus the asymptotic approximation to the G, db–ω locus of any linear system can be constructed from inspection of the transfer function.

The phase contribution of individual transfer function factors can be similarly added algebraically, to give the system phase-frequency data.

Note that denominator factors act to attenuate the magnitude ratio locus as frequency is increased, while numerator factors act to magnify the magnitude ratio as frequency is increased.

Example 5.7: Construct the Bode diagram for the system whose transfer function is

$$\frac{\theta_o}{\theta_i} = \frac{10(1 + 2D)}{(1 + 0.2D)(1 + 0.05D)}$$

The asymptotic approximation to the magnitude ratio-frequency locus will be adequate. Use $G = (\theta_o/\theta_i)_{j\omega}$ for magnitude ratio.

Solution (Fig. 5.18):

(a) Recognize that the corner frequencies will be

$$\omega_1 = \frac{1}{2} = 0.5 \text{ rad/sec, associated with the numerator factor } (1 + 2D);$$

$$\omega_2 = \frac{1}{0.2} = 5 \text{ rad/sec, associated with the denominator factor } (1 + 0.2D);$$

$$\omega_3 = \frac{1}{0.05} = 20 \text{ rad/sec, associated with the denominator factor } (1 + 0.5D).$$

Locate these frequencies on the logarithmic abscissa of semi-log graph paper.

(b) Recognize that the initial asymptote for low frequencies ($\omega \rightarrow 0$) is a horizontal line in this case. Also that it is located at 10, db $= 20 \log_{10} 10 = 20$, as $G_{\omega=0} = K = 10$. If

$$G^* = \left| \frac{\theta_o}{K\theta_i} \right|_{j\omega} = \left| \frac{\theta_o}{10\theta_i} \right|_{j\omega}$$

had been plotted, the initial horizontal asymptote would have been 0, as with the previous example. Draw the line G, db $= 20$.

(c) Terminate the G, db $= 20$ line at $\omega_1 = 0.5$ rad/sec; draw the upward sloping asymptote of slope 20 db/dec associated with ω_1 from this point.

(d) Terminate the 20 db/dec asymptote at $\omega_2 = 5$ rad/sec; change slope by -20 db/sec, as indicated by the slope associated with ω_2, producing a horizontal line.

(e) Extend the horizontal asymptote from ω_2 to $\omega_3 = 20$ rad/sec; at $\omega_3 = 20$ rad/sec, break down by -20 db/dec as indicated by the slope associated with

ω_3, producing an asymptote of slope -20 db/dec. This line continues indefinitely with ω.

Thus the asymptotic approximation to the magnitude ratio locus has been drawn.

(f) Recognize from the transfer function the phase relationship

$$\phi = \tan^{-1} 2\omega - \tan^{-1} 0.2\omega - \tan^{-1} 0.05\omega$$

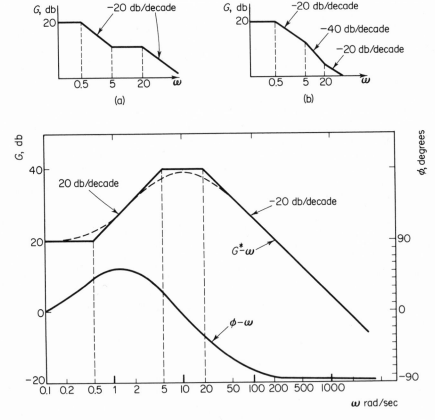

Fig. 5.18   Bode diagram for the system

$$\frac{\theta_o}{\theta_i} = \frac{10(1 + 2D)}{(1 + 0.2D)(1 + 0.05D)}$$

The inserts show the shapes of the G–ω curve for:

(a) $\dfrac{\theta_o}{\theta_i} = \dfrac{10(1 + 0.2D)}{(1 + 2D)(1 + 0.05D)}$;   (b) $\dfrac{\theta_o}{\theta_i} = \dfrac{10(1 + 0.05D)}{(1 + 0.2D)(1 + 2D)}$

Evaluate this for the range of ω established with the G–ω plot. It should be recognized that the ϕ–ω relationship will be asymptotic to $\phi = 0°$ for low frequencies, and to $\phi = -90°$ for high frequencies, i.e.,

$\omega =$	0	0.2	0.5	1	2	5	10	20	50	100	∞
$\phi° =$	0	$19\frac{1}{2}$	$37\frac{1}{2}$	50	48	25	-4	$-32\frac{1}{2}$	-62	-76	-90

Figure 5.18 shows the Bode diagram required. Conversion of the G–ω plot to read G^*–ω requires only that the G, db scale be shifted vertically so that the horizontal asymptote starts at G^*, db = 0 instead of G, db = 20.

Note that a good approximation to the true shape of the G–ω curve can be obtained by plotting the standard first-order error (3 db) at each corner frequency. The curve plotted on this basis is included in Fig. 5.18. Also, the shape of the G–ω curve for the present form of transfer function is highly dependent on the relative values of the time constants (2, 0.2, 0.05). The inserts included in Fig. 5.18 show

$$\text{(a)} \quad \frac{\theta_o}{\theta_i} = \frac{10(1 + 0.2D)}{(1 + 2D)(1 + 0.05D)}$$

$$\text{(b)} \quad \frac{\theta_o}{\theta_i} = \frac{10(1 + 0.05D)}{(1 + 0.2D)(1 + 2D)}$$

The ϕ–ω curves will also be of different shapes.

5.7 *EXPERIMENTAL FREQUENCY RESPONSE ANALYSIS*

5.7.1 Introduction

Experimental frequency response analysis is used where

(a) it is desired to ascertain the response characteristics of an existing physical component or system, whose transfer function is unknown or uncertain; hopefully the transfer function can be obtained by examining the experimental data;
(b) it is desired to confirm a mathematical analysis of a system, i.e., to check that the derived transfer function is satisfactory.

It is usually fairly easy to generate sinusoidal variations of physical variables. For example,

(a) a simple slider crank mechanism produces sinusoidally varying displacement of the slider;
(b) sinusoidal displacements of one end of a linear spring produce a sinusoidally varying force exerted by the other end of the spring on its support;
(c) electrical alternating current is due to a sinusoidally varying voltage;

(d) a piston reciprocating in a closed air cylinder can produce a sinusoidally varying pressure in the cylinder.

Sine wave generators are common items in dynamic analysis laboratories.

5.7.2 Procedure

The procedure for conducting an experimental frequency response analysis is as follows:

(a) Apply a disturbance (i.e., input signal) $\theta_i = H \sin \omega t$ to an appropriate variable of the system being examined. The initial value of the input variable can be any steady-state value, including zero. The sinusoidal disturbance is superimposed over the initial steady-state value.

(b) For a selected value of frequency ω and a constant amplitude H, allow the transient effects of the system response to die out. The variable chosen to represent the system response should then be varying sinusoidally* at a constant amplitude and at the same frequency as the input. Measure the amplitude of the response variable and its phase relative to the input sinusoid. Ordinarily, both input and response variables will be displayed on an oscilloscope or chart recorder.

(c) Holding the input amplitude H constant, repeat (b) for discrete values of ω, to cover the range of frequency to which the system will respond.

(d) Plot the response amplitude and phase against input frequency to obtain the frequency response characteristic of the system. Response amplitude can be plotted as magnitude ratio, simply by dividing it by the constant input amplitude H. The data can be plotted in either linear Cartesian, polar, or logarithmic (Bode) forms.

5.7.3 Interpretation

If the experimental data is of the form shown in Figs. 5.3 or 5.4, or in Figs. 5.13 or 5.14(a) (these diagrams are different forms of the same response data), it can be concluded immediately that the system tested is of the first-order form $K/(1 + T D)$. Moreover, the time constant T and the system gain constant K are immediately apparent.

If the experimental data is of the form shown in Figs. 5.6, 5.7, 5.12, or 5.15, it can be concluded immediately that the system tested is of the second-order form $K/(1 + K_2 D + K_1 D^2)$. Values of K, K_1, and K_2 (or ξ, T, and ω_n) can be found directly by using the second-order response relationships discussed previously.

It is of interest that the phase-frequency data is not essential for associating response data to simple first- and second-order systems. How-

---

*For linear systems.

ever, the ϕ–ω curve may be of assistance if any ambiguity exists in the G–ω data. With more complicated response data, it is usual that the ϕ–ω curve is of great assistance in the interpretation of experimental response data. The following example will illustrate this point.

Example 5.8: A servomechanism consists of the oil hydraulic positioner shown in Example 3.5 (p. 48) driving a load which can be modeled as the damped-spring-mass unit of Example 3.8 (p. 52). The position of the mass is controlled by the position of the lever input to the positioner. It is desired to establish experimentally the dynamic relationship between movement of the input lever x_i and position of the mass x. To achieve this, a sinusoidal displacement generator is fitted to drive the input lever according to $\theta'_i = 0.05 \sin \omega t$, 0.05 being the amplitude and ω the angular frequency of the variation of θ_i. A displacement transducer is fitted to the mass so that the mass position is shown on a continuous chart recorder. The steady-state sinusoidal response of the mass, $x' = B \sin (\omega t + \phi)$, is measured for a range of input frequencies. The response data, B and ϕ, is shown in the accompanying tabulation.

Input frequency ω, rad/sec	0	0.1	0.2	0.3	0.4	0.5	0.6	0.8
Response amplitude B, in.	5	5	4.72	4.5	4.25	3.75	3.35	2.8
Response phase lag, $-\phi°$	0	$12\frac{1}{2}$	25	36	46	54	60	72
Input frequency ω, rad/sec	1	2	4	10	20	40	80	100
Response amplitude B, in.	2.5	1.12	0.35	0.08	0.02	0.003	—	—
Response phase lag, $-\phi°$	80	109	139	182	213	237	255	260

It is required to establish the system transfer function $x/x_i = f(D)$.

Solution: The Bode diagram method of plotting the frequency response data is usually best for interpretation purposes. Dividing the response amplitude by the input amplitude 0.05 gives the magnitude ratio G, which is then expressed in decibels. Figure 5.19 shows the response data plotted in Bode diagram form.

Three facts are immediately apparent from the plots:

(a) The G–ω curve is asymptotic to the horizontal line $(G, \text{db}) = 40$ as $\omega \to 0$ rad/sec.
(b) The G–ω curve is asymptotic to a line of slope -60 db/dec as $\omega \to \infty$.
(c) The slope of the G–ω curve increases continually in a clockwise sense. There is no suggestion of inflection, i.e., no anticlockwise breakup in the slope.
(d) The ϕ–ω curve is asymptotic to $\phi = 0°$ for low frequencies, and to $\phi = -270°$ for high frequencies.

Observation (c) indicates that there are no D factors in the numerator of the system transfer function. The absence of maxima or minima peaks in the ϕ–ω curve supports this conclusion.

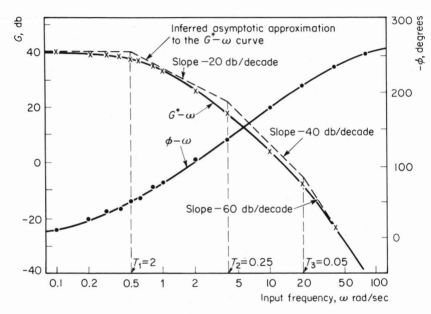

Fig. 5.19 Bode diagram of experimental data of Example 5.8; derived transfer function is

$$\frac{\theta_o}{\theta_i} = \frac{100}{(1 + 2D)(1 + 0.25D)(1 + 0.05D)}$$

In conjunction with (c), observation (b) indicates the presence of a third-order D term denominator of the transfer function. Observation (d) supports this conclusion, i.e., $\phi = 3 \times -90° = -270°$ as $\omega \to \infty$.

Observation (a) indicates that there are no zero factors present in the transfer function.

Hence it can be concluded that the transfer function is of the form

$$\frac{x}{x_i} = \frac{K}{K_1 D^3 + K_2 D^2 + K_3 D + 1}$$

This transfer function can be reduced further to one of the forms

(a) $\dfrac{K}{(1 + T D)^3}$

(c) $\dfrac{K}{(1 + T_1 D)(1 + T_2 D)(1 + T_3 D)}$

(b) $\dfrac{K}{(1 + T_1 D)(1 + T_2 D)^2}$

(d) $\dfrac{K}{(1 + T_1 D)(1 + 2\xi T D + T^2 D^2)}$

The absence of any upward peaking of the G–ω curve eliminates Case (d) (see Fig. 5.15). A cursory understanding of the actual physical system being tested would indicate the probability of Case (c) being the best model. On this basis, the 4-asymptote approximation to the curve, shown in Fig. 5.19, is drawn and the transfer function can be written

$$\frac{x}{x_i} = \frac{100}{(1 + 2D)(1 + 0.25D)(1 + 0.05D)}$$

i.e., K, db $= 20 \log_{10} K = 20 \log_{10} 100 = 40$ db, $1/2$, $1/0.25$, and $1/0.05$ rad/sec are the break points. Precise location of the break points would be assisted by knowing some or all of the actual system parameters such as piston area, load mass, input lever ratios, valve characteristics, etc., as the time constants are comprised of these values.

Example 5.9: A system yields the experimental frequency response data shown in the table; input amplitude (constant) $= 1$. Establish the transfer function of the system.

Input frequency, rad/sec	0.1	0.2	0.4	0.6	0.8	1	2
Response amplitude	1	0.95	0.75	0.6	0.47	0.4	0.25
Response phase lag, degrees	11	22	37	42	46	47	45
Input frequency, rad/sec	3	5	7	10	20	40	
Response amplitude	0.225	0.2	0.19	0.16	0.12	0.05	
Response phase lag, degrees	43	44	48	55	68	78	

Solution: The Bode plot of the response data is shown in Fig. 5.20.

The G–ω curve exhibits an initial slope of zero, followed by a breakdown at -20 db/dec, followed by a reduction of slope to zero, followed by a further breakdown to a final slope of -20 db/dec. It is immediately apparent that the initial breakdown in slope is due to a $1/(1 + T D)$ factor, that the breakup in slope to reinstate zero slope is due to a $(1 + T D)$ factor, and that the second breakdown is due to another $1/(1 + T D)$ factor. Thus, the transfer function is of the form

$$\frac{\theta_o}{\theta_i} = \frac{K(1 + T_2 D)}{(1 + T_1 D)(1 + T_3 D)}$$

The ϕ–ω curve is asymptotic to $\phi = 0$ and $\phi = -90°$, confirming this model. Drawing the best asymptotes of the appropriate slopes to the experimental curve (Fig. 5.20), the values of K, T_1, T_2 and T_3 are found to give

$$\frac{\theta_o}{\theta_i} = \frac{(1 + 0.5D)}{(1 + 2.5D)(1 + 0.1D)}$$

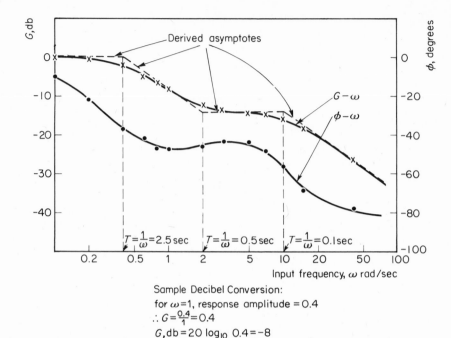

Sample Decibel Conversion:

for $\omega = 1$, response amplitude $= 0.4$

$\therefore G = \dfrac{0.4}{1} = 0.4$

$G, db = 20 \log_{10} 0.4 = -8$

Fig. 5.20 Bode diagram of experimental data of Example 5.9; derived transfer function is

$$\frac{\theta_o}{\theta_i} = \frac{(1 + 0.5D)}{(1 + 2.5D)(1 + 0.1D)}$$

The inflections in the ϕ–ω curve occur in the region of each critical frequency ($\omega = 1/T$), supporting the selected transfer function and its time constants.

It is more difficult to interpret experimental data accurately if the time constants are closer together than those of the two preceding Examples. It is often necessary to make an attempt to analyze the system mathematically in order to separate the transfer function factors.

5.8 SUMMARY

(a) A linear component or system which is subjected to a sinusoidally varying input disturbance exhibits a sinusoidally varying response after any transient response effects have died away in time.

(b) The frequency response characteristic of a linear system is essentially a plot of (1) the amplitude, and (2) phase relative to the input, of its steady-state response to a sinusoidal input disturbance, plotted against a wide range of input frequency.

(c) Frequency response analysis provides a way to describe the nature of a dynamic system without having to develop full solutions of system equations with various forcing functions.

(d) Frequency response data can be plotted in linear Cartesian, polar, or logarithmic forms. A polar plot has one curve containing both amplitude and phase data versus frequency. Cartesian plots require separate curves of amplitude and phase versus frequency.

(e) It is usual to represent response amplitude by the magnitude ratio

$$\frac{\text{amplitude of response sinusoid}}{\text{constant amplitude of input sinusoid}}$$

or

$$\frac{\text{amplitude of response}}{\text{system gain constant} \times \text{amplitude of input}}$$

(f) If the transfer function of a system is known, the frequency response data can be found by substituting $j\omega$ for D, and evaluating the consequent complex number as $G = f_1(\omega)$, $\phi = f_2(\omega)$ for various values of ω.

(g) The basic component factors of a system — i.e., first-order, second-order, and zero factors, in numerator or denominator of a transfer function — are well understood and readily interpreted in terms of frequency response.

(h) With logarithmic plotting, an asymptotic approximation to the magnitude ratio-frequency curve for any linear system can be easily constructed from inspection of its transfer function. The Bode diagram is a particularly descriptive form of logarithmic plot.

(i) The transfer function of a linear component or system can be established from experimental frequency response data. Bode plotting is particularly useful in establishing the form of a transfer function, and its constants. Phase-frequency data is not always essential, but can help in the interpretation of experimental data.

(j) Knowledge of the frequency response characteristics of a linear system enables direct interpretation of the system's response to other types of input disturbances (steps, ramps, etc.).

Further developments and aids to frequency response analysis are discussed in Chapter 8. The tabulation of G and ϕ values for the factor $G = 1 + j\omega T$ shown in Appendix C (pp. 416–417) is useful for evaluating magnitude ratios and phases. Appendix C also includes a decibel conversion table.

PROBLEMS

5.1 Show that the frequency response data given in the accompanying table applies to a simple second-order system, giving its damping ratio, natural undamped frequency, time constant, and system gain constant.

Input amplitude = 2 (constant)

Input frequency ω, rad/sec	0.2	0.25	0.32	0.4	0.5
Response amplitude	2.2	2.4	2.56	2.72	2.5
Response phase degrees	−20	−30	−41	−62	−90
Input frequency ω, rad/sec	0.55	0.65	0.8	1	2
Response amplitude	2.2	1.6	1.0	0.66	0.14
Response phase degrees	−104	−123	−140	−152	−166

Answer: $\dfrac{\theta_o}{\theta_i} = \dfrac{1}{1 + 1.6D + 4D^2}$; $\quad K = 1$; $\quad \xi = 0.4$; $\quad \omega_n = \dfrac{1}{T} = 0.5\,\text{rad/sec.}$

5.2 Obtain the frequency response characteristics in polar form for Problem 3.3 (p. 87).

5.3 Obtain the frequency response characteristics in Bode diagram form for Example 5.3 (p. 160).

5.4 Construct an accurate Bode diagram for the system

$$\frac{\theta_o}{\theta_i} = \frac{25(1 + 2D)}{(1 + 0.54D + 0.2D^2)}$$

5.5 Construct (1) the polar frequency response locus, and (b) the Bode diagram for the system

$$\frac{\theta_o}{\theta_i} = \frac{3D}{1 + 0.8D + D^2}$$

5.6 Construct the Bode diagram for the system

$$\frac{\theta_o}{\theta_i} = \frac{(1 + 5D)}{(1 + 30D)(1 + 150D)^2(1 + D)}$$

Use the asymptotic approximation for the G–ω curve.

5.7 Establish the transfer function of the system which yielded the experimental frequency data shown in the table.

Frequency, rad/sec	0.1	0.3	0.6	0.9	1
Amplitude ratio	9.95	3.19	1.42	0.96	0.69
Phase lag, degrees	97	110	128	138	146
Frequency, rad/sec	2	5	8	12	16
Amplitude ratio	0.21	0.028	0.008	0.0027	0.0012
Phase lag, degrees	175	214	231	242	250

Establish the constants associated with your transfer function.

6   *The stability of components and systems*

6.1 *INTRODUCTION*

The concept of the stability of an engineering system (either one component or a set of interconnected components) was introduced in Section 4.2.2. The stability condition of a linear system is associated with its characteristic equation, and is a characteristic of the system itself. An input (disturbance, or forcing function) applied to a system reveals the system's stability condition but does not cause or affect it. The response solution of a system equation to a specified forcing function contains two distinct terms. The steady-state term (the particular solution) is of the same form as the input disturbance* and cannot reveal a system's stability condition. The transient term (the complementary solution) is the solution of the system's homogeneous equation, and is of the general form

$$\theta_{o2} = \sum_{1}^{n} (B e^{\alpha t})$$

where n is the order of the system equation.

It was shown that $\alpha_1, \alpha_2, \ldots, \alpha_n$ are the distinct roots of the charac-

*Exceptions exist.

teristic equation. For a system to be stable, all terms $Be^{\alpha t}$ of the transient response must decay, in time, toward zero. This is achieved only if all roots α of the characteristic equation are negative, or have negative real parts if the roots are complex. The presence of one or more positive roots of the characteristic equation indicates the presence of terms in the transient response which increase with time. In this case, the transient term of the response to an input will increase with time, the system will never attain its steady-state value, and the system is unstable.

The first and main requirement of a dynamic engineering system is that it be stable. A linear system is stable if its response to an input

(a) reaches in time a steady-state condition which is unique and repeatable for a specified input, and is of the form of the input;
(b) dies away when the input is removed.

The system is unstable if its response

(c) increases continually with time;
(d) is self-sustained, such that it does not die away after the input disturbance is removed.

A borderline case exists between stable and unstable response, in which response achieves a finite oscillation about a steady-state condition. This stable-oscillating condition is usually undesirable.

Figure 6.1 shows some typical responses to a step input.

Thus the stability condition of a system can be ascertained

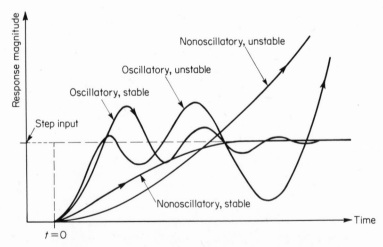

Fig. 6.1 Some possible responses of a system to a step input.

(e) by examining the roots of the system's characteristic equation;
(f) by examining the system's response to specified inputs.

As demonstrated in Chapter 4, both of these methods are very tedious when applied to any but the simplest of systems. A number of criteria have been developed which can be applied to reveal the stability condition of dynamic systems. The criteria reveal the presence or absence of positive roots of a system's characteristic equation, without evaluating the roots. Two such stability criteria, the Routh criterion and the Nyquist criterion, will be used in the present chapter. The root locus method of analysis, introduced in Chapter 7, provides another way of examining system stability.

6.2 ROOTS OF THE CHARACTERISTIC EQUATION

Several examples of extraction and examination of the roots of a characteristic equation to ascertain stability were given in Section 4.2.2. First- and second-order characteristic equations are readily handled in this manner. Extraction of the roots of a characteristic equation becomes increasingly difficult and tedious as the order of the equation increases. While methods have been developed for extracting the roots of high-order polynomials, it is usually preferable to use alternative techniques to examine the stability characteristics of a system.

Figure 6.2 shows the possible forms of the roots of a characteristic equation. The root forms are shown represented on the complex plane. The nature of the transient response associated with each form is also shown. It is apparent that all of the roots of a characteristic equation must be real and negative, or have negative real parts, if the transient term is to decay in time toward zero. Failure of the transient term to decay with time indicates an unstable system.

It should be kept in mind that complex or imaginary roots can exist only in conjugate pairs.

Example 6.1 (Section 6.3) illustrates the effect on system response of positive roots of the system's characteristic equation.

6.3 STABILITY FROM TIME RESPONSE

Chapter 4 was devoted to obtaining the time responses of systems, with specified forcing functions used to simulate input disturbances to the systems. Only stable systems were examined in detail. The stability condition of a system was immediately apparent from its time responses, as the transient terms decayed in time to zero leaving the system in a new steady-

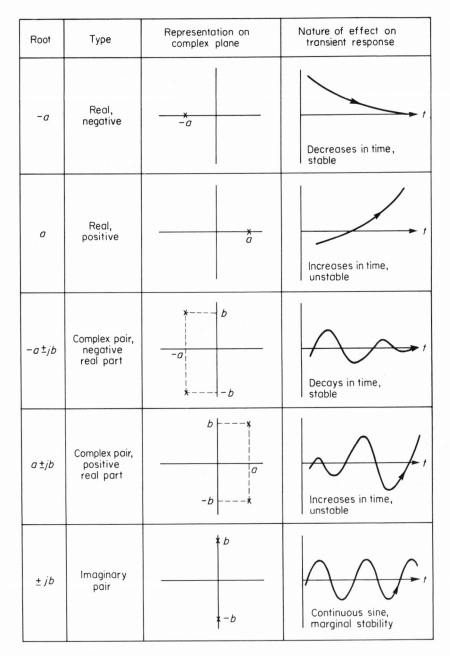

Fig. 6.2 Basic forms of characteristic equation roots and their natures.

state condition. The use of time response analysis to reveal the unstable condition of a system will be demonstrated in Example 6.1.

Example 6.1: A system has the transfer function

$$\frac{\theta_o}{\theta_i} = \frac{2}{2D^2 + 6D - 1}$$

Obtain the time response of the system for a step forcing function $\theta_i = 2$.

Solution: Assuming all initial conditions of θ_i and θ_o are zero, the transfer function is converted to the Laplace transform domain

$$\frac{\theta_o}{\theta_i}(s) = \frac{2}{2s^2 + 6s - 1} = \frac{1}{s^2 + 3s - 0.5} = \frac{1}{(s + 3.155)(s - 0.155)}$$

For $\theta_i = 2$, $\theta_i(s) = 2/s$, and

$$\theta_o(s) = \frac{2}{s(s + 3.155)(s - 0.155)}$$

Converting to time constant form,

$$\theta_o(s) = \frac{\left(\dfrac{2}{3.155}\right)(-0.155)}{s\left(\dfrac{s}{3.155} + 1\right)\left(\dfrac{s}{-0.155} + 1\right)} = \frac{-4}{s(0.317s + 1)(-6.45s + 1)}$$

$\theta(s)$ is now in a form recognizable as Function 11 in Table 4.2, with $T_1 = 0.317$, $T_2 = -6.45$. Inverse transformation yields

$$\theta_o(t) = -4\left[1 + \frac{1}{-6.45 - 0.317}(0.317e^{-3.155t} + 6.45e^{0.155t})\right]$$

$$= -4(1 - 0.046e^{-3.155t} - 0.954e^{0.155t})$$

Figure 6.3 shows that the magnitude of the system response increases continually with time, and hence that the system is unstable.

Alternatively, the system's instability is immediately recognizable if its characteristic equation,

$$2D^2 + 6D - 1 = 0$$

which is found by placing $\theta_i = 0$ in the transfer function and cross-multiplying, is factored to give

$$(D + 3.16)(D - 0.155) = 0$$

The roots of the characteristic equation are

$$D = \alpha_1 = -3.16, \quad D = \alpha_2 = 0.155$$

The complementary solution is of the form

$$\theta_o = B_1 e^{-3.16t} + B_2 e^{0.155t}$$

in which it is apparent that $B_2e^{0.155t}$ increases continually with time. That is, the positive root $D = 0.155$ causes instability.

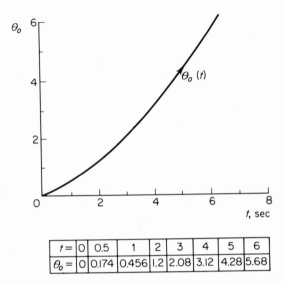

$t =$	0	0.5	1	2	3	4	5	6
$\theta_o =$	0	0.174	0.456	1.2	2.08	3.12	4.28	5.68

Fig. 6.3   Response of system $\theta_o/\theta_i = 2/(2D^2 + 6D - 1)$ to step input $\theta_i = 2$.

Figure 6.1 shows the time response of a typical system to a step input if:

(a) all roots of the system's characteristic equation are real and negative (nonoscillatory, stable);

(b) one or more roots are positive, the remaining roots being negative (nonoscillatory, unstable);

(c) one or more pairs of complex roots with negative real parts exist, the remaining roots being negative (oscillatory, stable);

(d) one or more pairs of complex roots with positive real parts exist, the remaining roots being negative (oscillatory, unstable);

(e) a pair of imaginary roots exist, the remaining roots being negative (marginally stable, or stable oscillating).

The first requirement of a dynamic engineering system is that it be stable. It is normally unnecessary to plot the time response of a system, as instability is readily revealed by quicker methods. However, affecting a time response solution with a computer may be a convenient method to establish a system's stability condition.

6.4 THE ROUTH CRITERION OF STABILITY

6.4.1 The Criterion

Only the criterion and its applications will be given. Its derivation is available in the literature.*

Routh's criterion shows the presence or absence of positive roots of a polynomial equation. The characteristic equation of a linear system is a polynomial in D. For example, the general form of a characteristic equation is

$$a_o D^n + a_1 D^{n-1} + a_2 D^{n-2} + \ldots + a_n = 0$$

To apply the criterion, the **Routhian array** associated with the polynomial must be formed. The Routhian array is an array of numbers derived in a specified pattern from the coefficients of the polynomial. Applied to the above general polynomial in D, the array is

$$
\begin{vmatrix}
a_o & a_2 & a_4 & \ldots & a_{n-1} \\
a_1 & a_3 & a_5 & \ldots & a_n \\
x_1 & x_2 & x_3 & \ldots & 0 \\
y_1 & y_2 & 0 & \ldots & 0 \\
z_1 & 0 & 0 & \ldots & 0 \\
. & . & . & . & . \\
. & . & . & . & . \\
. & . & . & . & . \\
0 & 0 & 0 & \ldots & 0
\end{vmatrix}
$$

where   row 1 is formed from the first, third, fifth, etc. coefficients;
   row 2 is formed from the second, fourth, sixth, etc. coefficients;
   row 3 is formed by combining rows 1 and 2 in the pattern

$$x_1 = \frac{a_1 a_2 - a_o a_3}{a_1}; \quad x_2 = \frac{a_1 a_4 - a_o a_5}{a_1}; \quad \text{etc.}$$

until continuous zeros appear in the row; row 4 is formed by combining rows 2 and 3 in the same pattern:

$$y_1 = \frac{x_1 a_3 - a_1 x_2}{x_1}; \quad y_2 = \frac{x_1 a_5 - a_1 x_3}{x_1}; \quad \text{etc.}$$

*See E. J. Routh, *Dynamics of a System of Rigid Bodies* (New York: Macmillan, 1877) and E. A. Guillemin, *The Mathematics of Circuit Anaylsis* (New York: John Wiley and Sons, Inc., 1949).

until only zeros appear. All subsequent rows are formed by similarly combining the two preceding rows, until only zeros appear in the array.

Example 6.2: Construct the Routhian array for the system

$$\frac{\theta_o}{\theta_i} = \frac{K(1 + 3D)}{D^5 + 3D^4 + 7D^3 + 20D^2 + 6D + 15}$$

Solution: The system's characteristic equation is

$$D^5 + 3D^4 + 7D^3 + 20D^2 + 6D + 15 = 0$$

The Routhian array is

$$
\begin{vmatrix}
1 & 7 & 6 \\
3 & 20 & 15 \\
x_1 = \frac{1}{3} & x_2 = 1 & x_3 = 0 \\
y_1 = 11 & y_2 = 15 & y_3 = 0 \\
z_1 = \frac{6}{11} & 0 & 0 \\
15 & 0 & 0 \\
0 & 0 & 0
\end{vmatrix}
$$

$$x_1 = \frac{3 \times 7 - 1 \times 20}{3} = \frac{1}{3}; \quad x_2 = \frac{3 \times 6 - 1 \times 15}{3} = 1;$$

$$x_3 = \frac{3 \times 0 - 1 \times 0}{3} = 0; \quad \text{etc.}$$

$$y_1 = \frac{\frac{1}{3} \times 20 - 3 \times 1}{\frac{1}{3}}; \quad y_2 = \frac{\frac{1}{3} \times 15 - 3 \times 0}{\frac{1}{3}} = 15; \quad y_3 = 0; \quad \text{etc.}$$

$$z_1 = \frac{11 \times 1 - \frac{1}{3} \times 15}{11} = \frac{6}{11}; \quad z_2 = 0$$

$$u_1 = \frac{\frac{6}{11} \times 15 - 11 \times 0}{\frac{6}{11}} = 15; \quad u_2 = 0$$

$$v_1 = \frac{15 \times 0 - \frac{6}{11} \times 0}{15} = 0$$

The Routh criterion

All roots of a polynomial are negative, if all elements in the first column of its Routhian array are positive. The Routh stability criterion can be stated as follows:

A system is stable if the Routhian array of its characteristic equation contains no negative elements in its first column.

Example 6.3: Investigate the stability condition of the system whose characteristic equation is

$$D^4 + 2D^3 + 3D^2 + 8D + 2 = 0$$

Solution: The Routhian array is

$$
\begin{vmatrix}
1 & 3 & 2 \\
2 & 8 & 0 \\
-1 & 2 & 0 \\
12 & 0 & \\
2 & 0 & \\
0 & &
\end{vmatrix}
$$

$$x_1 = \frac{2 \times 3 - 1 \times 8}{2} = -1, \quad \text{etc.}$$

$$y_1 = \frac{-1 \times 8 - 2 \times 2}{-1} = 12, \quad \text{etc.}$$

There is a negative number in the first column of the array. Hence the system is unstable, as its characteristic equation has at least one positive root.

Points to note

(1) All descending orders of the polynomial must be represented in order when forming the first two rows of the array. If any terms are missing from the characteristic equation, a zero must be used as its coefficient. Thus, the arrangement of the first two rows of $D^4 + 2D^2 + 3D + 4 = 0$ is

$$
\begin{vmatrix}
1 & 2 & 4 \\
0 & 3 & 0
\end{vmatrix}
$$

where the coefficient of D^3 is 0.
(2) The zeros which appear as the array is developed form a step pattern in pairs, until the first row of zeros appears. Examples 6.2 and 6.3 have such a pattern, shown by the broken lines.
(3) The number of sign changes which appear in the first column of the Routhian array indicates the number of positive roots (or complex roots with positive real parts) of the characteristic equation. Thus in Example 6.3 the sign changes twice (from $+2$ to -1, and from -1 to $+12$) indicating that there are two positive roots.
(4) All of the coefficients of the characteristic equations must be positive for a system to be stable. One or more negative coefficients will cause negatives to appear in the first column of the array.

(5) In the same manner that the first two rows of the Routhian array represent the original polynomial, any two successive rows represent a subsidiary equation of reduced order. For Example 6.2,

rows 1 and 2 represent $D^5 + 3D^4 + 7D^3 + 20D^2 + 6D + 15$;
rows 2 and 3 represent $3D^4 + \frac{1}{3}D^3 + 20D^2 + D + 15$;
rows 3 and 4 represent $\frac{1}{3}D^3 + 11D^2 + D + 15$;
rows 4 and 5 represent $11D^2 + \frac{6}{11}D + 15$;
rows 5 and 6 represent $\frac{6}{11}D + 15$.

Also, any single row of the array represents an expression containing alternate orders of D only. For Example 6.2,

row 1 represents $D^5 + 7D^3 + 6D$;
row 2 represents $3D^4 + 20D^2 + 15$;
row 4 represents $11D^2 + 15$.

(6) Any row of the Routhian array can be divided by a positive constant, without affecting the sign condition of the first column. Large numbers in a row can be reduced by such division for easier manipulation.

(7) Approximation of awkward numbers in the array is usually satisfactory unless there are near differences in any of the combinations of the products used to form an entry.

6.4.2 Some Special Cases

(1) If the first number in a row of the array is zero while other entries in the row are finite, the following row will contain indeterminate entries, and the array is indeterminate.

Example 6.4: For $2D^4 + 3D^2 + 2D + 1 = 0$, the array becomes

$$
\begin{vmatrix}
2 & 3 & 1 \\
0 & 2 & 0 \\
\infty & 0/0 &
\end{vmatrix}
$$

Note: $0D^3$ is used for the missing D^3 term.

For this situation, the characteristic equation can be multiplied by a factor $(D + k)$, where k is a positive number, and the array written for the resulting equation will be determinate. The stability condition associated with the original characteristic equation is unaffected as $D = -k$ represents a negative (and hence stable) additional root. It is best not to use $k = 1$ or $k = 2$, as this can lead to another indeterminate condition. For the present example, use $k = 3$ to give

$$(2D^4 + 3D^2 + 2D + 1)(D + 3) = 2D^5 + 6D^4 + 3D^3 + 11D^2 + 7D + 3 = 0$$

which now contains all descending orders of D.

The array becomes

$$
\begin{array}{cccc}
2 & 3 & 7 & 0 \\
6 & 11 & 3 & 0 \\
-\tfrac{2}{3} & 6 & 0 & \\
65 & 3 & 0 & \\
6* & 0 & & \\
3 & 0 & & \\
0 & & &
\end{array}
$$

*Actually $6\frac{2}{65}$; approximations are usually satisfactory, unless near differences in numbers occur.

indicating that the system represented is unstable. This will always be the case if any descending order of D is missing in the characteristic equation.

(2) If all of the numbers in a row are zero before the array is complete the criterion is indeterminate.

Example 6.5: For the characteristic equation

$$D^6 + D^5 - 2D^4 - 3D^3 - 7D^2 - 4D - 4 = 0$$

the array becomes

$$
\begin{array}{cccc}
1 & -2 & -7 & -4 \\
1 & -3 & -4 & 0 \\
1 & -3 & -4 & 0 \\
0 & 0 & 0 & \\
0/0 & 0/0 & 0/0 &
\end{array}
$$

Note: The presence of negative coefficients indicates instability. However, for purposes of illustration, the array is examined.

and the zeros of the fourth row have produced indeterminate entries in the fifth row, rendering the array indeterminate. To proceed, the subsidiary equation represented by the row preceding the row of zeros is differentiated, and substituted for the row of zeros. The array can then be completed to indicate the stability condition of the system.

The subsidiary equation of the present example is

$$D^4 - 3D^2 - 4$$

which can be differentiated with regard to D to give

$$4D^3 - 6D$$

the coefficients of which are substituted for the row of zeros to give

$$
\begin{vmatrix}
1 & -2 & -7 & -4 \\
1 & -3 & -4 & 0 \\
1 & -3 & -4 & 0 \\
4 & -6 & 0 &
\end{vmatrix}
$$

which can now be completed:

$$
\begin{vmatrix}
-1.5 & -4 & 0 \\
-16.7 & 0 & \\
-4 & 0 & \\
0 & &
\end{vmatrix}
$$

There is a sign change in the first column (from 4 to -1.5) and hence the system represented is unstable.

6.4.3 Conditional Stability

The Routh criterion can be used to indicate the range of a system parameter which will give stable response.

Example 6.6: A system has the characteristic equation

$$D^3 + 34.5D^2 + 7500D + 7500K = 0$$

It is required to establish the limits of K for the system to be stable. The Routhian array is

$$
\begin{vmatrix}
1 & 7500 & 0 \\
34.5 & 7500K & 0 \\
\left(\dfrac{258{,}750 - 7500K}{34.5}\right) & 0 & \\
7500K & 0 & \\
0 & &
\end{vmatrix}
$$

For stability, all entries in the first column of the array must be positive, i.e.,

$$\frac{258{,}750 - 7500K}{34.5} > 0 \quad \text{and} \quad 7500K > 0$$

from which $K < 34.5$, $K > 0$. Hence for the system to be stable, $0 < K < 34.5$.

Example 6.7: What are the limits of the parameter K for the system whose characteristic equation is

$$D^3 + 3K\,D^2 + (K + 2)\,D + 4 = 0$$

to be stable? The Routhian array is

$$
\begin{vmatrix}
1 & K+2 \\
3K & 4 \\
\left[\dfrac{3K(K+2)-4}{3K}\right] & 0 \\
4 & 0 \\
0 & 0
\end{vmatrix}
$$

For stability,
$$3K > 0 \tag{1}$$
and
$$\frac{3K(K+2)-4}{3K} > 0 \tag{2}$$

From (1), $K > 0$ for stability; from (2), $3K^2 + 6K - 4 > 0$, from which

$$K < -2.528 \quad \text{or} \quad K > 0.528$$

Thus $K > 0.528$ is the required solution.

6.4.4 Summary

The Routh stability criterion:

(a) is a quick and easy indicator of the stability condition of a linear system;
(b) indicates the number, if any, of positive roots of a system's characteristic equation;
(c) does not readily give the degree of stability of a system;
(d) can be used to specify values of system parameters for which a system is stable.

Some problems for solution appear at the end of the chapter.

6.5 THE NYQUIST CRITERION OF STABILITY

6.5.1 Introduction

The Nyquist stability criterion is a steady-state frequency response technique applicable to negative feedback systems. It requires understanding of the meaning of a system's **open loop transfer function,** which will be discussed in Section 6.5.2. Briefly, the criterion requires plotting of the polar frequency response locus of the open loop transfer function, by using $j\omega$ for D, for all possible values of frequency ω between $\pm \infty$. The location of the locus relative to the point $(-1, 0)$ establishes the stability condition of the system. Open loop polar plots are readily made.

Full derivation, application, and understanding of the Nyquist stability criterion require the use of abstract mathematical notions, and will not be given here. A complete analysis of the criterion and its application are readily available.* The present explanation and application is adequate for systems, classified as minimum phase systems, in which

(1) the individual components of the system are all stable;
(2) the denominator of the system transfer function is of higher order than its numerator.

These restrictions encompass most common control system situations. However, it should be realized that a closed loop system can be stable, even though one or more of its individual components are, in isolation, unstable. The stability of a closed loop system depends not so much on the stability of the individual components, as on the manner in which the components are connected to form the system. Components connected together to form a loop interact with each other.

6.5.2 The Open Loop Transfer Function

The block diagram of Fig. 6.4(a) represents the general form of a negative feedback system which has been reduced to one block in the forward feed, $K_1 f_1(D)$, and to one block in the feedback, $K_2 f_2(D)$. It is common that $K_2 f_2(D) = 1$, giving a unity negative feedback system [Fig. 6.4(b)]. The system transfer function is

$$\frac{\theta_o}{\theta_i} = \frac{K_1 f_1(D)}{1 + K_1 f_1(D) \cdot K_2 f_2(D)} = \frac{K_1 f_1(D)}{1 + K_o f(D)} \tag{6.1}$$

where $K_o = K_1 K_2$ and $f(D) = f_1(D) \cdot f_2(D)$.
The forward transfer function is

$$\frac{\theta_o}{\theta} = K_1 f_1(D) \tag{6.2}$$

The feedback transfer function is

$$\frac{\theta_{on}}{\theta_o} = K_2 f_2(D) \tag{6.3}$$

where θ_{on} is the signal at the summing sign due to feedback. Note that θ_{on} *represents* the response variable θ_o, but *equals* θ_o only for unity negative feedback systems, when $K_2 f_2(D) = 1$. Note also that θ_{on} has the same dimensions as the input θ_i, and consequently the error $\theta = \theta_i - \theta_{on}$.

*Kuo, B. C., *Automatic Control Systems* (Prentice-Hall, Inc., Englewood Cliffs, N. J. 1962).

The characteristic equation of the system is represented by

$$1 + K_o f(D) = 0 \qquad (6.4)$$

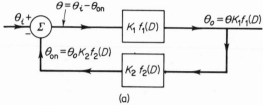

(a)

General negative feedback system

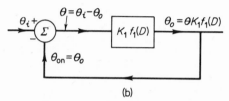

(b)

True unity negative feedback system,
where $K_2 f_2(D) = 1$

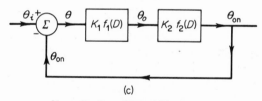

(c)

Normalized condition of (a), above,
to achieve unity negative feedback
representation

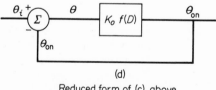

(d)

Reduced form of (c), above,

$$\frac{\theta_{on}}{\theta} = K_o \ f(D) = K_1 \ f_1(D) \cdot K_2 \ f_2(D)$$

is the open-loop transfer function

Fig. 6.4   Obtaining the open loop transfer function of a negative feedback system.

although some simplification is required to yield the actual characteristic equation, the root conditions of which decide stability (see origin of following Eq. 6.7).

Using θ_{on} to represent the condition of the response variable, the system block diagram can be rearranged to the unity negative feedback form of Fig. 6.4(c). Note that there are no changes in the basic relationships of the system variables:

$$\theta = \theta_i - \theta_{on}; \quad \frac{\theta_o}{\theta} = K_1 f_1(D); \quad \frac{\theta_{on}}{\theta_o} = K_2 f_2(D)$$

Figure 6.4(d) shows the reduced form of the rearranged block diagram. The **normalized system** so obtained has the transfer function

$$\frac{\theta_{on}}{\theta_i} = \frac{K_o f(D)}{1 + K_o f(D)} \tag{6.5}$$

which is nondimensional, as θ_{on} and θ_i are of the same dimensions.

It is of vital importance to perceive that the original system transfer function, Eq. 6.1, and the normalized system transfer function, Eq. 6.5, have the same characteristic equation (Eq. 6.4). *Hence a stability analysis made using the normalized system is equally applicable to the original system.* Now the relationship

$$\frac{\theta_{on}}{\theta} = K_o f(D) \tag{6.6}$$

which is apparent from each diagram of Fig. 6.4, is called the **open loop transfer function** of the system. The open loop transfer function relates the signal at the summing sign, which represents the condition of the response variable, to the error signal flowing forward from the summing sign.

For the case of the true unity negative feedback system (Fig. 6.4b), the open loop transfer function $\theta_{on}/\theta = K_o f(D)$ becomes simply

$$\frac{\theta_o}{\theta} = K_1 f_1(D) \tag{6.6a}$$

where $\theta_{on} = \theta_o$, $K_1 = K_o$, and $f_1(D) = f(D)$ when $K_2 f_2(D) = 1$.

In general, $f_1 D$, $f_2(D)$, and $f(D)$ will each be a ratio of polynomials in D. For example, Fig. 6.5(a) shows a system in which the forward transfer function is

$$\frac{\theta_o}{\theta} = \frac{6}{D(1 + 2D)} = K_1 f_1(D) = K_1 \frac{f_{1n}(D)}{f_{1d}(D)}$$

where $f_{1n}(D)$ is the numerator polynomial of $f_1(D)$ and $f_{1d}(D)$ is the denominator polynomial of $f_1(D)$. For this case, $K_1 = 6$, $f_{1n}(D) = 1$, and $f_{1d}(D) = D(1 + 2D)$.

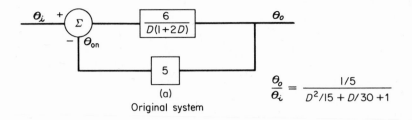

$$\frac{\theta_o}{\theta_i} = \frac{1/5}{D^2/15 + D/30 + 1}$$

(a)
Original system

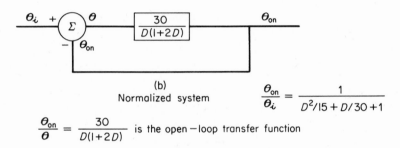

(b)
Normalized system

$$\frac{\theta_{on}}{\theta_i} = \frac{1}{D^2/15 + D/30 + 1}$$

$$\frac{\theta_{on}}{\theta} = \frac{30}{D(1+2D)} \quad \text{is the open-loop transfer function}$$

Fig. 6.5 Finding the open loop transfer function for the system of Example 6.8.

Hence the open loop transfer function, Eq. 6.6, can be written

$$\frac{\theta_{on}}{\theta} = K_o f(D) = \frac{K_o f_n(D)}{f_d(D)}$$

and the expression representing the characteristic equation, Eq. 6.4, becomes

$$1 + K_o f(D) = 1 + \frac{K_o f_n(D)}{f_d(D)} = 0 \qquad (6.4a)$$

which can be multiplied by $f_d(D)$ to give

$$f_d(D) + K_o f_n(D) = 0 \qquad (6.7)$$

which is the characteristic equation of the system, the roots of which dictate the system stability condition.

Equation 6.7 is quite significant, showing that the feedback system's characteristic equation is equal to the sum of the numerator and denominator of the system's open loop transfer function.

Finally, if $f_1(D)$, $f_2(D)$, and hence $f(D)$ are in time constant form [that is, if they are composed of dimensionless factors $(1 + TD)$, $D(1 + TD)$, or $(1 + 2\xi TD + T_2 D^2)]$, then

$$K_1 \quad \text{is the forward gain constant}$$

$$K_2 \quad \text{is the feedback gain constant}$$

$$K_o \quad \text{is the open loop gain constant}$$

Example 6.8: Obtain the system transfer function, the normalized system transfer function, the open loop transfer function, and the open loop gain constant of the system shown in Fig. 6.5(a).

Solution: The system transfer function, in time constant form, is

$$\frac{\theta_o}{\theta_i} = \frac{1/5}{D^2/15 + D/30 + 1}$$

To normalize the system, move the feedback transfer function 5 back into the forward feed, so that θ_{on} is used to represent the system response. Figure 6.5(b) shows the result. Thus the normalized system transfer function, in time constant form, is

$$\frac{\theta_{on}}{\theta_i} = \frac{1}{D^2/15 + D/30 + 1}$$

This process could easily be carried out without drawing Fig. 6.5(b):

$$\frac{\theta_o}{\theta_i} = \frac{1/5}{D^2/15 + D/30 + 1}$$

and $\theta_{on}/\theta_o = 5$; hence

$$\frac{\theta_{on}}{\theta_i} = \frac{\theta_o}{\theta_i} \cdot \frac{\theta_{on}}{\theta_o} = \frac{1}{D^2/15 + D/30 + 1}$$

The open loop transfer function, in time constant form, is

$$\frac{\theta_{on}}{\theta} = \frac{30}{D(1 + 2D)}$$

and hence the open loop gain constant is $K_o = 30$.

The system's characteristic equation is

$$\frac{D^2}{15} + \frac{D}{30} + 1 = 0$$

which is apparent from both the θ_o/θ_i and θ_{on}/θ_i relationships.

6.5.3 The Nyquist Stability Criterion

Subject to the restriction (discussed in Section 6.5.1) that analysis be confined to systems comprised of stable components, the Nyquist stability criterion can be stated as follows:

If the polar frequency response locus of a system's open loop transfer function, for all possible real values of frequency between $\pm$ infinity, encircles the point $(-1, 0)$ in a clockwise sense, the system is unstable. If the point $(-1, 0)$ is not encircled, the system is stable. If the locus passes through $(-1, 0)$, the system is marginally stable — that is, it is on the borderline between stability and instability.

It is only necessary to calculate the frequency response data for positive values of frequency, in the range $\omega = 0 \rightarrow \infty$. The locus for negative values of ω, in the range 0 to $-\infty$, is a mirror image about the horizontal axis of the locus obtained for positive ω. Proper application of the Nyquist criterion requires that the mirror image locus for negative ω be drawn.

Example 6.9: Ascertain the stability condition of the system whose partially reduced block diagram is shown in Fig. 6.6(a).

Solution: The system is a unity negative feedback system. Its open loop transfer function is $\theta_{on}/\theta = \theta_o/\theta = 1/D(1 + D)$. For steady-state frequency response analysis substitute $j\omega$ for D to give

$$\left(\frac{\theta_o}{\theta}\right)_{j\omega} = \frac{1}{j\omega + (j\omega)^2} = \frac{1}{j\omega - \omega^2}$$

The magnitude ratio and phase of the open loop transfer function are

$$G_o = \frac{1}{(\omega^2 + \omega^4)^{1/2}} = \frac{1}{\omega(1 + \omega^2)^{1/2}}$$

$$\phi_o = -\tan^{-1}\frac{\omega}{-\omega^2} = -\tan^{-1}\frac{1}{-\omega} = -90 - \tan^{-1}\omega$$

(See previous Section 5.5 for zero factors in a transfer function).

Figure 6.6 shows tabulated evaluations of G_o and ϕ_o for several positive values of ω, together with the polar plot of this data. The plot for positive ω (heavy line) was commenced on the real axis ($0°$). The presence of the $1/D \equiv 1/j\omega$ term in the open loop transfer function causes an immediate rotation of $-90°$ at radius infinity for $\omega \equiv 0$, so that the locus starts curving inwards from infinity on the $-90°$ axis. The importance of including the infinite radius quadrant in the open loop frequency response locus will be discussed in Section 6.5.4. The plot for negative ω (broken line) is a mirror image of the positive ω plot. Point $(-1, 0)$ is not encircled, hence the closed loop system is stable.

Example 6.10: Determine the stability of the system whose open loop transfer function is

$$\frac{\theta_{on}}{\theta} = \frac{100}{D(1 + D/4)(1 + D/16)}$$

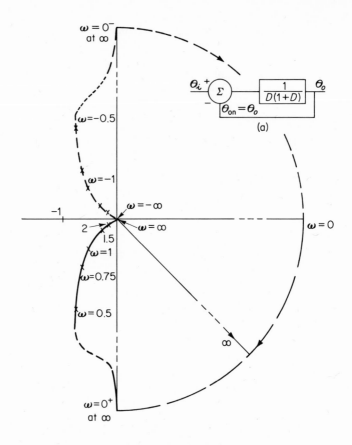

$\omega =$	0.2	0.5	0.75	1.0	1.5	2.0	rad/sec
$G_o =$	5	1.8	1.07	0.71	0.37	0.22	
$\phi_0 =$	−101°	−117°	−127°	−135°	−146°	−154°	

Fig. 6.6 Nyquist diagram for the system whose open loop transfer function is $\theta_{on}/\theta = 1/[D(1 + D)]$.

Solution: Substitute $j\omega$ for D to give

$$\left(\frac{\theta_{on}}{\theta}\right)_{j\omega} = \frac{100}{j\omega(1 + j\omega/4)(1 + j\omega/16)} \quad \text{or} \quad \frac{100}{-5/16\omega^2 + j(\omega - \omega^3/64)}$$

Then,

$$G_o = \frac{100}{\omega(1 + \omega^2/16)^{1/2}(1 + \omega^2/256)^{1/2}} \quad \text{or} \quad \frac{100}{[\frac{25}{256}\omega^4 + (\omega - \omega^3/64)^2]^{1/2}}$$

$$\phi_o = -90° - \tan^{-1}\frac{\omega}{4} - \tan^{-1}\frac{\omega}{16} \quad \text{or} \quad -\tan^{-1}\frac{1 - \omega^2/64}{-\frac{5}{16}\omega}$$

Figure 6.7 shows tabulated values of ω, G_o, and ϕ_o, together with the polar plot of the data, and its mirror image for negative values of ω. It is obvious that the point $(-1, 0)$ is encircled. Hence the system whose open loop transfer function was given is unstable. Note that the rotation of $-90°$ at infinite radius, for $\omega = 0$, was again included in the plot.

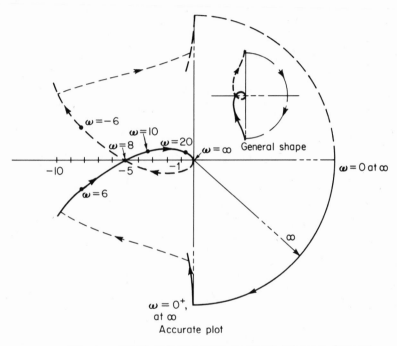

$\omega =$	0^+	1	2	4	6	8	10	20	50	∞
$\phi_0 =$	$-90°$	$-107°$	$-124°$	$-149°$	$-167°$	$-180°$	$-190°$	$-220°$	$-247°$	$-270°$
$G_o =$	∞	97	44	17	8.7	5	3.7	0.6	0.05	0

Fig. 6.7   Nyquist plot of the open loop transfer function

$$\frac{\theta_{on}}{\theta} = \frac{100}{D(1 + D/4)(1 + D/16)}$$

Points to note

(1) Open loop data (G_o, ϕ_o) was used to investigate the stability of the closed loop system.

(2) An open loop transfer function is usually simpler to handle than its corresponding closed loop transfer function.

(3) Only a few values of frequency were used to draw the plots. These values gave the full shape of the locus. For Example 6.9, nothing is gained by evaluating the frequencies higher than $\omega = 2$, as the $\omega = 2$ point is quite close to the $\omega = \infty$ point in this case.
(4) The positive ω open loop locus starts on the real axis ($0°$) for $\omega = 0$, and finishes at the origin for $\omega = \infty$ (minimum phase systems only).

6.5.4 Origin of the Nyquist Stability Criterion

The Nyquist criterion reveals the presence or absence of any positive roots of a system's characteristic equation. Rigid mathematical derivation of the criterion is somewhat abstract, and may be found in the work of Kuo.* A physical explanation of the origins of the criterion as it applies to systems composed only of stable components will be given here, as it promotes understanding of the criterion.

Consider two plotting planes:

(1) A plane with real and imaginary axes on which values for D can be represented, called the D plane (Fig. 6.8a).
(2) A plane with real and imaginary axes on which values of a function of D can be represented, called the $F(D)$ plane (Fig. 6.8b).

Two such planes are called **conformal planes,** and corresponding values of D and $F(D)$ are called **conformal points.**

Example:

$$F(D) = \frac{1}{D + 8}$$

The value $D = -3$ yields

$$F(D) = \frac{1}{-3 + 8} = \frac{1}{5}$$

Hence $D = -3$ on the D plane (Fig. 6.8a) and $F(D) = \frac{1}{5}$ on the $F(D)$ plane (Fig. 6.8b) are conformal points.

Also, a plot of points on the D plane, representing a locus of values of D, has a conformal plot of $F(D)$ on the $F(D)$ plane.

Some rules for conformal plots

(1) A closed path on the D plane transforms to a closed path on the $F(D)$ plane. The conformal closed paths are not necessarily of the same shape, or in the same relative location on their planes.
(2) A point inside a closed path on the D plane transforms to a point inside the conformal closed path on the $F(D)$ plane.

*Kuo, B. C., *Automatic Control Systems* (Prentice-Hall, Inc., Englewood Cliffs, N. J., 1962).

(3) If a vector drawn from a point inside a closed path on the D plane is rotated clockwise to pass through successive points 1, 2, 3, etc. on the path, then a vector drawn from a point inside the conformal closed path on the $F(D)$ plane will also rotate clockwise through successive conformal points $1'$, $2'$, $3'$, etc.

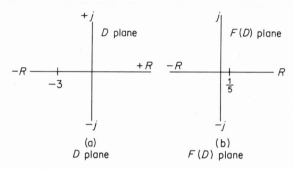

(a)
D plane

(b)
$F(D)$ plane

Showing conformal points $D = -3$ and $F(D) = \frac{1}{5}$

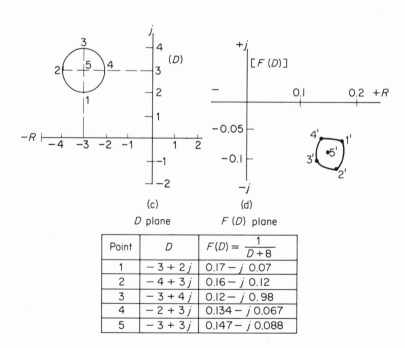

(c)
D plane

(d)
$F(D)$ plane

Point	D	$F(D) = \dfrac{1}{D+8}$
1	$-3 + 2j$	$0.17 - j\,0.07$
2	$-4 + 3j$	$0.16 - j\,0.12$
3	$-3 + 4j$	$0.12 - j\,0.98$
4	$-2 + 3j$	$0.134 - j\,0.067$
5	$-3 + 3j$	$0.147 - j\,0.088$

Fig. 6.8   Examples of conformal plotting for the function $1/(D+8)$.

It must be appreciated that these rules are not necessarily reversible. That is, all points inside a closed $F(D)$ contour are not necessarily inside the corresponding D plot.

Example:

$$F(D) = \frac{1}{D + 8}$$

Consider a circle of radius 1 drawn from the center point $(-3, j3)$ on the D plane (Fig. 6.8c). Points 1, 2, 3, 4 outline the circle; point 5 is the center. A table of D and $F(D)$ values can be prepared, and the $F(D)$ plot made. Note that $F(D)$ reduces to a complex number-vector relationship of the type handled previously in frequency response analysis. For example, consider point 1 on the D plane:

$$D = -3 + j2; \quad F(D) = \frac{1}{(-3 + j2) + 8} = \frac{1}{5 + j2}$$

The magnitude and angle of the vector representing this $F(D)$ point are found with the procedures used for frequency response analysis:

$$\text{magnitude} = \frac{1}{(5^2 + 2^2)^{1/2}} = 0.19; \quad \text{angle} = -\tan^{-1}\frac{2}{5} = -22°$$

Hence point 1′ on the $F(D)$ plane is located at 0.19, $-22°$ (Fig. 6.8d). Alternatively,

$$\frac{1}{5 + j2} = \frac{1}{5 + j2} \times \frac{5 - j2}{5 - j2} = \frac{5 - j2}{25 - j^2 4} = \frac{5 - j2}{29}$$

and point 1′ lies at $\frac{5}{29} - j\frac{2}{29} = 0.17 - j0.07$, which is readily plotted directly on the $F(D)$ plane (Fig. 6.8d).

Note that the conformal plots of Figs. 6.8(c) and (d) satisfy all three of the preceding rules.

Any root of a characteristic equation, substituted for D,

(1) makes the characteristic function $f_d(D) + K_o f_n(D)$ equal to zero, giving the characteristic equation (Eq. 6.7);

(2) makes

$$\frac{f_d(D) + K_o f_n(D)}{f_d(D)} = 0$$

(3) makes

$$\frac{f_d(D) + K_o f_n(D)}{f_d(D)} = 1 + K_o f(D) = 0 \quad \text{(Eqs. 6.4 and 6.4a)}$$

(4) makes $K_o f(D) = -1$.

It follows from (4) that all roots of a system's characteristic equation, substituted for D in $f(D)$, make $K_o f(D) = -1$. If roots of a characteristic equation are plotted on the D plane, all of them will plot at the point $(-1, j0)$ on the $F(D) = K_o f(D)$ plane.

Example: For the system shown in Fig. 6.9,

$$\frac{\theta_o}{\theta_i} = \frac{1}{D + 9}$$

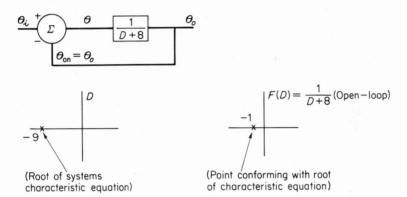

Fig. 6.9 Showing that roots of a system's characteristic equation plot at $(-1, j0)$ on the $F(D) = K_o f(D)$ plane.

is the system's transfer function. The system is a unity negative feedback system so $\theta_{on} = \theta_o$, and

$$\frac{\theta_{on}}{\theta} = \frac{1}{D + 8}$$

is the system's open loop transfer function. The system's characteristic equation is $1 + (D + 8) = 0$, or

$$D + 9 = 0$$

whose root is $D = -9$. For $D = -9$, the open loop transfer function becomes

$$\frac{\theta_{on}}{\theta} = F(D) = \frac{1}{D + 8} = \frac{1}{-9 + 8} = -1$$

Thus the root -9 on the D plane and the point -1 on the $F(D) = K_o f(D)$ plane are conformal points.

For steady-state frequency response analysis, we can replace D in transfer functions with $j\omega$. Thus we can work with conformal plots on the $j\omega$ and $F(j\omega)$ planes. All possible values of frequency can be represented on the imaginary axis of the $j\omega$ plane, as shown in Fig. 6.10(a). Positive values of ω, from 0 to ∞, occupy the positive imaginary axis, whereas negative values of ω occupy the negative imaginary axis.

Imagine now a semicircle of infinite radius drawn to completely encompass the righthand half of the $j\omega$ plane (Fig. 6.10b). A closed path has been formed, ranging from $\omega = 0$ to $\omega = \infty^+$ to $\omega = \infty^-$ to $\omega = 0$, with continuous clockwise rotation. The path encloses all possible positive real numbers and complex numbers with positive real parts.

Consider next a polar plot of the open loop transfer function $\theta_{on}/\theta = K_o f(D) = F_o(D)$, for $D = j\omega$ and for all values of ω. The plot is the frequency response locus of the open loop transfer function, for all possible values of ω. Figure 6.6 (Example 6.9) and Fig. 6.7 (Example 6.10) show several such plots. It was necessary to evaluate the open loop magnitude ratio G_o and the open loop phase angle ϕ_o only for some positive values of ω, as the curve for negative ω is a mirror image about the real axis of the positive ω curve. Figures 6.6 and 6.7 both show the general fact that the complete $\theta_{on}/\theta = F_o(j\omega)$ curve is a closed path. The path is clockwise in the sense of going from $\omega = 0$ to $\omega = \infty^+$ to $\omega = \infty^-$ to $\omega = 0$. Note that $\omega = \infty^+$ and $\omega = \infty^-$ coincide at the origin. Figure 6.10(c) shows a typical **Nyquist plot,** as the $\theta_{on}/\theta(j\omega)$ curve is known.

It follows that Figs. 6.10(b) and (c) are conformal plots, which obey the three rules given previously. Thus any point within the infinite semicircle of Fig. 6.10(b) must be within the plot of Fig. 6.10(c). Note that the infinite semicircle of Fig. 6.10(b) is conformal with an infinite number of $F_o(j\omega)$ plots, which depend on the particular $F_o(j\omega)$ considered. However, all $F_o(j\omega)$ plots will be closed paths rotating clockwise for ω varying from 0 to ∞^+ to ∞^- to 0.

Recall now that all roots of a characteristic equation will plot at $(-1, j0)$ on the $F_o(D) = F_o(j\omega)$ plane. Hence if point $(-1, j0)$ lies within the $F_o(j\omega)$ plot, then one or more roots of the characteristic equation of the system must lie within the infinite semicircle on the righthand half $j\omega$ plane. Such roots will be positive, indicating that the system is unstable.

Conversely, if a $\theta_{on}/\theta = F_o(j\omega)$ plot does not enclose the point $(-1, j0)$, then the conformal infinite semicircle on the righthand half $j\omega$ plane has not enclosed any roots of the system's characteristic equation, and hence no positive roots exist and the system is stable.

The effect of zero factors

It is common that an open loop transfer function contains first- or second-order zero factors in its denominator. It is possible, but less common, for higher-order zero factors to exist in the denominator or for zero factors to occur in the numerator. Previous examples, 6.8 and 6.9, both contained a first-order zero factor $1/D$. For the types of systems being

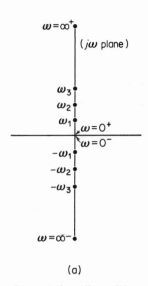

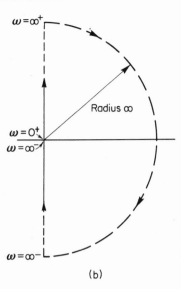

(a)

Representing all possible values of ω between $\pm\infty$, on the $D \equiv j\omega$ plane

(b)

The infinite semi-circle representing ω going from 0^+ to ∞^+ to ∞^- to 0^-, in a clockwise sense to encircle all possible positive numbers (real and complex)

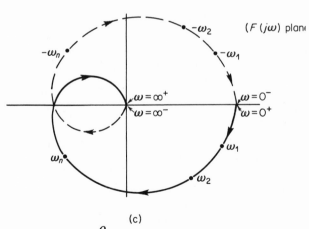

(c)

A typical $\dfrac{\theta_{on}}{\theta} = K_o f(j\omega) = F(j\omega)$ plot showing ω increasing from 0^+ to ∞^+ to ∞^- to 0^-; the plot is conformal with (b), above

Fig. 6.10 Conformal $j\omega$ and $F(j\omega)$ plots.

treated in this text, the presence of such zero factors can be recognized by starting the Nyquist plot on the real axis, and swinging through one quadrant at infinite radius for each zero factor present. Thus in Examples 6.8 and 6.9, the Nyquist phasor was rotated $-90°$ at infinite radius for $\omega = 0$ to locate G_o for $\omega = 0^+$ at infinity on the $-90°$ axis. If the open loop transfer function had contained $1/D^2$, the initial rotation would have been $-180°$ at infinite radius. If it had contained D as a numerator factor, the initial rotation would have been $+90°$.

While the foregoing procedure is adequate for most common feedback systems, the infinite radius rotations associated with zero factors have a deeper significance which is discussed in Kuo (*op. cit.*).

6.5.5 Summary of Application of Nyquist Criterion

To apply the Nyquist criterion of stability to negative feedback systems, which are composed of stable components,

(a) obtain the system's open loop transfer function;
(b) starting on the real axis for $\omega = 0$, plot the polar frequency response locus of the open loop transfer function, for positive values of ω between 0 and ∞; if zero factors $1/D$, $1/D^2$, D, etc. are present, the locus starts at ∞ on the real axis for $\omega = 0$ and swings through $\pm 90°$ for each such factor, to reach the appropriate axis for $\omega = 0^+$;
(c) draw the conjugate (mirror image about the real axis) of the curve, giving the locus for values of ω between $-\infty$ and 0;
(d) if the point $(-1, 0)$ has been encircled by the complete locus, the system is unstable; if not, the system is stable; if the locus passes through $(-1, 0)$, the system is marginally stable.

Points to note

(1) For simple open loop transfer functions containing no D terms in the numerator, the shape of the Nyquist plot is readily sketched. Figure 6.11 shows several such shapes. Each additional denominator factor $1/(1 + T D)$ or $1/D$ causes an additional $-90°$ rotation of the plot. It is obvious that zero factors of orders higher than unity (i.e., $1/D^2$, $1/D^3$, etc.) make such systems unstable, as $(-1, 0)$ must be encircled. It is also apparent that systems with open loop transfer functions of less than third order,

$$\frac{\theta_{on}}{\theta} = \frac{K}{T D}; \quad \frac{K}{1 + T D}; \quad \frac{K}{D(1 + T D)};$$

$$\frac{K}{(1 + T_1 D)(1 + T_2 D)}; \quad \frac{K}{1 + 2\xi T D + T^2 D^2}; \quad \text{etc.}$$

cannot be unstable.

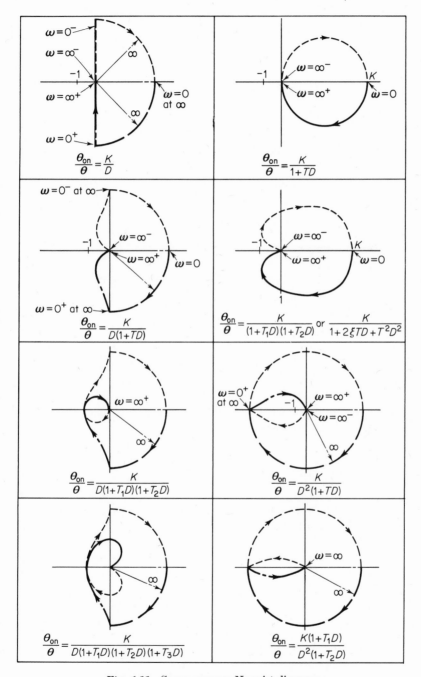

Fig. 6.11 Some common Nyquist diagrams.

(2) For systems whose open loop transfer functions contain D factors in the numerator, the precise shape of the Nyquist plot is not so readily sketched, as phase angle ϕ_o need not increase continually with frequency ω, and the Nyquist plot can have "bumps" in it. A D factor in the numerator has the effect of offsetting a similar factor in the denominator. However, the point at which $\omega = 0^+$ and the axis to which the locus is asymptotic as $\omega \to \infty$, are obvious. Each D or $(1 + T D)$ factor in the numerator contributes $+90°$ to the phase angle, and each factor in the denominator contributes $-90°$, as $\omega \to \infty$. Example 6.12 (Fig. 6.13) is such a case.

(3) It is often necessary to draw accurately only the section of the Nyquist plot in the region of point $(-1, 0)$.

(4) For the type of system under discussion, the mathematically rigid derivation of the Nyquist criterion (cf. Kuo, *op. cit.*) shows that the number of roots of a system's characteristic equation which are positive equals the number of times that the point $(-1, 0)$ is completely encircled by the Nyquist plot.

(5) For complicated systems, it is not always apparent if the point $(-1, j0)$ has been encircled. Figure 6.16 is an example of such a case. To check if the locus has encircled the Nyquist point,

    (a) draw a straight line from $(-1, 0)$ in any convenient direction;

    (b) where the line cuts each part of the locus, place an arrow on the locus against the line, in the direction of the locus at that point; the direction must be ascertained in the sense of ω going from 0^+ to ∞^+ to ∞^- to 0^-;

    (c) if the number of clockwise arrows equals the number of anticlockwise arrows, the input $(-1, j0)$ is not encircled and the system being investigated is stable; if the algebraic sum of the arrows is not zero, the point $(-1, j0)$ is encircled by the $\theta_{on}/\theta = F(j\omega)$ plot, and the system is unstable.

    If $(-1, 0)$ lies at point c in Fig. 6.16, and a radial line is drawn from c to cut the locus, there is one clockwise and one anticlockwise arrow against the line, indicating that the net encirclement of $(-1, 0)$ is zero and that the system is stable.

6.5.6 Some Examples

Example 6.11: Figure 6.12 shows the Nyquist diagram of the system whose open loop transfer function is

$$\frac{\theta_{on}}{\theta} = \frac{10}{D(1 + D/4)(1 + D/16)}$$

The point $(-1, 0)$ is not encircled and the system is stable.

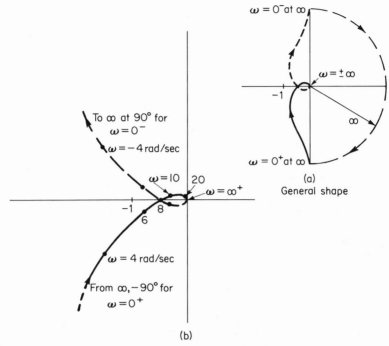

$\omega = 0^-$ at ∞

$\omega = \pm \infty$

-1

∞

$\omega = 0^+$ at ∞

(a)
General shape

To ∞ at 90° for
$\omega = 0^-$

$\omega = -4$ rad/sec

$\omega = 10$ 20

$\omega = \infty^+$

-1 8

6

$\omega = 4$ rad/sec

From ∞, $-90°$ for
$\omega = 0^+$

(b)

Accurate plot in the region of $(-1, 0)$

$\omega =$	0	1	2	4	6	8	10	20	50	∞
$\phi_0 =$	$-90°$	$-107°$	$-123°$	$-149°$	$-167°$	$-180°$	$-190°$	$-220°$	$-247°$	$-270°$
$G_0 =$	∞	9.7	4.45	1.73	0.8	0.5	0.37	0.063	0.005	0

Fig. 6.12   Nyquist plot for

$$\frac{\theta_{on}}{\theta} = \frac{10}{D(1 + D/4)(1 + D/16)}$$

Example 6.12: Establish the stability condition of the system whose open loop transfer function is

$$\frac{\theta_{on}}{\theta} = \frac{5(1 + 4D)}{D^2(1 + D/4)(1 + D/10)}$$

Solution: Substitute $j\omega$ for D to get

$$G_o = \frac{5(1 + 16\omega^2)^{1/2}}{\omega^2(1 + \omega^2/16)^{1/2}(1 + \omega^2/100)^{1/2}}$$

$$\phi_o = -180° + \tan^{-1} 4\omega - \tan^{-1} \omega/4 - \tan^{-1} \omega/10$$

(Use the table in Appendix C to evaluate G_o, ϕ_o.)

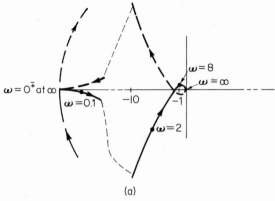

(a)

Accurate plot (part only)

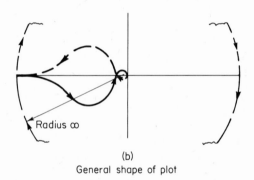

(b)

General shape of plot

$\omega =$	0^+	0.1	0.5	1	2	4	6	8	10	∞
$\phi_0 =$	$-180°$	$-160°$	$-126°$	$-124°$	$-135°$	$-160°$	$-180°$	$-193°$	$-203°$	$-270°$
$G_0 =$	∞	540	45	20	9	3.3	1.6	0.9	0.5	0

Fig. 6.13 Nyquist diagram of the system whose open-loop transfer function is

$$\frac{\theta_{on}}{\theta} = \frac{5(1 + 4D)}{D^2(1 + D/4)(1 + D/10)}$$

Figure 6.13 shows the Nyquist plot for the system. The point $(-1, 0)$ is encircled by the plot and the system is unstable.

6.5.7 The Degree of Stability

The nearer the Nyquist plot comes to encircling the point $(-1, j0)$, the closer the system represented is to instability. Conversely, the larger the margin between the Nyquist plot and encirclement of $(-1, j0)$, the more stable the system. With the simpler shapes of Nyquist plots which cut the $\pm180°$ axes only once for positive values of ω, the degree of stability can be described by the **gain margin** and the **phase margin** defined in Fig. 6.14.

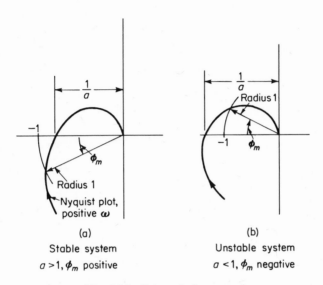

(a)

Stable system

$a > 1, \phi_m$ positive

(b)

Unstable system

$a < 1, \phi_m$ negative

Fig. 6.14 Gain and phase margins.

Gain margin a describes the proximity of the Nyquist locus to $(-1, j0)$ as it crosses the real $(\pm180°)$ axis. As defined, a will be greater than 1 for stability, and less than 1 for instability, for systems whose Nyquist loci cut the $\pm180°$ axis once only.

Phase margin ϕ_m describes the proximity of the Nyquist locus to $(-1, j0)$ by denoting the angle $\phi_m = (180° + \phi_o')$ where ϕ_o' is the phase angle when the open loop magnitude ratio G_o is 1; ϕ_m is found by scribing an arc of radius 1 centered on the origin, to cut the G_o, ϕ_o–ω curve. As defined, ϕ_m is positive for a stable system and negative for an unstable system.

It is common for a designer to specify minimum values of gain margin and phase margin to ensure an adequate degree of stability. For example, $a > 1.5$ and $\phi_m > 45°$ are reasonable specifications for a servomechanism.

Gain margin and phase margin become somewhat ambiguous terms for systems the Nyquist plots of which cut the $\pm180°$ axis more than once, as in Example 6.12.

6.5.8 The Effect of Gain K_o on Stability

The value of a system's open loop gain constant K_o, which is composed of system's constants, affects the stability condition of the system. As shown in Eqs. 6.4 and 6.7, K_o appears in a system's characteristic equation, and will affect its roots. The effect of K_o on system stability is readily appreciated from the Nyquist plot. Consider the general form of open loop transfer function

$$\frac{\theta_{on}}{\theta} = K_o f(D) = \frac{K_o f_n\,(D)}{f_d\,(D)}$$

and

$$\frac{\theta_{on}}{\theta} = K_o f(j\omega)$$

for the Nyquist plot.

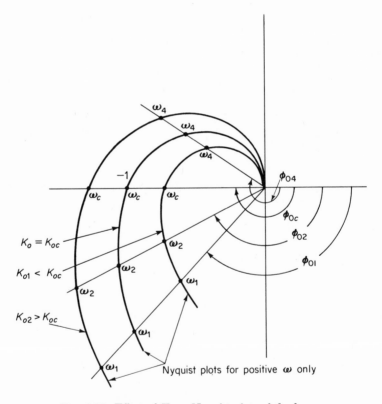

Fig. 6.15   Effect of K_o on Nyquist plots of the form

$$\frac{\theta_{on}}{\theta} = \frac{K_o}{D^n(1 + TD)(\quad)\ldots}$$

At any particular frequency, K_o affects the open loop magnitude ratio G_o, but not the phase ϕ_o; i.e., $K_o = (K_o + j0)$ has magnitude K_o but zero phase angle as $\phi = \tan^{-1} 0/K_o = 0$. Hence increasing K_o causes a Nyquist plot to expand radially in the manner shown in Fig. 6.15. Conversely, reducing K_o causes a radial shrinking of the Nyquist plot. The system whose open loop frequency response plot is shown in Fig. 6.15 is

(a) stable when $K_o = K_{o1}$;
(b) unstable when $K_o = K_{o2}$, where $K_{o2} > K_{o1}$;
(c) marginally stable when $K_o = K_{oc}$, where $K_{o2} > K_{oc} > K_{o1}$

The systems of previous Examples 6.10 and 6.11 had identical open loop transfer functions, except for the values of open loop gain constant. For $K_o = 10$, Example 6.11 (Fig. 6.12), the system is stable. For $K_o = 100$, Example 6.10 (Fig. 6.7), the system is unstable. Note that the frequency associated with any given value of ϕ_o is the same on both Nyquist plots. Figure 6.7 is just a radially expanded version of Fig. 6.12. The value of K_o for which this system is critically stable is readily found as follows:

$$\frac{\theta_{on}}{\theta} = \frac{K_o}{D(1 + \frac{1}{4}D)(1 + \frac{1}{16}D)}$$

$$\left(\frac{\theta_{on}}{\theta}\right)_{j\omega} = \frac{K_o}{-\frac{5}{16}\omega^2 + j(\omega - \omega^3/64)}$$

$$G_o = \frac{K_o}{[\frac{25}{256}\omega^4 + (\omega - \omega^3/64)^2]^{1/2}}$$

$$\phi_o = -\tan^{-1}\frac{\omega - \omega^3/64}{-\frac{5}{16}\omega^2} = -\tan^{-1}\frac{1 - \omega^2/64}{-\frac{5}{16}\omega}$$

The G_o, ϕ_o–ω curve crosses the $\pm 180°$ (real) axis when $\phi_o = -180°$, for which case $\omega = \omega_c$ rad/sec, and the phase expression becomes

$$\phi_o = -180° = -\tan^{-1}\frac{1 - \omega_c^2/64}{-\frac{5}{16}\omega_c}$$

Taking the tangents of both sides yields

$$0 = -\frac{1 - \omega_c^2/64}{-\frac{5}{16}\omega_c}$$

from which $-1 + \omega_c^2/64 = 0$, or $\omega_c = 8$ rad/sec. For marginal stability, $G_o = 1$ when $\phi_o = -180°$, which occurs when $\omega = \omega_c = 8$ rad/sec. Hence K_{oc} can be found from the magnitude ratio expression,

$$K_{oc} = 1 \cdot \left[\frac{25}{256} \cdot 8^4 + \left(8 - \frac{8^3}{64}\right)^2\right]^{1/2} = 20$$

It can be concluded that the system is

(a) stable for $K_o < 20$;
(b) unstable for $K_o > 20$;
(c) marginally stable for $K_o = 20$.

For systems whose open loop transfer functions have D terms in the numerator, it is common for the Nyquist plot to cut the $\pm 180°$ axis at several points as ω varies from 0^+ to ∞^+. For such cases, the systems

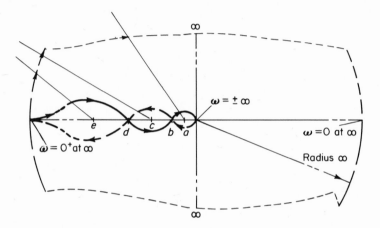

Fig. 6.16 Nyquist diagram of the conditionally stable system whose open loop transfer function is

$$\frac{\theta_{on}}{\theta} = \frac{K_o(1 + T_1 D)(1 + T_2 D)}{D^2(1 + T_3 D)(1 + T_4 D)(1 + T_5 D)}$$

represented may be stable over intermediate ranges of K_o, outside of which they are unstable. Figure 6.16 shows the form of the Nyquist plot of an open loop transfer function

$$\frac{\theta_{on}}{\theta} = \frac{K_o(1 + T_1 D)(1 + T_2 D)}{D^2(1 + T_3 D)(1 + T_4 D)(1 + T_5 D)}$$

If K_o is such that the Nyquist point $(-1, j0)$ lies at a, the system is unstable, as indicated by the net two clockwise arrows against the radial line drawn from a.

If K_o is such that $(-1, 0)$ lies at c, the system is stable, as the radial line has zero net rotation.

If K_o is such that $(-1, 0)$ lies at e, the system is unstable, as the radial line has a clockwise net rotation.

If K_o is such that $(-1, 0)$ lies at b or d, the system is marginally stable.

It can be concluded that the system is stable only for that intermediate range of K_o which produces $(-1, 0)$ in position c. The limits of K_o for stability are the values which produce $(-1, 0)$ at b and d.

6.5.9 Stability from the Open Loop Bode Plot

So far, the open loop frequency response data, $\theta_{on}/\theta = K_o f(j\omega)$ for $\omega = 0^+ \to \infty^+$, has been plotted in polar form. The G_o–ω and ϕ_o–ω data can also be plotted in Bode diagram form, using the procedures used with system frequency response analysis in Chapter 5.

Figure 6.17 shows the open loop frequency response data of previous Example 6.9 in Bode diagram form. The characteristic slope of the G_o–ω asymptote for zero factors such as $1/D = 1/j\omega$ was discussed in Section 5.6.5. The system has one value of open loop magnitude ratio G_o for open

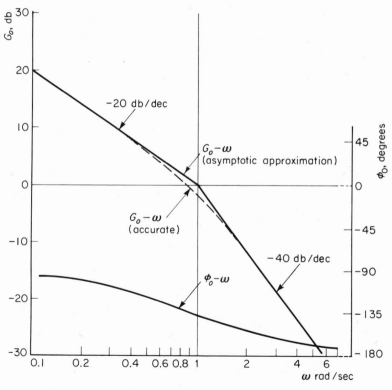

Fig. 6.17 Bode diagram of $\theta_{on}/\theta = 1/[D(1 + D)]$ (cf. previous Example 6.9, Fig. 6.6).

loop phase $\phi_o = -180°$. It is apparent from Fig. 6.6 that the system is stable so long as $G_o < 1$ when $\phi_o = -180°$. If $G_o > 1$ for $\phi_o = -180°$ [the point where the $(\theta_{on}/\theta)_{j\omega}$ locus cuts the $-180°$ axis], then the Nyquist point $(-1, 0)$ is enclosed by the open loop locus, and the system represented is unstable. Obviously, $G_o = 1$ at $\phi_o = -180°$ is the case of marginal stability. Now, $G_o = 1$ corresponds to G_o, db = 0 on the Bode plot. The present system's stability condition is directly apparent from its Bode diagram. So long as the G_o, db curve passes from the +db to the $-$db region before ϕ_o reaches $-180°$, the system is stable.

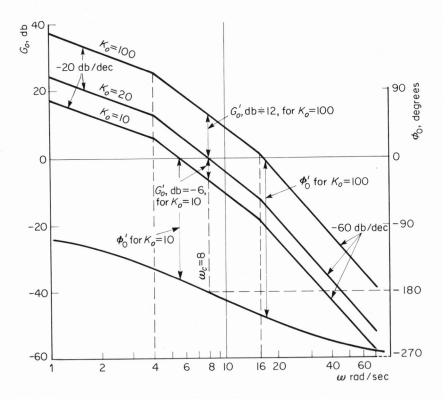

Fig. 6.18 Open loop Bode diagram for

$$\frac{\theta_{on}}{\theta} = \frac{K_o}{D(1 + D/4)(1 + D/16)}$$

(1) for $K_o = 10$ (previous Example 6.10, Fig. 6.7);
(2) for $K_o = 100$ (previous Example 6.11, Fig. 6.12);
(3) for $K_o = 20$ (discussed in Section 6.5.8).
Gain Margin, a, db $= -G_o'$, db; **Phase Margin,** $\phi_m = 180° + \phi_o'$.

Figure 6.18 shows the Bode diagram representation of the open loop frequency response data of previous Examples 6.10 and 6.11, in which only the value of the open loop gain constant varied. The $\phi_o - \omega$ curve is the same for each case. At $\phi_o = -180°$,

(1) G_o, db is positive for $K_o = 100$, indicating instability;
(2) G_o, db is zero for $K_o = 20$, indicating marginal stability;
(3) G_o, db is negative for $K_o = 10$, indicating stability.

Note that increasing K_o acts to lift the G_o, db–ω curve vertically upwards, increasing the tendency toward instability.

Figure 6.18 illustrates the interpretation of gain and phase margins from the open loop Bode diagram.

Gain margin: the reciprocal of G_o at $\phi_o = -180°$ (Fig. 6.11), i.e.,

$$a = \frac{1}{G_o'} \quad \text{or} \quad \frac{1}{a} = G_o'$$

where G_o' is the open loop magnitude ratio at $\phi_o = -180°$.
Now, G_o, db $= 20 \log_{10} G_o$; and at $\phi_o = -180°$,

$$G_o', \text{db} = \frac{1}{a}, \text{db} = 20 \log_{10} 1 - 20 \log_{10} a = -20 \log_{10} a = -a, \text{db}$$

$\therefore$ a, db $= -G_o'$, db. Hence if G_o', db is -6 then gain margin is 6, db, which corresponds to $a = 2$ and a stable system. Note that gain margin is minus the actual magnitude ratio in db at $\phi_o = -180°$. An unstable system will have a positive G_o', db and hence a negative a, db, which makes $a < 1$ and the system unstable.

Phase margin (Fig. 6.14): described by

$$\phi_m = 180° + \phi_o'$$

where ϕ_o' is the open loop phase angle when $G_o = 1$; here $G_o = 1$ corresponds to G_o, db $= 0$ on the Bode diagram. Thus the phase margin is readily read from the open loop Bode plot. Phase margin is positive if ϕ_o' is less than $-180°$ when G_o, db $= 0$, and negative if ϕ_o' is greater than $-180°$ when G_o, db $= 0$. Positive phase margin implies that a system is stable, whereas negative phase margin indicates instability.

The open loop frequency response plots of systems having D factors in the numerators of their open loop transfer functions can have several values of G_o for $\phi_o = -180°$. Figure 6.16 shows such a case. An open loop Bode diagram for this example is shown in Fig. 6.19, showing clearly the two values of G_o for $\phi_o = -180°$. In this case, the requirement for stability is that the phase margin be positive. The system is stable.

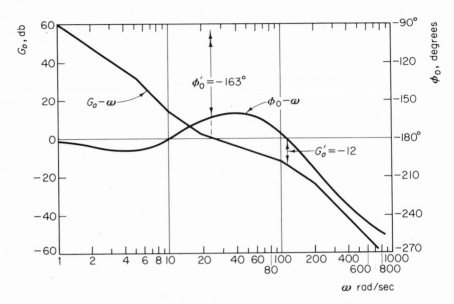

Fig. 6.19 Open loop Bode diagram of

$$\frac{\theta_{on}}{\theta} = \frac{1000(1 + D/10)(1 + D/20)}{D^2(1 + D/5)(1 + D/100)(1 + D/200)}$$

Corresponding closed loop system is stable: **Gain Margin,** a, db $= -G'_o$, db $= 12$; $a = 4$; **Phase Margin,** $\phi_m = 180° + \phi'_o = 180° - 163° = 17°$.

6.6 SUMMARY

A linear system is stable if its response to an input disturbance passes through a transient stage to approach a steady-state condition of the form of the input.

A linear system is stable only if all roots of its characteristic equation have negative real parts. Thus if the characteristic equation's roots can be ascertained, the system's stability condition can be established. Extraction of the roots of high-order characteristic equations is not easily achieved.

The Routh criterion of stability provides a simple numerical procedure for establishing the signs of the roots of a characteristic equation. Thus the stability condition of a system can be ascertained without evaluation of the roots of its characteristic equation.

The Nyquist stability criterion provides a graphic procedure for establishing the stability condition of a system without evaluation of the roots of its characteristic equation. The open loop transfer function of the system is subjected to frequency response analysis. Value(s) of the open loop magnitude ratio when the open loop phase is $-180°$ are used to disclose the system's stability condition.

Stability of response is the primary condition to be satisfied in control system analysis.

PROBLEMS

6.1 Use the Routh criterion to investigate the stability condition of systems the characteristic equations of which are:

(a) $3D^3 + 4D^2 + D + 1 = 0$
(b) $D^5 + 2D^4 + 2D^3 + 46D^2 + 89D + 260 = 0$
(c) $D^4 + 2D^3 + 11D^2 + 18D + 18 = 0$
(d) $D^5 + 3D^4 + 2D^3 + 4D^2 + 5D + 65 = 0$

> **Answers:** (a) stable;   (b) unstable, 2 positive roots;
> (c) stable;   (d) unstable, 2 positive roots.

6.2 A system can be represented as shown in Fig. 6.20. Use the Routh criterion

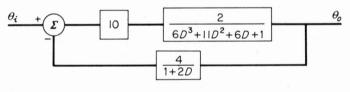

Fig. 6.20

to investigate its stability condition.

> **Answer:** System is unstable.

6.3 Find the range of values for K for which the system

$$\frac{\theta_o}{\theta_i} = \frac{K}{D(1 + D/4)(1 + D/16) + K}$$

is stable, using the Routh criterion.

> **Answer:** System is stable if $0 < K < 20$.

6.4 Use the Nyquist criterion to investigate the stability condition of the systems the open loop transfer functions of which are

(a) $\dfrac{\theta_{on}}{\theta} = \dfrac{8}{D(D+8)}$

(b) $\dfrac{\theta_{on}}{\theta} = \dfrac{6(1+3D)}{D(1+2D)(1+4D)}$

(c) $\dfrac{\theta_{on}}{\theta} = \dfrac{20(1+D/6)}{D(1+D/4)(1+D/16)(1+D/8)}$

(d) $\dfrac{\theta_{on}}{\theta} = \dfrac{16}{D^2(1+4D)}$

Answers: (a) stable;   (b) stable, gain margin $= \infty$, phase margin $= 14°$;   (c) stable, gain margin $= 0.2$, phase margin $= 5°$;   (d) unstable.

6.5 (a) Use the Nyquist criterion to investigate the stability condition of the system of Problem 6.2.
(b) For what range of values of open loop gain is this system stable?

Answers: (a) unstable;   (b) stable if $K_o < 6$.

6.6 What is the normalized system transfer function, and the characteristic equation, of each system in Problem 6.4?

6.7 A system has the open loop transfer function

$$\frac{\theta_{on}}{\theta} = \frac{10^4(1+0.2D)(1+0.025D)}{D^3(1+0.001D)(1+0.005D)}$$

(a) Ascertain the stability condition of the system.
(b) For what range(s) of the open loop gain constant is this system stable?

Answers: (a) stable;   (b) stable for $1200 < K_o < 105,000$.

6.8 Construct the open loop Bode diagram for Problem 6.7, and investigate system stability from it.

7 *The root locus method of analysis*

7.1 INTRODUCTION

The frequency response approach presented in Chapter 5 gave a method of analysis which is readily applied and which circumvents the necessity of making full solutions of system equations in order to understand the dynamic nature of a system. The root locus approach is another short-cut method of analysis which is readily applied and which gives insight into the dynamic nature of a system. The frequency response approach utilizes the steady-state part of a system response solution, whereas the root locus approach is associated with the transient part. Because of its association with the transient part of response, the root locus method is particularly useful for examining the stability characteristics of a system, and can be used to set limits on the system constants outside of which the system will be unstable. It is particularly useful in the design or synthesis stage of development of a control system, when the designer has some latitude in the selection of system parameters.

It was shown in Chapter 4 that the transient behavior of a continuous linear system is governed by the condition of the roots of the characteristic equation of the system. The nature of the transient behavior (i.e., oscillatory, exponential decay, or oscillatory decay, etc.) was shown to be independent of the particular forcing function applied to the system, as well as independent of any initial conditions associated with the system.

It was clearly established that the roots of a characteristic equation are dependent on the values of system constants, and hence on the values of system gain constants. The root locus method is essentially a graphic procedure which provides the locus of each root as any suitable system parameter (for example, the gain constant) is varied from zero to infinity. As the roots can be real, imaginary, or complex, root locus plots are drawn on the complex plane. From the loci of the roots,

(a) the stability of a system can be studied;
(b) the effect on response of varying system constants (and hence the gain constants) can be studied, and limits of such constants can be established.

The nature of a root locus plot is illustrated in Section 7.2. The common basis for root locus analysis is given in Sections 7.2 and 7.3, following which the short-cut methods from which root loci can be rapidly plotted are developed.

7.2 THE NATURE OF A ROOT LOCUS PLOT

Figure 7.1 shows one branch, i.e., the path or locus of one root, of the root locus plot of a hypothetical system. The plot shows the manner in which

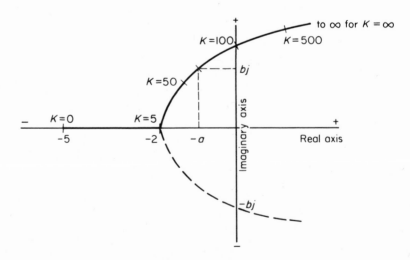

Fig. 7.1 A possible locus of a root as K is varied.

the characteristic equation root α_1 varies as the system gain constant K is varied from 0 to ∞. The root

(a) has a value of -5 when $K = 0$;
(b) is real and negative when K lies between 0 and 5;
(c) is complex with a negative real part when K lies between 5 and 100;
(d) is imaginary when $K = 100$;
(e) is complex with a positive real part when $K > 100$;
(f) has a value of ∞ when $K = \infty$.

It should be apparent that complex roots appear only in mirror image pairs, and hence that a second root follows the path shown as a broken line in Fig. 7.1. The system represented is unstable for $K > 100$.

A root locus plot for a system comprises the root paths of all roots of the system's characteristic equation. There will be as many separate paths on a root locus plot as there are roots of the characteristic equation.

Example 7.1 (Fig. 7.2a): A system has the transfer function

$$\frac{\theta_o}{\theta_i} = \frac{K(D + 2)}{D^2 + (4 + K)D + 2K}$$

where K is a constant. It is desired to study the effect of the constant K on the nature of the system.

Solution: The system characteristic equation is

$$D^2 + (4 + K)D + 2K = 0$$

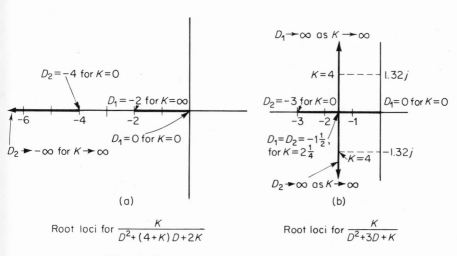

(a)

Root loci for $\dfrac{K}{D^2 + (4+K)D + 2K}$

(b)

Root loci for $\dfrac{K}{D^2 + 3D + K}$

Fig. 7.2 Root locus plots for Examples 7.1 and 7.2.

the roots of which are

$$D_1 = \frac{-(4 + K) + (16 + K^2)^{1/2}}{2} \quad \text{and} \quad D_2 = \frac{-(4 + K) - (16 + K^2)^{1/2}}{2}$$

There are two roots, and hence two paths on the root locus plot. For $K = 0$,

$$D_1 = \frac{-4 + 4}{2} = 0 \quad \text{and} \quad D_2 = \frac{-4 - 4}{2} = -4$$

which give the starting points of the two loci, as shown in Fig. 7.2(a).

Now, $16 + K^2$ can never be negative, as K is a positive real number in any real system; hence the roots D_1 and D_2 cannot be complex for any value of K. Also $(K^2 + 16)^{1/2}$ must always be less than $(4 + K)$, i.e.,

$$(4 + K)^2 = 16 + K^2 + 8K$$

which is $8K$ greater than $16 + K^2$. Thus the roots will be real and negative for all values of K.

As $K \to \infty$,

(a) root $D_1 \to (-4 - \infty + \infty)/2 \to -2$; hence the locus of root D_1 is a line from 0 to -2 on the real axis (Fig. 7.2a);

(b) root $D_2 \to (-4 - \infty - \infty)/2 \to -\infty$; hence the locus of root D_2 is a line from -4 to $-\infty$ on the real axis (Fig. 7.2a).

Intermediate values of K can be fitted onto the two loci by evaluating the roots, thus completing the root locus plot, i.e.,

$$\left. \begin{aligned} D_1 &= \frac{-9 + 41^{1/2}}{2} = -1.3 \\[2mm] D_2 &= \frac{-9 - 41^{1/2}}{2} = -7.7 \end{aligned} \right\} \text{for } K = 5 \text{ (Fig. 7.2a)}$$

The stability of the present system for all values of K is reflected in the absence of any part of the root locus plot from the righthand half plane of Fig. 7.2(a).

Example 7.2 (Fig. 7.2b): Obtain a root locus plot for the system

$$\frac{\theta_o}{\theta_i} = \frac{K}{D^2 + 3D + K}$$

Solution: The roots of the characteristic equation are

$$D_1 = \frac{-3 + (9 - 4K)^{1/2}}{2} \quad \text{and} \quad D_2 = \frac{-3 - (9 - 4K)^{1/2}}{2}$$

$$\left. \begin{aligned} D_1 &= \frac{-3 + 3}{2} = 0 \\[2mm] D_2 &= \frac{-3 - 3}{2} = -3 \end{aligned} \right\} \text{when } K = 0 \text{ (Fig. 7.2b)}$$

The roots will both be negative real numbers when $9 - 4K$ is positive, which occurs if K lies between 0 and $9/4$;

$$\left. \begin{array}{l} D_1 = -1\frac{1}{2} \\ D_2 = -1\frac{1}{2} \end{array} \right\} \text{ for } K = 2\frac{1}{4} \text{ (Fig. 7.2b)}$$

When $K > 2\frac{1}{4}$, the roots are a complex pair. The real part of each root is a constant $-1\frac{1}{2}$; the imaginary part $\pm(9 - 4K)^{1/2}/2$ increases with K, to reach infinity as $K \to \infty$, i.e.,

$$\left. \begin{array}{l} D_1 = \dfrac{-3 + 2.64j}{2} = -1.5 + 1.32j \\[2mm] D_2 = \dfrac{-3 - 2.64j}{2} = -1.5 - 1.32j \end{array} \right\} \text{ for } K = 4 \text{ (Fig. 7.2b)}$$

Thus the root locus plot of Fig. 7.2(b) is obtained. The system is shown to be stable for all values of K, as the root loci are confined to the lefthand half plane. It also shows that

(a) for $0 < K < 2\frac{1}{4}$, the system response tends to be heavily damped (real roots);

(b) as K increases from $2\frac{1}{4}$, the system becomes increasingly oscillatory in nature.

7.3 THE OPEN LOOP TRANSFER FUNCTION

The definition of a system's open loop transfer function was given and its significance discussed in Section 6.5.2. Because of its importance to this chapter, and because some students may require to study this chapter prior to Chapter 6, the work will be briefly restated.

The block diagram of Fig. 7.3(a) shows the general form of a feedback system having time-dependent terms, i.e., D functions, in both the forward feed and the feedback transfer functions, $K_1 f_1(D)$ and $K_2 f_2(D)$ respectively.

The system transfer function is

$$\frac{\theta_o}{\theta_i} = \frac{K_1 f_1(D)}{1 + K_1 K_2 \cdot f_1(D) \cdot f_2(D)} = \frac{K_1 f_1(D)}{1 + K_o f(D)} \tag{7.1}$$

where $K_o = K_1 K_2$; $f(D) = f_1(D) \cdot f_2(D)$ is in dimensionless, i.e., time constant, factor form. The **characteristic function** is represented by

$$1 + K_o f(D)$$

which, when equated to zero, becomes

$$1 + K_o f(D) = 0 \tag{7.2}$$

which represents the characteristic equation of the system whose root condition decides stability. For analysis, it is convenient to render the system transfer function nondimensional, by using the feedback signal at

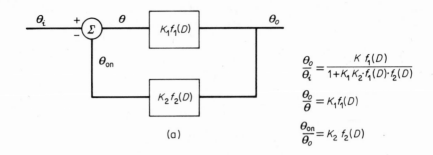

(a)

$$\frac{\theta_o}{\theta_i} = \frac{K\,f_1(D)}{1+K_1\,K_2 \cdot f_1(D) \cdot f_2(D)}$$

$$\frac{\theta_o}{\theta} = K_1 f_1(D)$$

$$\frac{\theta_{on}}{\theta_o} = K_2\,f_2(D)$$

(b)

K_1 is forward feed gain
K_2 is feedback gain
K_o is open-loop gain ($K_o = K_1 K_2$)
$f_1(D)$, $f_2(D)$, and $f(D)$ are in dimensionless
(i.e. time constant) form

$$\frac{\theta_{on}}{\theta_i} = \frac{K_o\,f(D)}{1+K_o\,f(D)}$$

$$\frac{\theta_{on}}{\theta} = K_o\,f(D)$$

Fig. 7.3 (a) Original form of system. (b) Nondimensionalized form of system.

the summing sign θ_{on} to represent system response. Thus the system is represented by Fig. 7.3(b), which has unity negative feedback, and from which

$$\frac{\theta_{on}}{\theta_i} = \frac{K_o f(D)}{1 + K_o f(D)} \tag{7.3}$$

is the system transfer function in nondimensional form, and

$$\frac{\theta_{on}}{\theta} = K_o f(D) \tag{7.4}$$

is the open loop transfer function of the system; K_o is the **open loop gain** of the system. Note that the denominator of the original system transfer function, and hence also the characteristic equation, are unaltered by the nondimensionalizing process.

Example 7.3: Obtain the system transfer function, the nondimensional system transfer function, the open loop transfer function, and the open loop gain of the system shown in Figure 7.4(a).

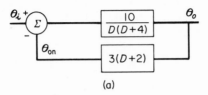

(a)

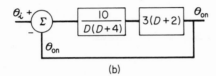

(b)

Fig. 7.4

Solution:

(a) The system transfer function is

$$\frac{\theta_o}{\theta_i} = \frac{10}{D^2 + 34D + 60}$$

(b) Adjust the block diagram to the form of Fig. 7.4(b). Then,

(c) $\dfrac{\theta_{on}}{\theta_i} = \dfrac{30(D + 2)}{D^2 + 34D + 60}$ (system)

(d) $\dfrac{\theta_{on}}{\theta} = \dfrac{30(D + 2)}{D(D + 4)}$ (open loop)

$\qquad = \dfrac{15(\frac{1}{2}D + 1)}{D(\frac{1}{4}D + 1)}$ (dimensionless factor form)

(e) $K_o = 15$

7.4 THE POLE-ZERO CONCEPT

It is convenient to use the notion that an expression can have poles and zeros defined by:

(a) **pole:** A pole of an expression is a solution which makes the expression become infinite.
(b) **zero:** A zero of an expression is a solution which makes the expression equal to zero.

For example, consider the expression

$$3D + 6 \quad \text{or} \quad 3(D + 2)$$

$D = -2$ makes the equation zero and hence is a *zero* of the equation. $D = \infty$ makes the expression infinite, hence ∞ is a *pole* of the expression. See further practice examples in Problem 7.1.

The pole-zero concept is readily adapted to transfer functions. For example,

$$\frac{\theta_o}{\theta_i} = \frac{K}{1 + TD} = \frac{K/T}{1/T + D}$$

from which $D = -1/T$ is recognized as a pole, rendering the transfer function infinite. There are no finite zeros of the transfer function, although $D = \infty$ can be considered as a zero because it renders the transfer function equal to 0. To aid in the ready recognition of poles and zeros, a transfer function is written to contain factors of the form $D + \alpha_1$, $D + \alpha_2$, etc. For example,

$$\frac{\theta_{on}}{\theta} = \frac{15(1 + \frac{1}{2}D)}{D(1 + \frac{1}{4}D)}$$

$$= \frac{[(15 \times 4)/2](2 + D)}{D(4 + D)}$$

$$= \frac{30(2 + D)}{D(4 + D)}$$

from which the poles are, by inspection,

$$D = 0 \quad \text{and} \quad D = -4$$

and the only finite zero is $D = -2$. Note that $D = \infty$ is also a zero.

It is important to observe that the constant associated with a transfer function changes when the transfer function is changed from time constant form to pole-zero form. For the present example,

(a) $K_o = 15$ is the **open loop gain constant** associated with the time constant form.

(b) $K_o' = 30$ is the **open loop sensitivity** associated with the pole-zero form;

(c) K_o and K_o' are related by a constant composed of the system time constants.

It should be recalled that factors of a transfer function can be real, imaginary, or complex, and hence that poles and/or zeros can be real, imaginary, or complex. For example,

$$\frac{1}{D^2 + 6D + 25} = \frac{1}{(D + 3 + 4j)(D + 3 - 4j)}$$

TABLE 7.1: *Poles and Zeros of Several Transfer Functions*

	Transfer function				
	Expanded form	Factored form[a]	Root locus form	Poles	Finite zeros
(a)	$\dfrac{K}{3D^2+4D+1}$	$\dfrac{K}{(3D+1)(D+1)}$	$\dfrac{K/3}{(D+\frac{1}{3})(D+1)}$	$D=-\frac{1}{3}$ $D=-1$	
(b)	$\dfrac{K(1+2D)}{D^2+6D+25}$	—	$\dfrac{2K(D+\frac{1}{2})}{(D+3+4j)(D+3-4j)}$	$D=-(3+4j)$ $D=-(3-4j)$	$D=-\frac{1}{2}$
(c)	$\dfrac{15(\frac{1}{2}D+1)}{\frac{1}{4}D^2+D}$	$\dfrac{15(\frac{1}{2}D+1)}{D(\frac{1}{4}D+1)}$	$\dfrac{30(D+2)}{D(D+4)}$	$D=0$ $D=-4$	$D=-2$
(d)	$\dfrac{KD}{D^3+3D^2+29D+52}$	$\dfrac{(K/52)D}{(\frac{1}{4}D+1)\left(\frac{D^2}{13}+\frac{4D}{13}+1\right)}$	$\dfrac{KD}{(D+4)(D+2+3j)(D+2-3j)}$	$D=-4$ $D=-(2+3j)$ $D=-(2-3j)$	$D=0$
(e)	$\dfrac{K(D+3)}{D^3+7D^2}$	—	$\dfrac{K(D+3)}{D^2(D+7)}$	$D=0$ $D=0$ $D=-7$	$D=-3$

[a] Time Constant Form.

for which the poles are $D = -(3 + 4j)$ and $D = -(3 - 4j)$ while there is no finite zero.

Poles and zeros are readily represented on the complex plane. Table 7.1 and Fig. 7.5 show the poles and zeros of a number of transfer functions.

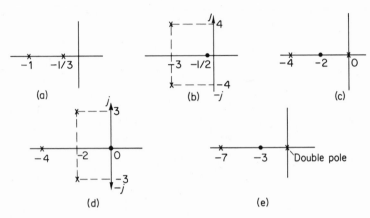

Fig. 7.5 Pole ($\times$) and zero ($\bullet$) plots associated with Table 7.1.

At this point, it does not matter whether the transfer functions given are normal, nondimensionalized, or open loop system transfer functions. Note that a repeated factor, i.e., D^2 in case e, requires a repeated pole or zero.

For practice problems see Problem 7.1. Note that the poles of a transfer function are in fact the root values of its denominator. In the case of a system's transfer function, the poles are the roots of the characteristic equation. The finite zeros of a transfer function are the root values of its numerator.

It is important to realize that a system's transfer function, its non-dimensional transfer function, its open loop transfer function, and its characteristic equation will each have their own distinctive pattern of poles and zeros.

7.5 CRITERIA USED FOR RAPID PLOTTING OF ROOT LOCUS

7.5.1 Introduction and Basic Concept

It was demonstrated in Section 7.2 that root locus plots can be drawn from comprehensive evaluation of the roots of a system's characteristic equation. If comprehensive evaluations of these roots were necessary, then the root locus method of analysis would be extremely tedious. The popularity and utility of the method owes itself to well-founded criteria from which the critical points, slopes, and intersects of root loci can be located rapidly with a minimum of calculation. The construction criteria and their origins will now be introduced and discussed.

As with the Nyquist frequency response stability criterion, the open loop transfer function is utilized to give closed loop system response data. The open loop transfer function is normally much simpler and easier to manipulate than the system transfer function.

Consider the general form of the characteristic equation expressed in Eq. 7.2, Section 7.3,

$$1 + K_o f(D) = 0 \quad \text{or} \quad 1 + K_o' f'(D) = 0$$

where K_o = open loop gain constant; K_o' is open loop sensitivity; $K_o f(D)$ and $K_o' f'(D)$ are open loop transfer functions in time constant and pole-zero forms respectively. The equation can be written

$$K_o' f'(D) = -1 \tag{7.5}$$

which must be satisfied if any root of the characteristic equation is substituted for D.

Equation 7.5 can be expressed in polar notation,

$$K_o' f'(D) = 1, \quad \angle(n \times 180°) \tag{7.5a}$$

where n is any odd number

The notion expressed in Eq. 7.5(a) is a very useful aid to the rapid plotting of root loci, as

(a) any point on the complex plane which satisfies the open loop transfer function angularity requirement

$$\Phi = n \times 180°; \quad n = \pm 1, \pm 3, \pm 5, \text{ etc.} \tag{7.6}$$

is a *possible* root of the characteristic equation, and hence will lie on the root locus;

(b) a point satisfying Eq. 7.6 *will* have an open loop sensitivity which satisfies the magnitude requirement

$$|K_o' f'(D)| = 1 \tag{7.7}$$

Applying the angular requirement

In general, an open loop transfer function can be factored into the form

$$K_o f(D) = K_o' f'(D) = \frac{K_o'(D - Z_1)(D - Z_2)\dots}{(D - P_1)(D - P_2)(D - P_3)\dots} \tag{7.8}$$

where Z_1, Z_2, etc. are finite zeros of $K_o f(D)$ and P_1, P_2, P_3, etc. are poles of $K_o f(D)$.

Each $D - Z$ and $D - P$ factor can be represented as a vector on the

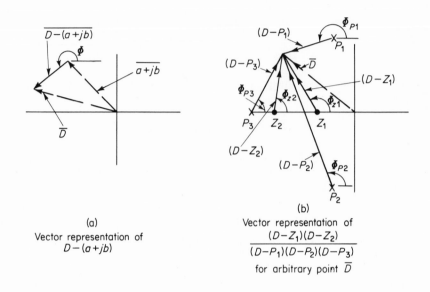

(a)
Vector representation of
$D - (a + jb)$

(b)
Vector representation of
$$\frac{(D-Z_1)(D-Z_2)}{(D-P_1)(D-P_2)(D-P_3)}$$
for arbitrary point $\overline{D}$

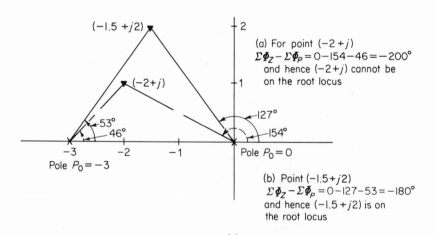

(a) For point $(-2+j)$
$\Sigma \Phi_Z - \Sigma \Phi_P = 0 - 154 - 46 = -200°$
and hence $(-2+j)$ cannot be
on the root locus

(b) Point $(-1.5+j2)$
$\Sigma \Phi_Z - \Sigma \Phi_P = 0 - 127 - 53 = -180°$
and hence $(-1.5+j2)$ is on
the root locus

(c)
Application to the system whose open loop transfer function is

$$\frac{\theta_{on}}{\theta} = \frac{K_o'}{D(D+3)}$$

Fig. 7.6 The angular criterion for root locus plotting.

complex plane, as illustrated in Fig. 7.6(a). When seeking the angle associated with $K_o f(D)$, $D - Z$ angles can be regarded as positive, whereas the denominator $D - P$ angles are regarded as negative, in the manner used previously with frequency response analysis. Figure 7.6(b) shows the $D - Z$ and $D - P$ vectors drawn to an arbitrary point $\bar{D}$ on the complex plane, for an arbitrary open loop transfer function. The angle associated with the open loop transfer function is

$$\Phi_{z1} + \Phi_{z2} - \Phi_{p1} - \Phi_{p2} - \Phi_{p3} = \Phi$$

where Φ_z is a zero angle; and Φ_p is a pole angle. Φ must be an odd multiple of 180° if point $\bar{D}$ lies on the root locus of the system considered. Note that Φ is independent of K_o'.

In this manner, the angular requirement of Eq. 7.6 can be used to ascertain the possibility of any selected value of D being on the root locus, by locating on the complex plane the following:

(a) the poles and finite zeros of the open loop transfer function;
(b) the point to be investigated;
(c) the vectors connecting each pole and finite zero to this point.

Then, for any point on the root locus,

$$\sum \Phi_z - \sum \Phi_p = n \times 180°, \quad n = \pm 1, \pm 3, \ldots \quad (7.9)$$

Equation 7.9 is a useful form of the **angular criterion** which must be satisfied for a point to lie on the root locus.

Example 7.4 (Fig. 7.6): Use the angular criterion to ascertain if the points (a) $-2 + j$, and (b) $-1.5 + j2$ can be on the root locus plot of the system the open loop transfer function of which is

$$\frac{\theta_{on}}{\theta} = \frac{K_o'}{D(D + 3)}$$

where $D = 0$ and $D = -3$ are the open loop poles. There are no finite open loop zeros. Figure 7.6(c) shows the poles, the points (a) and (b) requiring investigation, and the vectors joining the poles to each point.

Solution: For (a), $\Phi = \sum \Phi_z - \sum \Phi_p = 0 - 154° - 46° = -200°$, which is not an odd number multiple of 180°. For (b), $\Phi = 0 - 127° - 53° = -180°$, which satisfies the angular requirement. Hence $-2 + j$ cannot be on the root locus, but $-1.5 + j2$ will be.

Applying the magnitude requirement

The value of open loop sensitivity K_o' associated with a point on the root locus is found by evaluating the *magnitude* of the vector relationship in Eq. 7.7. Using Eq. 7.8 for $K_o' f'(D)$, the requirement becomes

$$\left| \frac{K_o'(D - Z_1)(D - Z_2)\ldots}{(D - P_1)(D - P_2)(D - P_3)\ldots} \right| = 1 \quad (7.10)$$

where D is the value of the point considered. Hence,

$$K'_o = \left| \frac{(D - P_1)(D - P_2)(D - P_3)\ldots}{(D - Z_1)(D - Z_2)\ldots} \right|$$

or

$$K'_o = \frac{|(D - P_1)|\cdot|(D - P_2)|\cdot|(D - P_3)|\ldots}{|(D - Z_1)|\cdot|(D - Z_2)|\ldots} \qquad (7.10a)$$

In the absence of finite open loop zeros, this expression becomes

$$K'_o = |(D - P_1)|\cdot|(D - P_2)|\ldots \qquad (7.10b)$$

Equations 7.10, 7.10(a), and 7.10(b) are readily evaluated by calculation, or graphically.

Example 7.4 (Fig. 7.6, continued): Find the value of sensitivity K'_o at the point $-1.5 + j2$, which was shown by the angular criterion to lie on the root locus.

By calculation:

$$\frac{K'_o}{D(D + 3)} = 1 \quad \text{or} \quad K'_o = D(D + 3)$$

For $D = -1.5 + j2$,

$$K'_o = [(-1.5)^2 + 2^2]^{1/2}\cdot(1.5^2 + 2^2)^{1/2} = 6.25$$

Note that open loop gain $K_o = K'_o/3 = 2.08$.

Graphically: As shown in Figs. 7.6(a) and (b), the line drawn from a pole or finite zero to the point considered is the vector $\overline{D - P}$ or $\overline{D - Z}$ respectively. Its magnitude is readily scaled from the open loop pole-zero diagram. For the point $-1.5 + j2$, (Fig. 7.6c), Eq. 7.10(b) yields

$$K'_o = 2.5 \times 2.5 = 6.25$$

7.5.2 Rules for Rapid Plotting, and Their Origins

Rule 1: Number of paths

> There are as many separate branch loci as there are roots of the characteristic equation.

Example: Previous Examples 7.1 and 7.2 (Fig. 7.2) have second-order characteristic equations which must have two roots. Figure 7.2 shows that both root locus plots have two separate root paths.

Justification: Each characteristic equation root will have its own unique path on the complex plane as sensitivity is varied from 0 to ∞. In general, the number of branch loci also equals

(a) the order of the system equation or transfer function (closed loop);
(b) the number of poles of the system transfer function;
(c) the number of poles of the open loop transfer function.

Rule 2: *Starting and finishing points*

> Root locus branches start at the poles (for $K'_o = 0$) of the open loop transfer function and end at its zeros (for $K'_o = \infty$).

Example: The open loop transfer function for previous Example 7.2 (Fig. 7.2b) is readily shown to be

$$\frac{\theta_o}{\theta} = \frac{K}{D(D+3)}$$

where $\theta_o = \theta_{on}$ and $K = K'_o$ for this case as the system transfer function is already nondimensional. The poles of this equation are $D = 0$ and $D = -3$, and the zeros are $D = \infty$. Previous examination of the system transfer function showed that 0 and -3 were the starting points of the branch loci, and that the branches finished at ∞.

Example: The open loop transfer function of previous Example 7.1 (Fig. 7.2a) is readily shown to be

$$\frac{\theta_o}{\theta} = \frac{K(D+2)}{D(D+4)}$$

where $\theta_o = \theta_{on}$ and $K = K'_o$, as for the previous example. The poles for this equation are $D = 0$ and $D = -4$, and the zeros are $D = -2$ and $D = \infty$. These open loop pole and zero values correspond with the branch starting and finishing points previously established.

Justification: In effect, Rule 2 states the following:

(a) The poles of the open loop transfer function (P_o) have the same values as the roots of the characteristic equation have when $K'_o = 0$.
(b) The zeros of the open loop transfer function Z_o have the same values as the roots of the characteristic equation have when $K'_o = \infty$.

Now the characteristic equation can be represented (Eq. 7.5)

$$1 + K'_o f'(D) = 0 = 1 + K'_o \frac{f_n(D)}{f_d(D)}$$

where $f'_d(D)$ is the denominator, and $K'_o f_n(D)$ is the numerator, of the open loop transfer function $K'_o f'(D)$.
The characteristic equation is

$$f_d(D) + K'_o f_n(D) = 0$$

For $K'_o = 0$, the characteristic equation becomes

$$f_d(D) = 0$$

Hence the poles of the open loop transfer function have the same values as the roots of the characteristic equation when $K'_o = 0$.

For $K'_o \to \infty$, the characteristic equation approaches

$$K'_o f_n(D) = 0,$$

the roots of which are the zeros of the open loop transfer function. Hence the zeros of the open loop transfer function are identical with the roots of the characteristic equation when $K'_o \to \infty$.

Rule 3: Location of infinite zero asymptotes

It has been established that the separate branches of a root locus plot start at open loop poles and end at open loop zeros. Hence there must be

$$N_p - N_z$$

open loop zeros at infinity. N_p = number of open loop poles; N_z = number of finite open loop zeros.

A locus approaching infinity for $K'_o \to \infty$ does so asymptotically. The angle and location of such asymptotes can be found from

(a) the angles which infinite open loop zero asymptotes make with the real axis, which are given by

$$\alpha^\circ = \frac{n \times 180}{N_p - N_z}, \quad n = \pm 1, \pm 3, \ldots$$

(b) the point on the real axis at which such asymptotes start, which is given by

$$x = \frac{\sum P_o - \sum Z_o}{N_p - N_z}$$

where $\sum P_o$ = sum of open loop poles; $\sum Z_o$ = sum of open loop zeros.

Example: Consider previous Example 7.2 (Fig. 7.2b), the open loop transfer function of which is

$$\frac{\theta_o}{\theta} = \frac{K'_o}{D(D + 3)}$$

The number of infinite zeros is

$$N_p - N_z = 2 - 0 = 2$$

and hence two asymptotes are required:

$$\alpha = \frac{\pm 1 \times 180}{2} = \pm 90°$$

The asymptotes start on the real axis at

$$x = \frac{(0 - 3) - 0}{2} = -1\tfrac{1}{2}$$

Figure 7.2(b) confirms both location and angles of the $K \rightarrow \infty$ asymptotes.

Example: A system has the open loop transfer function

$$\frac{\theta_{on}}{\theta} = \frac{K'_o}{D(D + 3)(D + 5)}$$

The poles are $D = 0$, -3, -5. There are no finite zeros, hence 3 zeros exist at infinity. The angles of the infinite zero asymptotes are

$$\alpha = \frac{\pm 1 \times 180}{3} = \pm 60°$$

and

$$\alpha = \frac{\pm 3 \times 180}{3} = 180°$$

The asymptotes intersect the real axis at

$$x = \frac{(0 - 3 - 5) - 0}{3} = -\frac{8}{3}$$

These three asymptotes are illustrated in Fig. 7.7(a).

Justification:

(a) *Angle:* When a branch locus approaches infinity, lines drawn to it from all of the poles and finite zeros will approach a constant slope (α of Fig. 7.7b). The angular criterion applied to this situation yields

$$\sum \Phi_z - \sum \Phi_p = N_z \cdot \alpha - N_p \cdot \alpha = \alpha(N_z - N_p) = n \cdot 180°$$

where n is an odd number, i.e.,

$$\alpha = \frac{n \cdot 180°}{N_z - N_p}$$

(b) *Location:* An established property of polynomial equations is that the sum of the roots of the equation equals minus the coefficient of the second-highest-order term, when the coefficient of the highest-order term is unity, i.e., for

$$D^3 + 9D^2 + 8D + K_o = 0, \qquad \sum \text{roots} = -9$$

or more generally,

$$D^n + \alpha_{n-1} D^{n-1} + \ldots \alpha_1 D + \alpha_o = 0, \qquad \sum \text{roots} = -\alpha_{n-1}$$

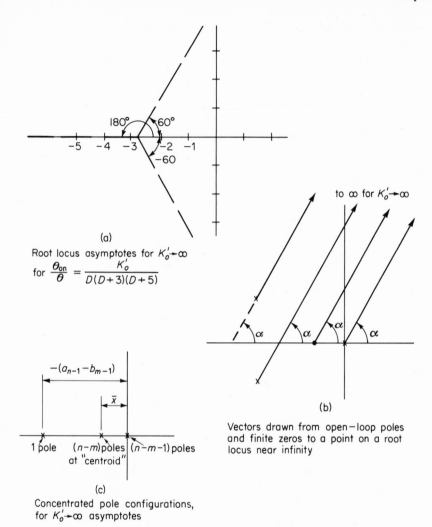

(a)

Root locus asymptotes for $K_o' \to \infty$

for $\dfrac{\theta_{on}}{\theta} = \dfrac{K_o'}{D(D+3)(D+5)}$

(b)

Vectors drawn from open−loop poles and finite zeros to a point on a root locus near infinity

(c)

Concentrated pole configurations, for $K_o' \to \infty$ asymptotes

Fig. 7.7 Root locus asymptotes for infinite zero configurations.

In the most general case, an open loop transfer function is in the form of a ratio of polynomials, as shown in Eq. 7.8, which could be written

$$\frac{\theta_{on}}{\theta} = K_o' f'(D) = \frac{K_o'(D^m + b_{m-1} D^{m-1} + \ldots b_1 D + b_o)}{D^n + a_{n-1} D^{n-1} + \ldots a_1 D + a_o} \qquad (7.11)$$

Dividing numerator and denominator by $(D^m + b_{m-1} D^{m-1} + \cdots)$ yields

$$K_o' f'(D) = \frac{K_o'}{(D^n + a_{n-1} D^{n-1} + \ldots)/(D^m + b_{m-1} D^{m-1} + \ldots)}$$

Using the conventional procedure for dividing polynomials,

$$K'_o f'(D) = \frac{K'_o}{D^{n-m} + (a_{n-1} - b_{m-1})D^{n-m-1} + \ldots} \tag{7.11a}$$

In this manner, the open loop transfer function is reduced to a form containing only open loop poles, with no finite zeros.

For large values of D, i.e., for points on the root locus far out along the asymptotes, the denominator of Eq. 7.11(a) can be approximated by its first two terms only, i.e.,

$$K'_o f'(D) \approx \frac{K'_o}{D^{n-m} + (a_{n-1} - b_{m-1})D^{n-m-1}} \quad \text{for } D \to \infty$$

which can be written

$$K'_o f'(D) = \frac{K'_o}{D^{n-m-1}[D + (a_{n-1} - b_{m-1})]}$$

Thus for $D \to \infty$, the original open loop pole-zero configuration can be replaced with $n - m - 1$ poles at the origin, and one pole at the real point, $-(a_{n-1} - b_{m-1})$, as shown in Fig. 7.7(c).

The "centroid" of these $n - m$ poles is found by taking moments about the imaginary axis, i.e.,

$$1 \text{ pole} \times -(a_{n-1} - b_{m-1}) = (n - m) \text{ poles} \times \bar{X}$$

and

$$\bar{X} = \frac{-(a_{n-1} - b_{m-1})}{n - m}$$

In this manner, a single real point is located at which all of the open loop poles can be considered to be concentrated when drawing the root locus branches in the regions where K'_o is very large. The branches approach their asymptotes as K'_o becomes very large. Thus the straight line approximation to the root locus in the regions of large K'_o can be considered to start from the "centroid," as they must start from open loop poles.

Now referring to Eq. 7.11,

(a) $-a_{n-1}$ is the sum of the roots of the denominator; and hence
(b) $-a_{n-1} = \sum \text{poles of } K_o f(D) = \sum P_o$.

Also, $-b_{m-1}$ is the sum of the roots of the numerator, and hence

(c) $-b_{m-1} = \sum \text{zeros of } K_o f(D) = \sum Z_o$.

Also, n is the number of poles and m is the number of zeros of $K_o f(D)$,

$$\therefore n - m = N_p - N_z$$

$$\bar{x} = \frac{\sum P_o - \sum Z_o}{N_p - N_z}$$

Rule 4: Location on real axis

A root locus exists only on portions of the real axis; the portions are determined by the locations of only real poles and zeros of the open loop transfer function.

A point on the real axis lies on the root locus if the total number of real open loop poles and zeros to its right is an odd number.

Example: The open loop poles and zeros of Example 7.1 (Fig. 7.2a) were established for Rule 2 as 0, -4, and -2.

(a) There are no real poles and zeros to the right of the origin, and hence no part of the positive real axis lies on the root locus.

(b) There is one real pole (0), and no real zeros to the right of -2, hence the line -2 to 0 lies on the root locus.

(c) There is one real pole (0), plus one real zero (-2) to the right of -4, giving a total of two real poles and zeros. Hence the region -4 to -2 on the real axis is not on the root locus.

(d) There are three real poles and zeros $(-4, -2, 0)$ to the right of any point on the real axis between -4 and $-\infty$. Hence this portion of the real axis lies on the root locus.

Example: For Example 7.2 (Fig. 7.2b), it was established for Rule 2 that real poles of the open loop transfer function exist at 0 and -3, whereas there are no real finite zeros. Hence Rule 3 yields the following:

(a) The number of the real poles and zeros to the right of the origin is 0. Hence the positive real axis does not lie on the root locus.

(b) The number of real poles and zeros to the right of any point lying between -3 and 0 is one. Hence the -3 to 0 region of the real axis lies on the root locus.

(c) The number of real poles and zeros to the right of any point between $-\infty$ and -3 on the real axis is two, and hence the root locus cannot occur in this region.

Justification: Complex poles and/or zeros can only exist in conjugate pairs. Hence the sum of the angles of the vectors drawn from such a pair of points to any point on the real axis is 360°, as illustrated in Fig. 7.8(a). As 360° is effectively the same as 0°, a complex conjugate pair of points cannot affect the angular criterion applied to points on the real axis.

All real open loop poles and/or zeros to the left of a point on the real axis have vector angles of 0° associated with them, as shown in Fig. 7.8(b), and hence cannot affect an application of the angular criterion. It should be apparent that the root locus cannot exist to the right of the algebraically largest real open loop pole or root.

All real open loop poles and/or zeros to the right of a point on the real axis have an angle of 180° associated with them if a vector is drawn from them to the point considered (Fig. 7.8c). The $\Sigma \, \Phi_z - \Sigma \, \Phi_p$ sum of the vector angles for any even number of such poles and/or zeros is readily seen to be either 0° or 360°, depending upon the distribution of poles and zeros.

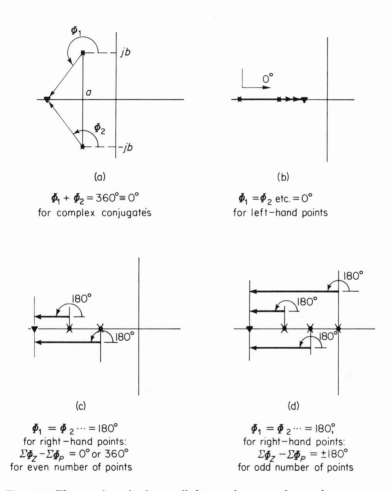

(a)

$\Phi_1 + \Phi_2 = 360° \equiv 0°$
for complex conjugates

(b)

$\Phi_1 = \Phi_2$ etc. $= 0°$
for left−hand points

(c)

$\Phi_1 = \Phi_2 \cdots = 180°$
for right−hand points:
$\Sigma\Phi_Z - \Sigma\Phi_P = 0°$ or 360°
for even number of points

(d)

$\Phi_1 = \Phi_2 \cdots = 180°$,
for right−hand points:
$\Sigma\Phi_Z - \Sigma\Phi_P = \pm 180°$
for odd number of points

Fig. 7.8 The angular criterion applied to various open loop pole–zero configurations (the point being considered is identified by a triangle).

If there is an odd number of real poles and/or zeros to the right of the point considered (Fig. 7.8d), the $\Phi_z - \Phi_p$ sum of the vector angles is readily seen to be $\pm n \times 180°$, with n an odd number. Hence the angular criterion is satisfied only by this condition, and the root locus will be on the real axis only when this condition is satisfied.

Rule 5: Symmetry of root locus plot

A root locus plot is symmetrical about the real axis.

Example: Example 7.2 (Fig. 7.2b) illustrates the rule, which was also mentioned in association with Fig. 7.1.

Justification: A root locus leaves the real axis only if complex roots of the characteristic equation exist. Complex roots can only exist in mirror image pairs (conjugates). Hence a complete root locus will be symmetrical about the real axis.

Rule 6: Location of breakaway and breakin points

(a) It follows from Rule 5 that loci which start on the real axis and then leave the real axis as open loop gain is increased must leave it in pairs from a common point. Such a point is called a **breakaway point.**

A breakaway point will exist between two adjacent real poles of the open loop transfer function if the root locus exists between such poles. The breakaway point is located by taking the differential dK'_o/dD of the characteristic equation, and then solving this expression equated to zero for D.

Example: In Example 7.2 (Fig. 7.2b), -3 and 0 are adjacent poles of the open loop transfer function, and the root locus exists between the points. Hence a breakaway point exists between -3 and 0. The characteristic equation is:

$$D_2 + 3D + K'_o = 0$$

from which

$$K'_o = -D^2 - 3D \qquad \text{(a)}$$

$$\frac{dK'_o}{dD} = -2D - 3$$

which is zero for a breakaway point, i.e.,

$$2D + 3 = 0 \quad \text{and} \quad D = -1\tfrac{1}{2}$$

From (a), $K'_o = 2\tfrac{1}{4}$ for $D = -1\tfrac{1}{2}$. Hence $D = -1\tfrac{1}{2}$ is the breakaway point, which is confirmed in Fig. 7.2(b).

For this example, the breakaway point and the asymptote starting point found from Rule 3 are identical. In general, the breakaway point and the asymptote point do not coincide. Following Example 7.5 (Fig. 7.12) illustrates a case when this coincidence does not apply.

Justification: Each branch locus starts at an open loop pole and ends at an open loop zero. Two root paths starting from adjacent real open loop poles and moving towards each other along the real axis must depart from the real axis in order to seek an open loop zero (real or infinite) as their finishing points. To satisfy Rule 5, the breakaway must occur at the point where the pair of paths meet.

Location of a breakaway point is based on recognition that K'_o, against which the root locus plot is being made, is a maximum for that portion of the real axis immediately adjacent to the breakaway point — i.e., in Fig. 7.2(b), $K'_o = 2\frac{1}{4}$ at the breakaway point $(-1\frac{1}{2})$ is a maximum for that part of the root locus on the real axis. That is, the slope of the K'_o versus real D relationship is zero at a breakaway point. The K'_o versus D relationship is the characteristic equation.

For example, consider the characteristic equation

$$D^2 + 3D + K'_o = 0; \quad K'_o = -D^2 - 3D \tag{a}$$

$$\frac{dK'_o}{dD} = -2D - 3 = 0$$

for a maximum value of D, i.e., $D = -1\frac{1}{2}$ is the breakaway point.

Having found the breakaway value of D, the associated value of K'_o is readily found from expression (a) above, i.e.,

$$K'_o = -(-1\frac{1}{2})^2 - 3(-1\frac{1}{2}) = 2\frac{1}{4}$$

as shown previously in Fig. 7.2(b).

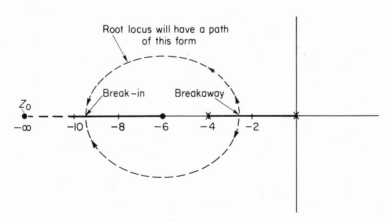

Fig. 7.9 Location of breakaway and breakin points for

$$\frac{\theta_{on}}{\theta} = \frac{K'_o(D + 6)}{D(D + 4)}$$

(b) Just as a pair of loci can break away from the real axis, a pair of loci can return to the real axis as gain is increased from values which made the roots complex. A point of entry or re-entry to the real axis is called a **breakin point.**

A breakin point will necessarily exist if a real open loop zero is not joined by a branch locus to an adjacent real pole (Fig. 7.9). A breakin point will be located by the differentiation procedure given for breakaway points. In effect, a local minimum zero slope of the real D versus K_o' relationship is established.

Example: Consider the open loop transfer function

$$\frac{\theta_{on}}{\theta} = \frac{K_o'(D + 6)}{D(D + 4)}$$

the poles of which are at 0 and -4, and the only finite zero of which is at -6 (Fig. 7.9). Rule 1 indicates that there are two locus branches starting from 0 and -4 and ending at -6 and ∞. Rule 2 indicates that the infinite zero exists at 180°. Rule 4 shows that the root locus exists on the real axis between -4 and 0, and between $-\infty$ and -6. Rule 6(a) shows that there must be a breakaway point between -4 and 0. Examination of Fig. 7.9 shows that the branches which break away from the region -4 to 0 must return to the real axis between $-\infty$ and -6, or the locus cannot be complete. Note that there is no branch starting point in the $-\infty$ to -6 region.

The characteristic equation is

$$D^2 + (4 + K_o')D + 6K_o' = 0$$

from which

$$K_o' = \frac{-D^2 - 4D}{D + 6}$$

$$\frac{dK_o'}{dD} = \frac{-D^2 - 12D - 24}{(D + 6)^2}$$

[from $(d/dx)(u\,v) = v(du/dx) + u(dv/dx)$, with $u = -D^2 - 4D$ and $v = (D + 6)^{-1}$], which must be zero for maxima and minima, i.e., $D^2 + 12D + 24 = 0$ for break points, and $D = -2.5$ and -9.5. Hence $D = -2.5$ is the breakaway point and $D = -9.5$ is the breakin point (Fig. 7.9).

The differentiation procedure becomes tedious if the characteristic equation is of high order or if it is complicated by K_o'. An experienced plotter of the root locus would then prefer to locate breakpoints by trial and error, using the angular criterion.

Rule 7: Crossing imaginary axis

Putting the imaginary number jb for D in the characteristic equation and solving for b reveals the number and locations of any points at which root locus branches cross the imaginary axis. The value of open loop sensitivity at which such crossings occur is also revealed.

Example: Consider the open loop transfer function

$$\frac{\theta_{on}}{\theta} = \frac{K_o'}{D(D + 3)(D + 5)}$$

The characteristic equation for this system is

$$D(D + 3)(D + 5) + K'_o = D^3 + 8D^2 + 15D + K'_o = 0$$

Substituting jb for D yields

$$j^3b^3 + 8j^2b^2 + 15jb + K'_o = 0 = -(8b^2 - K'_o) + jb(15 - b^2)$$

For the complex number to be zero, both parts must be zero:

$$-(8b^2 - K'_o) = 0$$

$$15 - b^2 = 0$$

from which $b = 15^{1/2}$, and $K'_o = 120$, i.e., loci cross the imaginary axis at $\pm j \cdot 15^{1/2}$ for $K'_o = 120$. Example 7.6 (Fig. 7.12) is a typical application.

Justification: If a branch of a root locus plot touches the imaginary axis, the value of the associated root at the touching point is imaginary. Substituting the imaginary number jb for D in the characteristic equation and solving for b reveals presence or absence of such touching or crossing points. If b is finite, it must occur as a conjugate pair $\pm b$ to satisfy the symmetry requirement of Rule 5.

Rule 8: Angles of departure and arrival

The poles of an open loop transfer function can be complex, indicating that root locus branches can start from complex points. The angle at which a locus leaves a complex pole is called the **angle of departure.** Evaluation of an angle of departure gives the tangent to the root locus at its complex starting point.

An angle of departure is found from the relationship

$$\psi = \sum \Phi_z - \sum \Phi_p - n \times 180°$$

where $\sum \Phi_z$ is the sum of the angles of the lines drawn from finite zeros to the complex pole being examined; $\sum \Phi_p$ is the sum of the angles of the lines drawn from the poles to the complex pole being examined; n is an odd number.

Example:

$$\frac{\theta_{on}}{\theta} = \frac{K'_o(D + 1)}{D^2 + 3D + 3.25} = \frac{K'_o(D + 1)}{[D + (1.5 + j1)][D + (1.5 - j1)]}$$

Open loop poles exist at $-1.5 \pm j1$ and a finite open loop zero exists at -1, as shown in Fig. 7.10(a). The angle of departure for the root locus branch which starts at the pole $-1.5 + j1$ is

$$\psi = \sum \Phi_z - \sum \Phi_p - n \times 180°$$

$$= 117° - 90° - 180° = -153° = 207°$$

Obviously, the angle of departure from the pole $-1.5 - j1$ is $153°$.

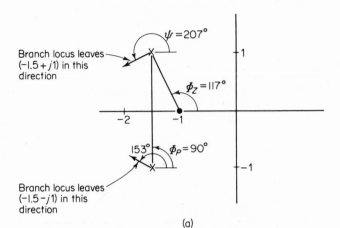

(a)

Angles of departure for the system whose open

loop transfer function is $\dfrac{\theta_{on}}{\theta} = \dfrac{K_o'(D+1)}{D^2+3D+3.25}$

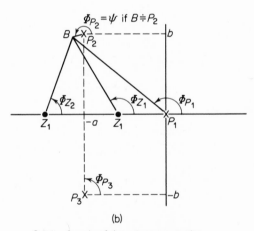

(b)

Origin of angle of departure expression

Fig. 7.10 Angles of departure.

Justification: Figure 7.10(b) shows open loop pole-zero configuration, with complex poles at $-a \pm jb$. Consider an arbitrary point B close to the pole $P_2 = -a + jb$. For B to lie on the root locus, the angular criterion (Eq. 7.9) must be satisfied:

$$\Phi_{z1} + \Phi_{z2} - \Phi_{p1} - \psi - \Phi_{p2} = n \times 180$$

where $\psi = \Phi_{p2}$; n is an odd number.

Now, if B is very close to P_2, angles Φ_{z1}, Φ_{z2}, Φ_{p1}, and Φ_{p3} are almost identical to the angles of the lines drawn from the poles and zeros to P_2 itself, i.e.,

$$\psi = \sum \Phi_z - \sum \Phi_p - n \times 180°$$

where $\sum \Phi_z$ and $\sum \Phi_p$ were previously defined.

In complicated systems, it is possible to have a pair of complex open loop zeros, at which points root locus branches will finish for $K_o' = \infty$. The angle of the tangent to a branch as it reaches a complex zero is called the **angle of arrival,** and can be found in the same manner as established for angles of departure.

Rule 9: Sum of the roots of the characteristic equation

As discussed under Rule 3, *Justification:*

> For a characteristic equation of the form
> $$D^n + a_{n-1} D^{n-1} + \cdots + a_1 D + a_o = 0$$
> $$\sum \text{roots} = -a_{n-1}$$

This property of polynomials can be useful in locating values of open loop sensitivity K_o on root locus branches. Following Example 7.5 illustrates its use.

Rule 10: Scaling the root locus

The general technique for assigning values of open loop sensitivity K_o' to the root locus was given in Section 7.5.1. Applying the magnitude requirement:

> The open loop sensitivity K_o' for a point on the root locus can be calculated by substituting the point for D in the expression $K_o' = f'(D)^{-1}$, where $K_o' f'(D)$ is the open loop transfer function. The rule can be applied graphically by using
> $$K_o' = \frac{|\bar{P}_1| \cdot |\bar{P}_2| \cdot \ldots}{|\bar{Z}_1| \cdot |\bar{Z}_2| \cdot \ldots}$$
> where $\bar{P}$ is a vector drawn from an open loop pole to the point considered; $\bar{Z}$ is a vector drawn from a finite open loop zero to the point considered.

An example and justification of this rule was given in Section 7.5.1.

7.5.3 Summary of Rapid Plotting Criteria and Rules

The angular criterion

A point on the root locus must satisfy the angular expression

$$\sum \Phi_z - \sum \Phi_p = n \times 180°$$

where Φ_z is the angle of a line drawn from a finite open loop zero to the point considered; Φ_p is the angle of a line drawn from an open loop pole to the point considered; n is an odd number.

The magnitude criterion

The value of open loop sensitivity for a point on the root locus is found by satisfying the magnitude expression

$$|K'_o f'(D)| = 1 \quad \text{or} \quad K'_o = |f'(D)^{-1}|$$

Rule 1: There are as many separate branch loci as there are roots of the characteristic equation.

Rule 2: Root locus branches start at the poles (for $K'_o = 0$) of the open loop transfer function, and end at its zeros (for $K'_o = \infty$).

Rule 3: The angles and location of any infinite zero asymptotes to root locus branches are given by

$$\alpha° = \frac{n \times 180°}{N_p - N_z} \quad \text{and} \quad x = \frac{\sum P_o - \sum Z_o}{N_p - N_z}$$

where $N_p =$ number of open loop poles; $N_z =$ number of open loop zeros; $\sum P_o =$ sum of open loop poles; $\sum Z_o =$ sum of open loop zeros.

Rule 4: A point on the real axis lies on the root locus if the number of real open loop poles and zeros to its right is an odd number.

Rule 5: A root locus plot is symmetrical about the real axis.

Rule 6: If the root locus occupies the real axis between two adjacent real open loop poles, it will break away from the real axis at a point between such poles.

    If a real open loop zero is not joined to an adjacent real open loop pole by a locus on the real axis, then a locus must break in to the real axis from the complex region.

    Breakaway points will be maxima and breakin points minima of the $K'_o - D$ relationship of the characteristic equation, and can be found from $dK'_o/dD = 0$.

Rule 7:   The location of any points at which the root locus crosses the imaginary axis, and the value of open loop sensitivity at which such crossings occur, can be found by substituting jb for D in the characteristic equation.

Rule 8:   A root locus branch leaves a complex open loop pole (for $K_o' \, 0) =$ at the angle of departure

$$\psi = \sum \Phi_z - \sum \Phi_p - n \times 180°$$

where Φ_z and Φ_p vectors are drawn to the complex pole, and n is an odd number.

A root locus branch enters a complex open loop zero (for $K_o' = \infty$) at an angle of arrival given by the same expression

Rule 9:   The sum of the roots of a characteristic equation is minus the coefficient of the second-highest-order term.

Rule 10: The sensitivity K_o' for a point on the root locus can be calculated by using the magnitude criterion $K_o' = f'(D)^{-1}$. The criterion can be applied graphically by using

$$K_o' = \frac{|\bar{P}_1| \cdot |\bar{P}_2| \dots}{|\bar{Z}_1| \cdot |\bar{Z}_2| \dots}$$

$\bar{P}$ is a vector drawn from an open loop pole to the point considered; $\bar{Z}$ is a vector drawn from a finite open loop zero to the point considered.

7.5.4 Further Comments on Root Locus Plotting

Further ideas and extensions to the rules given can be gained with experience in root locus plotting.

The differentiation approach of Rule 6 for finding breakaway and break-in points becomes tedious for complicated transfer functions. It becomes more feasible to locate points on the root locus near the break points by experienced trial and error, using the angular criterion.

Having used all of the guides to rapid plotting to locate critical points and asymptotes, it is often necessary to get intermediate points to complete the plot with acceptable accuracy. Trial and error location of points using the angular criterion is quite rapidly applied by an experienced operator.

Experience is a great aid to root locus plotting. A diagram showing common root locus forms is most useful. Figure 7.11 shows some common root locus plots. A student should satisfy himself that the plots are authentic.

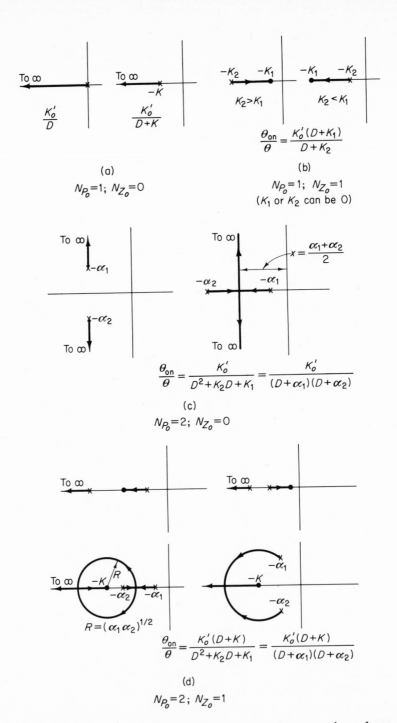

Fig. 7.11 Some common root locus forms; N_{P_o}, N_{z_o} are numbers of open loop poles and zeros.

Use of the Spirule, an aid to rapid plotting of root loci by trial and error, will be discussed in Section 7.7.

7.6 EXAMPLES WITH SOLUTIONS

Example 7.5 (Fig. 7.12): A system has the open loop transfer function

$$\frac{\theta_{on}}{\theta} = \frac{K'_o}{D(D + 1)(D + 8)}$$

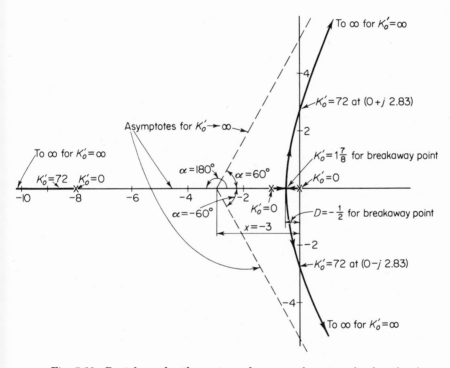

Fig. 7.12 Root locus for the system whose open loop transfer function is

$$\frac{\theta_{on}}{\theta_o} = \frac{K'_o}{D(D + 1)(D + 8)}$$

Construct the root locus of this system and establish the values of K'_o for which the system will be stable.

Solution (Fig. 7.12):

(Rule 1) There are three branch loci, as there are three roots of the characteristic equation.

(Rule 2) Loci start at 0, -1, and -8 (the poles of θ_{on}/θ), and end at infinity (θ_{on}/θ having no finite zeros).

(Rule 3) The asymptote angles are

$$\alpha^\circ = \frac{n \times 180^\circ}{N_p - N_z} = \frac{\pm 180}{3 - 0} = \pm 60^\circ$$

and

$$\alpha^\circ = \frac{3 \times \pm 180}{3} = 180^\circ$$

The asymptotes intersect the real axis at

$$x = \frac{\Sigma P_o - \Sigma Z_o}{N_p - N_z} = \frac{(-1 - 8) - 0}{3 - 0} = -3$$

(Rule 4) Loci exist on the real axis between 0 and -1, and between -8 and $-\infty$.

(Rule 6) A breakaway point occurs between 0 and -1 (i.e., 0 and -1 are adjacent real poles with the root locus joining them). The characteristic equation of the system is

$$D^3 + 9D^2 + 8D + K'_o = 0$$

That is,

$$K'_o = -D^3 - 9D^2 - 8D \qquad\qquad \text{(a)}$$

$$\frac{dK'_o}{dD} = -3D^2 - 18D - 8 = 0$$

for a breakin point, i.e.,

$$3D^2 + 18D + 8 = 0$$

$$D = -3 \pm \frac{(18^2 - 96)^{1/2}}{6} = -0.5 \quad \text{and} \quad -5.5$$

Hence $D = -0.5$ is the breakaway point required. From expression (a) above,

$$K'_o = -(-0 \cdot 5)^3 - 9(-0 \cdot 5)^2 - 8(-0 \cdot 5) = 1.875$$

at the breakaway point.

(Rule 7) Substitute jb for D in the characteristic equation:

$$j^3 b^3 + 9 j^2 b^2 + 8 j b + K'_o = 0$$

$$(K'_o - 9 b^2) + j b (8 - b^2) = 0$$

hence

$$K'_o - 9 b^2 = 0$$

and

$$j b (8 - b^2) = 0$$

from which $b = \pm 8^{1/2}$, and $K'_o = 72$, i.e., root loci cross the imaginary axis at ± 2.83, at which points $K'_o = 72$.

(Rule 8) There are no complex open loop poles or zeros, and hence no angles of departure or arrival.

(Rule 9) The sum of the roots of the characteristic equation is -9 (coefficient of second-highest-order term). For $K_o' = 72$, two of the roots are 2.83 and -2.83; hence, the third root must be $-9 - 2.83 + 2.83 = -9$, and $K_o' = 72$ is located at -9 on the branch locus from -8 to $-\infty$.

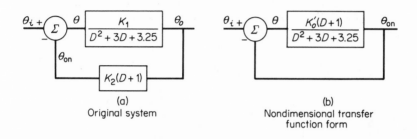

(a)
Original system

(b)
Nondimensional transfer
function form

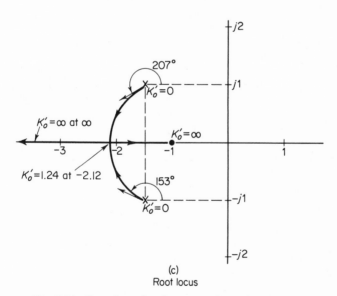

(c)
Root locus

Fig. 7.13   Root locus for the system shown in Diagram (a).

From this data the root locus can be sketched (Fig. 7.12). It is apparent that the system is stable for values of $K_o' < 72$. For $K_o' = 72$ the system is critically stable, whereas for $K_o' > 72$ the system is unstable.

If a more accurate plot is required, more points on the root locus must be found. The approach would be as follows:

(a) Consider only the upper complex locus from -0.5 to ∞.

(b) From the sketched curve, select a trial point. For example, point $-0.25 + j2$ could be tried.

(c) Apply the angular criterion to this point. Make necessary adjustments to the point to satisfy the criterion with acceptable accuracy.

(d) Evaluate K_o' for the acquired point by multiplying together the magnitudes of the vectors drawn from the poles.

(e) Repeat for as many points as needed to draw the curve accurately.

(f) The lower complex locus is a mirror image of the upper one.

(g) Locate values of K_o' on the real root locus from -8 to $-\infty$, using the sum-of-the-roots technique of Rule 9, or Rule 10. Use of a Spirule, discussed in Section 7.7, greatly speeds this procedure.

Example 7.6 (Fig. 7.13): Sketch the root locus for the system shown in Fig. 7.13(a), the transfer function of which is

$$\frac{\theta_o}{\theta_i} = \frac{K_1}{D^2 + (3 + K_1K_2)D + (3.25 + K_1K_2)}$$

Solution: The open loop transfer function is found by rearranging the system block diagram to the nondimensional form of Fig. 7.13(b). Then

$$\frac{\theta_{on}}{\theta} = \frac{K_o'(D + 1)}{D^2 + 3D + 3.25}$$

where $K_o' = K_1K_2$.

The characteristic equation is second-order, and hence has two roots. There must be two root locus branches. (Alternatively, there are two poles to the open loop transfer function and hence there are two root locus branches.)

The branch loci start at open loop poles given by

$$D^2 + 3D + 3.25 = [D + (1.5 + j1)][D + (1.5 - j1)]$$

i.e., $D = -1.5 \pm j1$, for which starting points $K_o' = 0$ (Fig. 7.13c).

The branch loci end at open loop zeros $D = -1$, and $D = \infty$ for $K_o' = \infty$. The $D = \infty$ zero lies along the 180° real axis, as

$$\alpha = \frac{\pm 180}{N_p - N_z} = \frac{\pm 180}{2 - 1} = 180°$$

The root locus occupies the real axis between $-\infty$ and -1.

The two poles are complex, whereas the two zeros lie on the real axis. Hence there must be a breakin point on the root locus. The breakin point will lie between $-\infty$ and -1 (real open loop zeros having no real poles between them). The characteristic equation

$$D^2 + (3 + K_o')D + (3.25 + K_o') = 0$$

can be written

$$K_o' = \frac{-D^2 - 3D - 3.25}{D + 1}$$

$$\therefore \frac{dK_o'}{dD} = \frac{(D + 1)(-2D - 3) + D^2 + 3D + 3.25}{(D + 1)^2} = \frac{-D^2 - 2D + 0.25}{(D + 1)^2}$$

and from $dK'_o/dD = 0$ for a breakin point,

$$D^2 + 2D - 0.25 = 0$$

and $D = -2.12$ is the breakin point. For $D = -2.12$,

$$K'_o = \frac{-(-2.12)^2 - 3(-2.12) - 3.25}{-2.12 + 1} = 1.24$$

The angles of departure of the branch loci are

$$\psi = \sum \Phi_z - \sum \Phi_p - n \times 180°$$

where n is an odd number. For the pole $-1.5 + j1$, $\psi = 117° - 90° - 180° = -153° = 207°$. For the pole $-1.5 - j1$, $\psi = 153°$ (either evaluate separately or from symmetry).

Figure 7.13(c) shows the root locus sketched from the calculated data.

Intermediate points on the root locus, together with the appropriate values of K'_o, can be found by using the angular criterion to locate a point by trial and error, and then using Rule 10 to evaluate K_o at that point.

Example 7.7 (Fig. 7.14): Consider the damped-spring-mass system of Examples 3.8 and 3.14. It was shown in Example 3.14 that the systems could be reduced to the block diagram shown in Fig. 7.14(a). The nondimensional transfer function form required for root locus analysis is shown in Fig. 7.14(b). The open loop transfer function is

$$\frac{F_s}{F} = \frac{k}{(W/g)\, D^2 + c\, D}$$

which is put into the following form for root locus analysis:

$$\frac{F_s}{F} = \frac{gK/W}{D(D + cg/W)} = \frac{K'_o}{D(D + A)}$$

where $K'_o = gk/W$ and $A = cg/W$.

There are two open loop poles (0 and $-A$) and hence there are two root locus branches, starting at 0 and $-A$ for $K'_o = 0$. There are no finite open loop zeros, and hence both branches finish at ∞ for $K'_o = \infty$.

The angle and location of the infinite zero ($K'_o = \infty$) asymptotes are

$$\alpha = \frac{\pm 180}{2} = \pm 90°$$

$$\bar{x} = \frac{-cg/W}{2} = -\frac{cg}{2W} = -\frac{1}{2} A$$

The root locus occupies the real axis between 0 and $-A$. A breakaway point exists at $-\frac{1}{2}A$. (Check by getting and differentiating the characteristic equation.)

Figure 7.14 shows the form of the root locus for this system. Note the following points for this type of system:

(a) The root locus occupies the real axis between 0 and $-A$.

(b) Breakaway occurs at $\pm 90°$ at $-\frac{1}{2}A$, and the locus maintains these angles as K_o' is increased.

(c) A increases linearly with the damping coefficient c.

(d) K_o' increases linearly with the spring constant k.

Comments (a) and (b) above apply to all systems having an open loop transfer

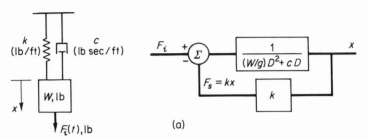

(a)

Partially reduced block diagram

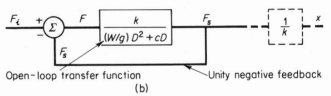

Open-loop transfer function   Unity negative feedback

(b)

Nondimensional open-loop transfer function form of block diagram, required for root locus analysis

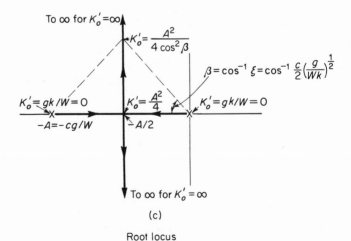

(c)

Root locus

Fig. 7.14   Root locus of damped-spring-mass system.

function of the form $K_o'/D(D + A)$. It must be recognized that all second-order systems the system transfer function of which is of the form

$$\frac{\theta_o}{\theta_i} = \frac{K}{T^2 D^2 + 2\xi T D + 1}$$

do not have the present form of open loop transfer function. The reader can satisfy himself on this point by seeking the open loop transfer functions of some of the second-order systems examined in Chapter 3.

Example 7.8 (Fig. 7.15): A system has the open loop transfer function

$$\frac{\theta_{on}}{\theta} = \frac{K_o'}{D(D^2 + 2D + 2)}$$

Construct the root locus of the system. Locate several intermediate points on the locus branches, and assign their appropriate values of open loop sensitivity K_o'.

Solution (Fig. 7.15):

(a) The open loop transfer function can be written

$$\frac{\theta_{on}}{\theta} = \frac{K_o'}{D(D + 1 + j1)(D + 1 - j1)}$$

(b) There are three open loop poles 0, $-(1 + j)$, and $-(1 - j)$; hence there are three branch loci, starting from these points for $K_o' = 0$.
(c) There are no finite open loop zeros; hence each branch locus finishes at ∞. The asymptotes which the branch loci approach as K_o' becomes large are at the angles

$$\alpha = \pm\frac{180}{3} = \pm60° \quad \text{and} \quad \alpha = \pm\frac{3 \times 180}{3} = 180°$$

The asymptotes intersect the real axis at

$$\bar{x} = \frac{-2}{3} = -\frac{2}{3}$$

(d) The root locus completely occupies the negative real axis. Hence one branch starts at 0 for $K_o' = 0$ and follows the negative real axis to $-\infty$ for $K_o' = \infty$.
(e) There are no breakaway or breakin points.
(f) The root locus crosses the imaginary axis at $\pm b$, where b is obtained by substituting jb for D in the characteristic equation, i.e.,

$$D^3 + 2D^2 + 2D + K_o' = 0 \quad \text{(characteristic equation)}$$

Substituting jb for D,

$$(-2b^2 + K_o') + j\,[(-b(b^2 - 2)] = 0$$

That is,

$$-2b^2 + K_o' = 0; \quad -b(b^2 - 2) = 0$$

$$b = \pm1.414; \quad K_o' = 4$$

and loci cross the imaginary axis at $\pm j \times 1.414$, for $K_o' = 4$.

(g) Angles of departure exist at $(-1 + j)$ and $(-1 - j)$.

$\psi_1 = 0 - 135 - 90 - 180° = -405° = -45°$ for pole $(-1 + j)$

$\psi_2 = 45°$ (Symmetry) for pole $(-1 - j)$

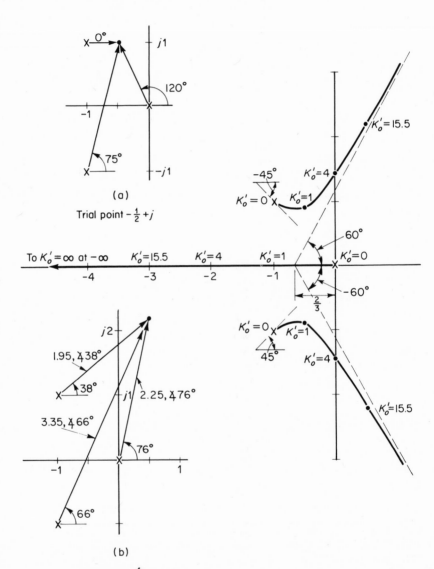

Fig. 7.15 Root locus for the system whose open loop transfer function is

$$\frac{\theta_{on}}{\theta} = \frac{K'_o}{D^3 + 2D^2 + 2D}$$

(h) The root locus can be sketched from the data obtained so far (Fig. 7.15).
(i) A point in the region $(-\frac{1}{2} + j)$ seems to lie near the upper root locus branch. Applying the angular criterion to this point (Fig. 7.15a),

$$\sum \Phi_{zo} = 0; \quad \sum \Phi_{po} = 120° + 75° + 0° = 195°$$

$$\therefore \sum \Phi_{zo} - \sum \Phi_{po} = -195° \neq 180°$$

and the point $(-\frac{1}{2} + j)$ does not lie on the root locus.
Try point $(-\frac{1}{2} + j0.9)$:

$$\sum \Phi_{zo} - \sum \Phi_{po} = 0 - 119° - 74° - 348° = -541 = 181°$$

Hence point $(-\frac{1}{2} + j \times 0.9)$ lies on the root locus. From symmetry, point $(-\frac{1}{2} - j \times 0.9)$ lies on the lower branch locus. Using the magnitude criterion (Rule 10),

$$K'_o = 1 \times 2 \times \tfrac{1}{2} = 1 \quad \text{for points } (-\tfrac{1}{2} \pm j \times 0.9)$$

(j) Points $(\frac{1}{2} \pm j \times 2.2)$ also seem to be on the root locus. Applying the angular criterion (Fig. 7.15b),

$$\sum \Phi_{zo} - \sum \Phi_{po} = 0 - 76° - 66° - 38° = -180°$$

which confirms that $(\frac{1}{2} \pm j \times 2.2)$ lies on the root locus.
Also,

$$K'_o = 2.25 \times 3.55 \times 1.95 = 15.5$$

for these points.

(k) Rule 9 can be used to locate the $K'_o = 1$, 4, and 15.5 points on the third (real axis) branch of the root locus, i.e., for $K'_o = 4$, two characteristic equation root values are $(\pm j \times 1.414)$. From the characteristic equation,

$$\sum \text{roots} = -2$$

therefore $(\pm j \times 1.414) + \alpha_3 = -2$, and $\alpha_3 = -2$ where α_3 is the value of the third root for $K'_o = 4$.
  Thus $K'_o = 4$ can be located at -2 on the real axis. Similarly, $K'_o = 1$ can be located at -1, and $K'_o = 15.5$ can be located at -3.
(l) Sufficient data is now available to complete Fig. 7.15 with reasonable accuracy.
(m) It is apparent from Fig. 7.15 that the system
  (1) is stable for $K'_o < 4$ (all roots have negative real parts);
  (2) approaches instability as $K'_o \to 4$, i.e., becomes oscillatory;
  (3) is critically stable for $K'_o = 4$ (has two imaginary roots);
  (4) is unstable for $K'_o > 4$, i.e., has two characteristic equation roots with positive real parts.

Example 7.9: Sketch the root locus for the system whose open loop transfer function is

$$\frac{\theta_{on}}{\theta} = \frac{K'_o(D + 12)}{D^2(D + 20)}$$

Solution (Fig. 7.16): There are three open loop poles; one at -20 and two at 0, i.e., the double pole associated with D^2. There is one finite zero (-12). Hence two root locus branches start at 0 for $K_o' = 0$, while the third starts at -20 for $K_o' = 0$. One branch finishes at -12 for $K_o' = \infty$, while the other two branches finish at ∞.

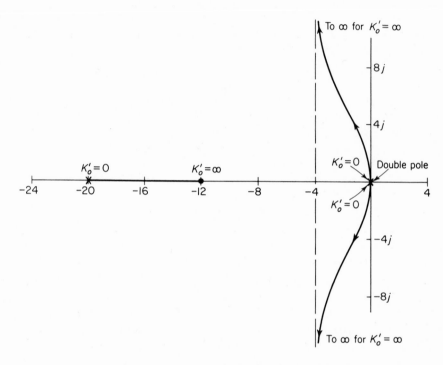

Fig. 7.16 Form of root locus for system whose open loop transfer function is

$$\frac{\theta_{on}}{\theta} = \frac{K_o'(D + 12)}{D^2(D + 20)}$$

The infinite zero asymptotes are located by

$$\alpha = \frac{\pm 180}{2} = \pm 90$$

$$\bar{x} = \frac{-20 - (-12)}{2} = -4$$

The root locus occupies the real axis only between -12 and -20. The root locus does not cut the imaginary axis.

7.7 USE OF THE SPIRULE

A number of aids to rapid plotting of root locus are available.* In particular, the Spirule technique[†] is widely used.

Root locus construction requires the ability to locate values of D which satisfy the angular criterion (Eq. 7.9). When the locus is drawn, it is scaled or calibrated for sensitivity by using the magnitude criterion (Eq. 7.7). It has been shown (Section 7.5.1) that both criteria can be applied graphically using only a rule and a protractor. The Spirule is essentially a protractor and rule combined into one unit.

Figure 7.17 shows the basic construction of a Spirule. A transparent arm (the rule) is attached to a transparent circular protractor so that it can be rotated around it. There is sufficient friction at the pivot so that arm and protractor can be rotated together when required.

To apply the angular criterion at a test point, i.e., to sum the angles of the lines drawn from all finite open loop zeros and poles to the point considered, proceed as follows:

(1) Place the eye of the Spirule over the test point, with the reference line R on the rule lying through 0° (Fig. 7.17a).
(2) Choose an open loop pole P_{o1} and rotate the Spirule assembly so that the line R lies through the pole (Fig. 7.17a).
(3) Either (a) if there are no finite open loop zeros, hold the protractor fixed and return the arm so that line R is horizontal through the test point (Fig. 7.17c); *or* (b) hold the protractor fixed and rotate the arm until line R coincides with an open loop zero (Fig. 7.17d).
(4) Rotate the assembly so that line R lies through the next pole.
(5) If there is more than one finite open loop zero, repeat 3(b). Otherwise repeat 3(a).
(6) Continue the process until all open loop singularities, i.e., poles or finite zeros, have been considered. The algebraic sum of the singularity angles, made according to the angular criterion, is then read as the angle where the reference line R cuts the protractor. If this angle is 180°, the test point is on the root locus. If not, make an interpolative second choice. In this manner, sufficient intermediate points can be obtained quickly to give an accurate root locus plot.

The scale on the rule is specially designed to permit the multiplication and division of vector magnitudes, as required for the scaling of root locus plots. To scale a point already established as being on the root locus, proceed as follows:

*See A. L. Bjorkstam, "Simplifying Root Locus Plotting," Parts 1 and 2, *Control Engineering* (March and April 1966); and J. E. Gibson, "A Dynamic Root Locus Plotter," *Control Engineering* (February 1956).
[†]Invented by W. R. Evans and manufactured by the Spirule Co., Whittier, Calif.

(1) Center the Spirule over the point, with the line R passing through 0°.
(2) Rotate the assembly until R passes through an open loop pole.
(3) Fix the protractor and rotate the arm until the curve S passes through the selected pole.

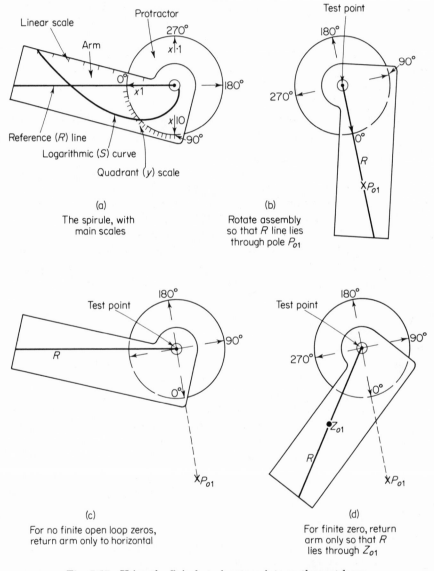

(a)

The spirule, with
main scales

(b)

Rotate assembly
so that R line lies
through pole P_{o1}

(c)

For no finite open loop zeros,
return arm only to horizontal

(d)

For finite zero, return
arm only so that R
lies through Z_{o1}

Fig. 7.17 Using the Spirule to locate points on the root locus.

(4) Repeat 2 and 3 for each open loop pole with the assembly in the condition after step 3.
(5) Rotate the assembly until the line S is on a finite zero.
(6) Fix the protractor and rotate the arm until R is over the zero.
(7) Repeat 5 and 6 until all zeros have been considered. On completion of this procedure, one of the three arrows (at 0°, 90°, and 270°) on the protractor will be on the mating quadrant scale on the arm. Read the scale and note which arrow is used, i.e., $x0.1$, $x1$ or $x10$. The open loop sensitivity is then

$$K'_o = A^n \cdot yx$$

where y is the quadrant scale reading; x is the factor associated with the protractor arrow (0.1, 1, or 10); A is a constant relating the Spirule scale to the scale of the root locus plot being made; n is $N_p - N_z$, the number of open loop poles minus the number of open loop zeros. The plot scale number, A, corresponds to the length 0 to 1 on the linear scale on the upper side of the Spirule arm. Thus A is 10 if the root locus is drawn to the scale 10 = length 0 to 1, i.e., 5 inches, on the linear Spirule scale.

7.8 FREQUENCY RESPONSE DATA FROM ROOT LOCUS

Though directly associated with the time domain and the transient component of system response, the root locus plot can be used to obtain frequency response data of the system. For given values of the system constants (and hence for a particular value of open loop gain or sensitivity) a root locus displays the values of the roots of the system's characteristic equation. The connection between the root locus and frequency response analysis will be shown through the following example.

Example 7.10: Consider Example 7.8, the root locus of which is shown in Fig. 7.15. The nondimensional system transfer function is

$$\frac{\theta_{on}}{\theta_i} = \frac{K'_o}{D(D^2 + 2D + 2) + K'_o}$$

For $K'_o = 1$, the transfer function becomes

$$\frac{\theta_{on}}{\theta_i} = \frac{1}{D^3 + 2D^2 + 2D + 1}$$

From the root locus (Fig. 7.15), the roots of the characteristic equation for $K'_o = 1$

are -1, $(-\frac{1}{2} + j \times 0.9)$, and $(-\frac{1}{2} - j \times 0.9)$. Hence the system transfer function can be written

$$\frac{\theta_{on}}{\theta_i} = \frac{1}{(D + 1)(D + \frac{1}{2} - j \times 0.9)(D + \frac{1}{2} + j \times 0.9)}$$

As established in Chapter 5, frequency response data (magnitude ratio and phase) can be obtained by substituting $j\omega$ for D in this expression, and evaluating it as a phasor on the complex plane. Consider now a factor $D + \alpha$, with $j\omega$ for D to give $j\omega + \alpha$. This factor can be represented on the $j\omega$ plane as shown in Fig. 7.18(a). The phasor $j\omega + \alpha$ can be represented also by the vector drawn from $-\alpha$ to $j\omega$, as shown in Fig. 7.18(b).

Figure 7.18(c) shows the application of the foregoing idea to the present example for $\omega = 0$. Vectors are drawn from the root value points -1, $(-\frac{1}{2} \pm j \times 0.9)$ to the origin for $\omega = 0$, $j\omega = 0$. Then,

$$\text{magnitude ratio} \quad G_n = \left|\frac{\theta_{on}}{\theta_i}\right|_{j\omega} = \frac{1}{1 \times 1 \times 1} = 1$$

and

$$\text{phase} \quad \phi_n = 0 - 0 - 60 + 60 = 0°$$

For $\omega = 1$, $j\omega = j1$ (Fig. 7.17d),

$$G_n = \frac{1}{1.4 \times 0.5 \times 2} = 0.715$$

$$\phi_n = -45 - 10 - 75 = -130°$$

The procedure can be repeated for sufficient values of ω to give the G_n-ω and ϕ_n-ω frequency response curves. The procedure can be applied for any selected value of K_o'. Note that the frequency response data obtained applies to the non-dimensionalized system transfer function. The characteristics will apply to the system transfer function only if the real system has unity negative feedback, in which case $\theta_{on} \equiv \theta_o$.

The reader can satisfy himself on the applicability of this method by completing the present example and by comparing his curves with those obtained by conventional frequency response analysis.

7.9 SUMMARY

A root locus branch shows the path of all possible values of one root of a system's characteristic equation. A root locus plot consists of the separate paths of all roots of the characteristic equation. A convenient system parameter is varied to cause the roots to vary. It is common to select a parameter which can be varied in a real situation. It is also common to

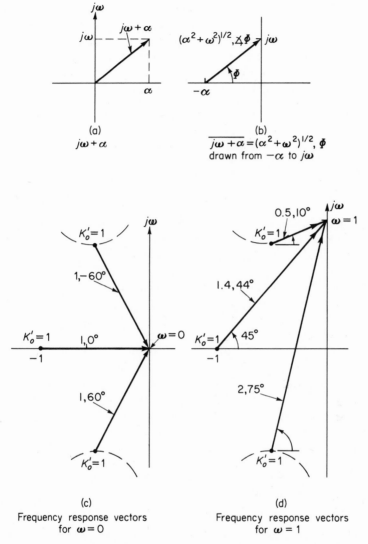

Fig. 7.18 Frequency response data from root locus (system $\theta_{on}/\theta = K'_o/(D^3 + 2D^2 + 2D)$ with $K'_o = 1$; cf. Fig. 7.14).

plot the root locus against the open loop sensivity; however, any constant which appears in this parameter can be used. The root locus actually gives the values of the roots of a system's characteristic equation for all values of the parameter against which the plot is made.

The relationship between a system's open loop transfer function and its system transfer function is utilized to produce the root locus plot of a system. The plot is made from the open loop transfer function, which is normally considerably simpler to handle than the system transfer function; but the plots obtained pertain to the closed loop system.

A set of easily applied rules has been developed from which a root locus plot can be quickly obtained. The basic origins of the rules are as follows:

(a) The root locus branches start at the poles of a system's open loop transfer function, and end at the zeros.
(b) The angle associated with the open loop vector is 180° for any root of the system's characteristic equation.
(c) The magnitude of the open loop vector is unity, for any root of the characteristic equation.

Apart from locating critical points, slopes, and asymptotes by these rules, points on a root locus are located by judicious trial and error. With experience, this can be a rapid process. There are a number of techniques and devices which aid rapid plotting. The Spirule is a particularly useful aid to trial-and-error location of intermediate points on a root locus.

Root locus techniques are particularly useful in the design stages of the development of a system, when there is still room for choice in the values of system constants. The root locus illustrates clearly the effects of the values of such constants on system stability and on the nature of its response to input disturbances (oscillatory, heavily damped, etc.).

For the root locus technique to be readily applied, a system's open loop transfer function must be in factored form, containing only first-order factors $(D + \alpha)$ and/or second-order factors $(D + k\,D^2 + k_2)$. When obtained from a basic analysis of a system, the open loop transfer function is normally in such a form.

While the root locus method is essentially a time domain or transient technique, it can be directly associated with the frequency response methods, i.e., a frequency domain, steady-state technique. Frequency response data (magnitude ratio and phase for selected frequencies) can be obtained directly from a root locus plot.

PROBLEMS

7.1 Find the poles and finite zeros of the following equations and transfer functions:

(a) $D(D^2 + 3D + 2)$ (b) $(3D + 1)(2D + 3D + 4)$

(c) $\dfrac{10}{(3D+1)(0.5D+1)(D+1)}$ (d) $\dfrac{6D(D+3)}{D^2+3D+2}$

(e) $\dfrac{K(\frac{1}{2}D+1)}{D^2(4D+1)(3D+2D+1)}$

Answers: (a) zeros at $D = 0, -2, -1$;   (b) zeros at $D = -\frac{1}{3}, -\frac{4}{5}$;
(c) poles at $D = -1, -2, -\frac{1}{3}$;   (d) zeros at $0, -3$; poles at $-2, -1$;
(e) zeros at $D = -2$; poles at $0, 0, -\frac{1}{4}, -\frac{1}{5}$.

7.2 Sketch the root locus of the system whose open loop transfer function is

$$\frac{K_o(\frac{1}{4}D+1)}{D(\frac{1}{2}D+1)}$$

7.3 Sketch the root locus for the system of Fig. 7.19.

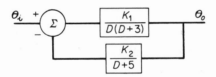

Fig. 7.19

7.4 Sketch the root locus of the system whose open loop transfer function is

$$\frac{\theta_{on}}{\theta} = \frac{K_o'}{D(D+3)(D^2+6D+64)}$$

7.5 Construct the root locus for the system shown in Fig. 7.20. Scale the diagram with values of constant K.

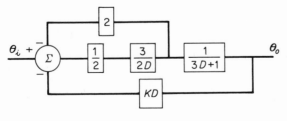

Fig. 7.20

7.6 A system with unity negative feedback has the transfer function

$$\frac{\theta_o}{\theta_i} = \frac{K}{D(D+2)(D+4)(D+6)+K}$$

Construct the root locus of the system.

7.7 Obtain an accurate root locus plot of the system the open loop transfer function of which is

$$\frac{\theta_{on}}{\theta} = \frac{K_o'(D+4)}{D^2 + 4D + 20}$$

8   *System characteristics from*
open loop data

8.1 INTRODUCTION

Stability is the first requirement to be satisfied in the analysis of engineering systems. If it is established that a system is unstable, then further performance analysis is pointless. After a system is shown to be stable, it is usually necessary to examine further the nature of the response of the system. One of the most useful analytical procedures is to examine stability with the Nyquist criterion and, if satisfactory, to then study the nature of the system by obtaining its frequency response characteristics.

Application of the Nyquist criterion requires evaluation of the frequency response characteristic of the system's open loop transfer function. The system frequency response characteristics can be evaluated from the closed loop system transfer function, which is considerably more complicated than the corresponding open loop transfer function.

By utilizing the relationship between a system's open loop and closed loop transfer functions, graphic procedures can be used to obtain the (closed loop) system frequency response directly from open loop frequency response data. Thus evaluation of the simple open loop data enables examination of both the system's stability condition and its closed loop frequency response characteristic.

Several methods for utilizing open loop data to obtain system characteristics will now be presented.

8.2 THE RELATIONSHIP BETWEEN OPEN LOOP AND SYSTEM TRANSFER FUNCTIONS

Figure 8.1(a) shows the basic normalized representation of a negative feedback system, discussed in detail in Section 6.5.2. Recall that the normalized system response θ_{on} equals the actual system response θ_o only for a unity negative feedback system. In general, θ_{on} and θ_o are related by

$$\theta_o = \frac{\theta_{on}}{H(D)}$$

where $H(D)$ is the feedback transfer function.

Now, the error which actuates the control system is

$$\theta = \theta_i - \theta_{on} \tag{8.1}$$

For frequency response (harmonic) analysis, Eq. 8.1 is a vector relationship which can be represented by the vector triangle QOP shown in Fig. 8.1(b).

Each vector of Fig. 8.1(b) can be divided by the magnitude θ to yield the vector relationship of Fig. 8.1(c):

$$\frac{\theta}{\theta} = 1 = \frac{\theta_i}{\theta} - \frac{\theta_{on}}{\theta}$$

Selecting point O as the origin,

(1) point Q becomes $(-1, 0)$;
(2) $OP = \theta_{on}/\theta$, and the locus of P for various values of ω is the open loop frequency response plot (Nyquist diagram), G_o and ϕ_o versus ω;
(3) $QP = \theta_i/\theta$, drawn from $(-1, 0)$ to the open loop locus, represents the closed-loop system input θ_i;
(4) $$\left|\frac{OP}{QP}\right| = \left|\frac{\theta_{on}/\theta}{\theta_i/\theta}\right| = \left|\frac{\theta_{on}}{\theta_i}\right|$$

represents the normalized closed loop system frequency response magnitude ratio G_n, for the value of frequency associated with the point P;
(5) the angle between the input and response vectors $Q\hat{P}O$ is the normalized system phase lag $-\phi_n$ for the value of ω associated with P, i.e., $\hat{\theta}_i - \hat{\theta}_o$.

$G_n = G$ and $\phi_n = \phi$, where G and ϕ are the actual system frequency response characteristics, only for unity negative feedback systems. In general,

$$G = \frac{G_n}{G_H} \quad \text{and} \quad \phi = \phi_n - \phi_H \qquad (8.2)$$

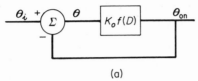

(a)

Basic normalized feedback diagram

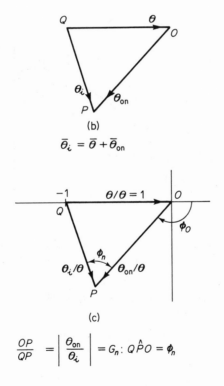

(b)

$$\bar{\theta}_i = \bar{\theta} + \bar{\theta}_{on}$$

(c)

$$\frac{OP}{QP} = \left| \frac{\theta_{on}}{\theta_i} \right| = G_n : Q\hat{P}O = \phi_n$$

Fig. 8.1 Frequency response relationships between open loop and closed loop transfer functions.

where G_H and ϕ_H are respectively the magnitude and phase associated with the feedback transfer function.

Obviously, the foregoing technique for getting system data from open loop data is most directly applied to unity negative feedback systems. However, feedback transfer functions are usually relatively simple and it is often an easy matter to adjust a derived G_n and ϕ_n versus ω relationship to a corresponding G and ϕ versus ω form.

Example 8.1: Obtain several values of system frequency response data for the system of Example 6.11 (Fig. 6.12).

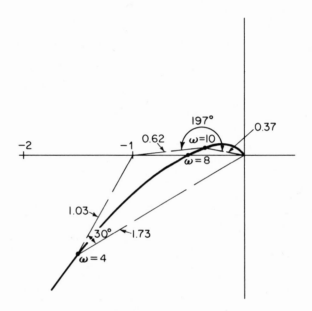

Fig. 8.2 Getting system frequency response data from the Nyquist (open loop) diagram (cf. previous Example 6.11; Fig. 6.12).

Solution: Figure 8.2 shows the partial Nyquist plot reproduced from Fig. 6.12. For $\omega = 4$,

$$G_n = \frac{1.73}{1.03} = 1.67; \quad \phi_n = -30°$$

For $\omega = 8$,

$$G_n = \frac{0.5}{0.5} = 1; \quad \phi_n = -180°$$

For $\omega = 10$,

$$G_n = \frac{0.37}{0.62} = 0.6; \quad \phi_n = -197°$$

From a more complete Nyquist plot, the complete G_n, ϕ_n–ω data could be obtained, and the full normalized system frequency response curve plotted.

8.3 CONSTANT CONTOURS OF SYSTEM MAGNITUDE RATIO AND PHASE ON THE NYQUIST PLANE

Substituting $j\omega$ for D in an open loop transfer function can always yield a simple complex number, $\theta_{on}/\theta = x + jy$.

For example,

$$\frac{\theta_{on}}{\theta} = \frac{K_o(1 + T_1 D)}{D(1 + T_2 D)}; \quad \left(\frac{\theta_{on}}{\theta}\right)_{j\omega} = \frac{K_o(1 + j\omega T_1)}{j\omega(1 + j\omega T_2)}$$

$$= \frac{K_o(1 + j\omega T_1)}{-\omega^2 T_2 + j\omega} = \frac{K_o(1 + j\omega T_1)}{-\omega^2 T_2 + j\omega} \cdot \frac{-\omega^2 T_2 - j\omega}{-\omega^2 T_2 - j\omega}$$

$$= \frac{K_o[\omega(T_1 - T_2) - j(1 - \omega^2 T_1 T_2)]}{\omega(1 - \omega^2 T_2^2)}$$

$$= x + jy$$

where

$$x = \frac{K_o(T_1 - T_2)}{(1 - \omega^2 T_2^2)}; \quad y = \frac{(\omega^2 T_1 T_2 - 1) K_o}{\omega(1 - \omega^2 T_2^2)}$$

The Nyquist plot can be made with this method by evaluating x and y for various values of ω and locating points on the complex plane.

Now, the normalized system transfer function has been shown to be

$$\frac{\theta_{on}}{\theta_i} = \frac{\theta_{on}/\theta}{1 + \theta_{on}/\theta} = \frac{x + jy}{1 + (x + jy)} = \frac{x + jy}{(1 + x) + jy}$$

The magnitude ratio G_n and phase ϕ_n can be written

$$G_n = \left|\frac{\theta_{on}}{\theta_i}\right|_{j\omega} = \left[\frac{x^2 + y^2}{(x + 1)^2 + y^2}\right]^{1/2} \tag{8.3}$$

$$\phi_n = \tan^{-1}\frac{y}{x} - \tan^{-1}\frac{y}{x + 1} \tag{8.4}$$

Constant G_n contours

Squaring both sides of Eq. 8.3 and cross-multiplying,

$$G_n^2 (x^2 + 2x + 1 + y^2) = x^2 + y^2$$

Gathering terms,

$$x^2(G_n^2 - 1) + 2xG_n^2 + G_n^2 + y^2(G_n^2 - 1) = 0$$

and

$$x^2 + \frac{2G_n^2}{G_n^2 - 1}x + y^2 = -\frac{G_n^2}{G_n^2 - 1} = \frac{G_n^2}{1 - G_n^2}$$

The x terms can be adjusted to yield

$$\left[\left(x + \frac{G_n^2}{G_n^2 - 1}\right)^2 - \left(\frac{G_n^2}{G_n^2 - 1}\right)^2\right] + y^2 = \frac{G_n^2}{1 - G_n^2}$$

and

$$\left(x + \frac{G_n^2}{G_n^2 - 1}\right)^2 + y^2 = \frac{G_n^2}{1 - G_n^2} + \left(\frac{G_n^2}{G_n^2 - 1}\right)^2 = \left(\frac{G_n}{G_n^2 - 1}\right)^2 \quad (8.5)$$

Equation 8.5 is the equation of a circle of radius

$$\frac{G_n}{G_n^2 - 1}$$

the center of which lies at

$$x_o = -\frac{G_n^2}{G_n^2 - 1} = \frac{G_n^2}{1 - G_n^2}; \quad y_o = 0$$

Hence contours of constant G_n on the Nyquist plane are a family of circles of radii $G_n/(G_n^2 - 1)$ and centers $G_n^2/(1 - G_n^2)$, 0. Figure 8.3(a) shows the constant G_n circles. An open loop frequency plot (Nyquist diagram for positive ω) plotted on Fig. 8.3 would cut a number of the G_n circles, giving the value of G_n at the frequency at which the intersection is made. The open loop plot of Fig. 8.2 is shown in Fig. 8.3. It can be seen that $G_n \approx 1.67$ for $\omega = 4$, as found in Example 8.1 (Fig. 8.2).

Constant ϕ_n contours

Using the identity $\tan^{-1} A - \tan^{-1} B = \tan^{-1}[(A - B)/(1 + AB)]$, Eq. 8.4 can be written

$$\phi_n = \tan^{-1} \frac{y/x - y/(x + 1)}{1 + y/x \cdot y/(x + 1)} = \tan^{-1} \frac{y}{x^2 + x + y^2}$$

$$\therefore \tan \phi_n = \frac{y}{x^2 + x + y^2}$$

Cross-multiplying, and dividing throughout by $\tan \phi_n$,

$$x^2 + x + y^2 - \frac{y}{\tan \phi_n} = 0$$

Adding $\frac{1}{4} + (1/2\tan \phi_n)^2$ to both sides

$$\left(x^2 + x + \frac{1}{4}\right) + \left[y^2 - \frac{y}{\tan \phi_n} + \left(\frac{1}{2 \tan \phi_n}\right)^2\right]$$

$$= \frac{1}{4} + \left(\frac{1}{2 \tan \phi_n}\right)^2 = \frac{1}{4}\left[1 + \left(\frac{1}{\tan \phi_n}\right)^2\right]$$

and

$$\left(x + \frac{1}{2}\right)^2 + \left(y - \frac{1}{2 \tan \phi_n}\right)^2 = \frac{1}{4}\left[1 + \left(\frac{1}{\tan \phi_n}\right)^2\right]$$

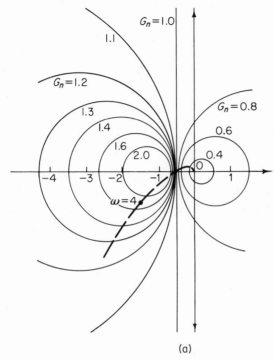

(a)

Circles of constant system magnitude ratio

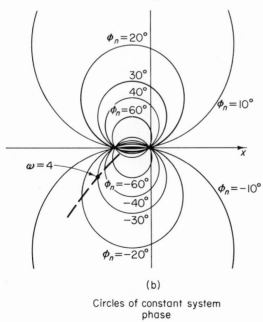

(b)

Circles of constant system
phase

Fig. 8.3 Contours of constant G_n and ϕ_n on Nyquist plane.

which is the equation of a circle the center of which is at

$$x = -\frac{1}{2}; \quad y = \frac{1}{2 \tan \phi_n}$$

and the radius of which is

$$\frac{1}{2}\left[1 + \left(\frac{1}{\tan \phi_n}\right)^2\right]^{1/2}$$

Thus contours of constant ϕ_n on the Nyquist plane are a family of circles, as shown in Fig. 8.3(b). The open loop plot of Fig. 8.2 is also shown in Fig. 8.3(b), and it is seen that ϕ_n is $-30°$ for $\omega = 4$, as shown in Example 8.1.

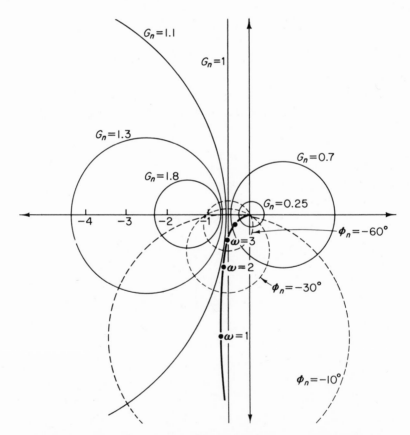

Fig. 8.4 Using G_n and ϕ_n circles to get system frequency response data from the Nyquist plot.

If the constant G_n and constant ϕ_n circles are printed on (or overlayed on, or underlayed on) a system's polar open loop (Nyquist) frequency response locus,

(1) the stability condition is apparent by the Nyquist criterion;
(2) the normalized system magnitude ratio G_n and phase ϕ_n for various values of frequency are readily read off the plot, and can be plotted separately to yield the normalized system's frequency response characteristic.

Example 8.2: A unity negative feedback system has the open loop transfer function

$$\frac{3}{D(0.05D + 1)(0.2D + 1)}$$

Use constant magnitude ratio and phase circles to ascertain the maximum sytems magnitude ratio and the phase angle corresponding to it.

Solution: Figure 8.4 shows part of the system's Nyquist plot, which indicates that the system represented is stable. For unity negative feedback,

$$\theta_o = \theta_{on}; \quad G = G_n; \quad \phi = \phi_n$$

where G and ϕ are the system magnitude ratio and phase.

The open loop locus just touches the $G = 1.1$ circle at $\omega = 2.5$ rad/sec. Hence $G = 1.1$ is the maximum system magnitude ratio; $\phi = -55°$ at $\omega = 2.5$ rad/sec (from constant ϕ circles).

8.4 *CONSTANT CONTOURS ON THE INVERSE NYQUIST PLANE*

The stability condition of a negative feedback system can be examined using the frequency response locus of the *inverse* of the system's open loop transfer function. This technique is sometimes used instead of the direct Nyquist plot, because the contours of constant system magnitude ratio and phase are a much simpler family of concentric circles and radial straight lines respectively, as shown in Fig. 8.5. The Nyquist point $(-1, 0)$ is the center for the G circles and for the radial straight lines of constant ϕ.

For $\theta_{on}/\theta = K_o f(D)$, the inverse is $\theta/\theta_{on} = [K_o f(D)]^{-1}$ and

$$G_o^{-1} = \left|\frac{\theta_{on}}{\theta}\right|^{-1} = \left|\frac{\theta}{\theta_{on}}\right|; \quad \phi_o^{-1} = \tan^{-1}[f(j\omega)]^{-1}$$

where ϕ_o^{-1} is the angle whose tangent is the inverse of that for ϕ_o.

Example: A system has the open loop transfer function

$$\frac{\theta_{on}}{\theta} = \frac{K_o}{(1 + T_1 D)(1 + T_2 D)}$$

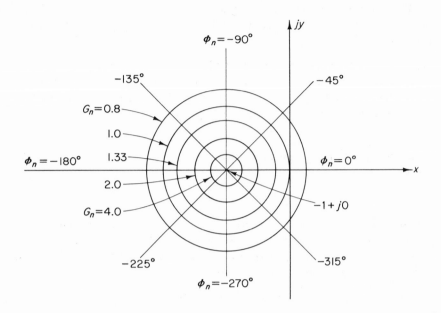

Fig. 8.5 Contours of constant system magnitude ratio and phase on the inverse Nyquist plane. Constant G_n contours are circles, radius $1/G_n^2$, center $(-1, 0)$

$$(x + 1)^2 + y^2 = 1/G_n^2$$

Constant ϕ_n contours are straight lines radiating from $(-1, 0)$

$$\phi_n = -\tan^{-1} \frac{y}{x + 1}$$

The inverse is

$$\frac{\theta}{\theta_{on}} = \frac{(1 + T_1 D)(1 + T_2 D)}{K_o}$$

The inverse open loop magnitude ratio is

$$G_o^{-1} = \frac{(1 + \omega^2 T_1^2)^{1/2}(1 + \omega^2 T_2^2)^{1/2}}{K_o}$$

The inverse open loop phase is

$$\phi_o^{-1} = \tan^{-1} \omega T_1 + \tan^{-1} \omega T_2$$

Figure 8.6 shows the form of the G_o^{-1}, ϕ_o^{-1} versus ω polar plot, including negative values of ω, which is known as the inverse Nyquist plot for the system.

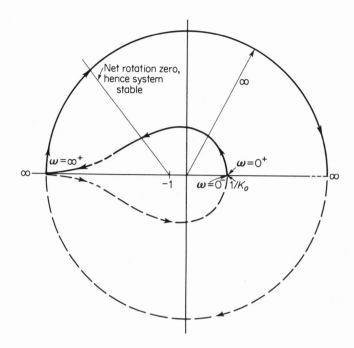

Fig. 8.6 Inverse Nyquist plot for $\theta_{on}/\theta = K_o/(1 + T_1 D)(1 + T_2 D)$.

The point $(-1, 0)$ is not enclosed by the plot and hence the system represented is stable.

If the constant G circles and the constant ϕ radial lines were drawn superimposed on Fig. 8.6, values of G and ϕ for selected values of ω could be easily read.

It is left to the reader to develop this alternative technique further.

8.5 CONSTANT CONTOURS ON LOGARITHMIC PLANES—THE NICHOLS CHART

Frequency response data (system, or open loop) can be plotted on Cartesian coordinates of magnitude ratio and phase, with frequency as a parameter on the curves. Figure 8.7 shows one form of phase-gain plot for the generalized simple second-order system, with magnitude ratio expressed in decibels. It should be recognized that Fig. 8.7 is only a variation of previous Figs. 5.6 and 5.13, which contained the same data in polar and Bode forms respectively.

Figure 8.8 shows the open loop frequency response data of Example 6.11 (Fig. 6.12) in a convenient phase-gain form known as a **Nichols plot.**

Contours of constant system magnitude ratio and phase can be developed for the Nichols plane in the same way as the constant G and ϕ circles were developed in Section 7.3 for the Nyquist plane. As before, the constant

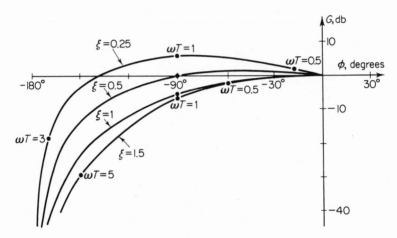

Fig. 8.7 Frequency response characteristics of the system

$$\frac{\theta_o}{K\theta_i} = \frac{1}{T^2 D^2 + 2\xi T D + 1}$$

for various values of ξ, in a phase-gain form.

contours will be for system magnitude ratio and phase if the particular system being investigated is a unity negative feedback system, but will be for normalized system magnitude ratio and phase if the system has a nonunity feedback transfer function.

For the Nichols coordinates of Fig. 8.8, it is necessary to express G_n and ϕ_n as functions of G_o and ϕ_o. For frequency response analysis only, the closed loop and open loop system transfer functions can be expressed

$$\left(\frac{\theta_{on}}{\theta_i}\right)_{j\omega} = G_n e^{j\phi_n} \tag{1}$$

$$\left(\frac{\theta_{on}}{\theta}\right)_{j\omega} = G_o e^{j\phi_o} \tag{2}$$

Also,

$$\frac{\theta_{on}}{\theta_i} = \frac{\theta_{on}/\theta}{1 + \theta_{on}/\theta} = \frac{G_o e^{j\phi_o}}{1 + G_o e^{j\phi_o}} = \frac{1}{e^{-j\phi_o}/G_o + 1}$$

$$= \frac{1}{1 + (\cos \phi_o)/G_o - (j \sin \phi_o)/G_o}$$

as $e^{-j\phi_o} = \cos\phi_o - j\sin\phi_o$.

$$\therefore G_n = \left|\frac{\theta_{on}}{\theta_i}\right|_{j\omega} = \frac{1}{\left(1 + \dfrac{2\cos\phi_o}{G_o} + \dfrac{\cos^2\phi_o}{G_o^2} + \dfrac{\sin^2\phi_o}{G_o^2}\right)^{1/2}}$$

$$= \left(1 + \frac{2\cos\phi_o}{G_o} + \frac{1}{G_o^2}\right)^{-1/2} \tag{3}$$

as $\cos^2\phi_o + \sin^2\phi_o = 1$.

Also,

$$\phi_n = -\tan^{-1}\frac{-(\sin\phi_o)/G_o}{1 + (\cos\phi_o)/G_o} = -\tan^{-1}\frac{-\sin\phi_o}{G_o + \cos\phi_o} \tag{4}$$

Equations (3) and (4) describe G_n and ϕ_n as functions of G_o and ϕ_o, and contours of constant G_n and of constant ϕ_n can be plotted onto the G_o, ϕ_o plane. For example, select a value for G_n and use it in Equation (3) to yield $G_o = f(\phi_o)$. For various values of ϕ_o, G_o can be evaluated and

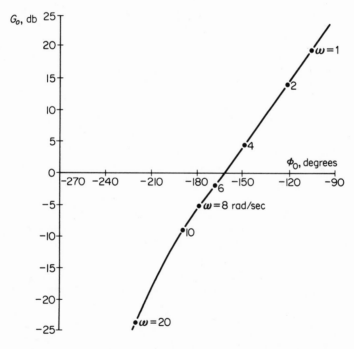

Fig. 8.8 Frequency response characteristic, in Nichols plot form, of the open loop transfer function

$$\frac{\theta_{on}}{\theta} = \frac{10}{D(1 + D/4)(1 + D/16)}$$

(cf. previous Example 6.11; Fig. 6.12).

the contour of constant G_n plotted. Constant phase contours are similarly developed.

Figure 8.9 shows contours of constant G_n and ϕ_n on the Nichols plane. Such a contour chart is called a **Nichols chart.** The Nichols chart is the

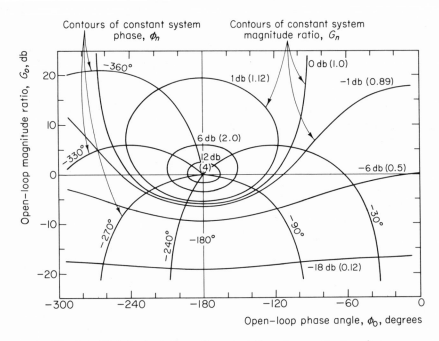

Fig. 8.9 Nichols chart: lines of constant G_n and ϕ_n on G_o, db–ϕ_o° plane.

most widely used of the constant contour techniques for obtaining system frequency response characteristics from open loop data used for the Nyquist plot.

It should be realized that the Nichols chart coordinates of G_o, db and ϕ_o° are a convenience. Phase-gain plots can be made with linear scales of G_o or with plain log scales rather than db. Whatever form of G_o–ϕ_o plot is desired, lines of constant G_n and ϕ_n can be added.

Example 8.3: A system has the open loop transfer function

$$\frac{\theta_{on}}{\theta} = \frac{10}{D(1 + D/4)(1 + D/16)}$$

Use a Nichols chart to obtain the normalized frequency response characteristics of the system.

Solution: The open loop frequency response data is given with Fig. 6.12 (Example 6.11), and was plotted in Fig. 8.8. Figure 8.10(a) shows the data plotted on a Nichols chart.

Consider the point $\omega = 6$ rad/sec. The G_o–ϕ_o curve cuts the constant contour G_n, db = 9.5 at this point. It also cuts the constant contour $\phi_n = -120°$ at $\omega = 6$.

Thus $G_n = 3$ (9.5, db) and $\phi_n = -120°$ for $\omega = 6$, to yield a point on the system frequency response, shown in Bode form in Fig. 8.10(b).

Figure 8.10(b) can be completed by observing the values of G_n and ϕ_n for selected values of ω on the G_o–ϕ_o curve.

8.6 STABILITY FROM THE NICHOLS PLOT

A system's stability condition is immediately recognizable from its Nichols plot. For the types of system covered in this text, it was shown in Section 6.5.7 that for the system to be stable,

(a) open loop magnitude ratio must be less than 1 when open loop phase is $-180°$;

(b) open loop phase lag must be less than 180° when open loop magnitude ratio is 1.

These conditions were described by gain margin and phase margin, as defined in Fig. 6.14.

Conditions (a) and (b) applied to the Nichols plot become

(c) G_o, db < 0, (i.e., G_o, db negative) for $\phi_o = -180°$;

(d) $\phi_o > -180°$ when G_o, db $= 0$ ($\phi_o > -180°$ means phase lag $< 180°$).

It is readily seen that the system whose open loop data is shown in Fig. 8.10(a) is stable. It should be apparent that the system whose open loop frequency response curve is shown in Fig. 8.11 is unstable. Thus:

> **A system is stable if its Nichols plot passes to the right of the point G_o, db $= 0$, $\phi_o = -180°$.**

For a conditionally stable system of the form illustrated in Fig. 6.16, the Nichols plot cuts the $\phi_o = -180°$ axis in several places, as shown in Figs. 8.12(a), (b), and (c). It follows that

(1) for case (a), the system is unstable and corresponds to the Nyquist point being at point *a* in Fig. 6.16;

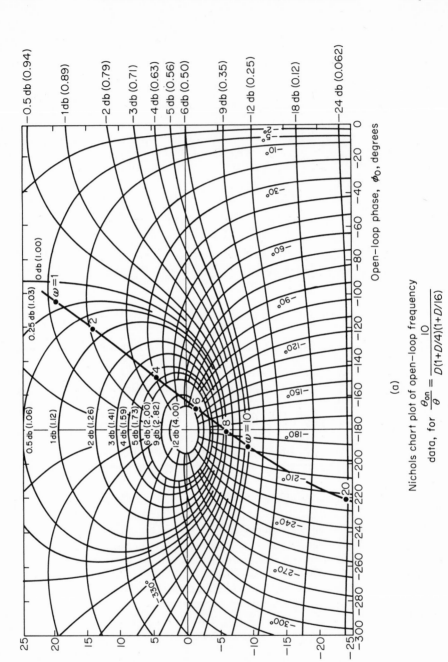

Nichols chart plot of open-loop frequency

data, for $\dfrac{\theta_{on}}{\theta} = \dfrac{10}{D(1+D/4)(1+D/16)}$

(a)

(2) for case (b), the system is stable and corresponds to the Nyquist point being at c in Fig. 6.16;

(3) for case (c), the system is unstable and corresponds to the Nyquist point being at e in Fig. 6.16.

The measurement of gain and phase margins from open loop plots in which G_o is measured in decibels was discussed in Section 6.5.9. It should be apparent that phase and gain margins are directly measurable as shown in Fig. 8.13, with ϕ_m positive in the sense shown and a db positive in the sense shown.

8.7 SUMMARY

The relationship between a system's closed loop and open loop transfer functions has been used to yield the system frequency response charac-

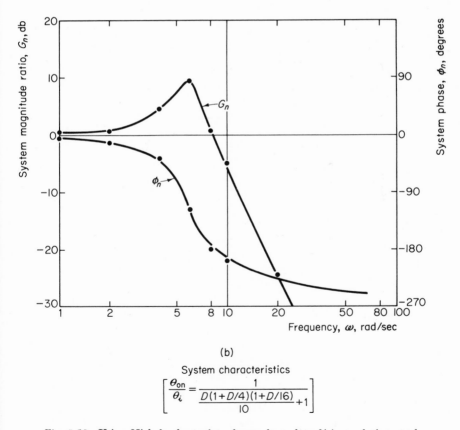

(b)

System characteristics

$$\left[\frac{\theta_{on}}{\theta_i} = \frac{1}{\dfrac{D(1+D/4)(1+D/16)}{10} + 1} \right]$$

Fig. 8.10   Using Nichols chart plot of open loop data [(a), *on facing page*] to get system frequency response characteristics [(b), *above*].

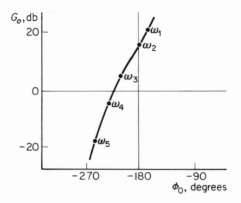

Fig. 8.11   Nichols plot of an unstable system.

teristics directly from the open loop frequency response data. The technique is very useful, as the open loop data can be used to investigate stability via the Nyquist criterion. If a system is stable, the next requirement is to examine its performance characteristics. It is commonly adequate to obtain its frequency response characteristic.

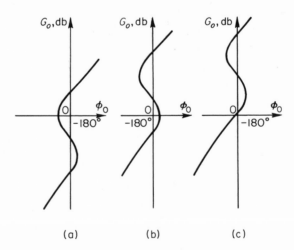

(a)   (b)   (c)

Fig. 8.12   Nichols plots of a conditionally stable system of form

$$\frac{\theta_{on}}{\theta_o} = \frac{K_o f_1(D)}{D^n f_2(D)}$$

in which only K_o varies: (a) for K_{o1}, system is unstable; (b) for K_{o2} ($> K_{o1}$), system is stable; (c) for K_{o3} ($> K_{o2}$), system is unstable.

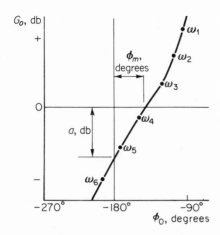

Fig. 8.13   Gain margin (a) and phase margin (ϕ_m) Nichols plot: a and ϕ_m are both positive in the sense shown.

Several variations of the open loop versus closed loop frequency response relationships exist. The most convenient is the Nichols plot, on which the open loop magnitude ratio expressed in decibels is plotted against open loop phase, with frequency as a parameter on the curve. Contours of constant system magnitude ratio and phase are projected onto the open loop plot and are used to directly read values of system magnitude ratio and phase. The logarithmic nature of the Nichols plot enables ready study of the effects of changes in a system's open loop gain constant, as multiplication of magnitudes become simple additions on the log plot. Stability condition, gain margin, and phase margin are readily interpreted directly from the Nichols plot. The Nichols plot is particularly useful in attempts to improve system performance and will be used for this purpose in Chapter 9.

PROBLEMS

8.1 Plot families of (a) constant system magnitude ratio circles, and (b) constant system phase angle circles, on the Nyquist plane and use them to obtain the closed loop system frequency response characteristics of the system the open loop transfer function of which is

$$\frac{\theta_{on}}{\theta} = \frac{10}{D(1 + D/4)(1 + D/16)}$$

(Example 6.11, Fig. 6.12).

8.2 Solve Problem 8.1 on the inverse Nyquist plane.

8.3 Plot the contours of the following on the Nichols plane:

(a) $G_n = -0.5$　(b) $G_n = 1$　　(c) $G_n = 2$

(d) $\phi_n = -10°$　(e) $\phi_n = -120°$

8.4 Use a Nichols plot to investigate the stability of the system the open loop transfer function of which is

$$\frac{\theta_{on}}{\theta} = \frac{6(1 + 3D)}{D(1 + 2D)(1 + 4D)}$$

Give gain and phase margins. If stable, use a Nichols chart to get the system frequency response characteristics.

8.5 Using a Nichols plot, investigate the stability of the system the open loop transfer function of which is

$$\frac{\theta_{on}}{\theta} = \frac{1000(1 + 0.1D)(1 + 0.05D)}{D^2(1 + 0.2D)(1 + 0.01D)(1 + 0.005D)}$$

If the system is stable: (a) give its gain margin and phase margin; and (b) use the Nichols chart to obtain the system's frequency response characteristics. (*Note:* Assume the system to have unity negative feedback. Take G_o, ϕ_o–ω data from Fig. 6.19.)

9 *Improving system performance*

9.1 *INTRODUCTION*

Chapters 1 through 8 provide the basic techniques required for the analysis of linear feedback systems. In summary, the reader should be able to do the following:

(a) write the dynamic mathematical relationships (models) of basic engineering phenomena;
(b) form from these the dynamic relationships which describe each component of a control system;
(c) combine the models of the components of a system formed by a series of interconnected components, to provide the dynamic relationship describing the system;
(d) establish the response characteristics of a component or a complete system by studying its response to input disturbances of known form;
(e) use the highly developed frequency response technique to describe the dynamic nature of a component or a complete system;
(f) investigate the stability condition of a component or a system by

(1) investigating the condition of the roots of the appropriate characteristic equation,

(2) applying the Routh criterion, and

(3) applying the Nyquist criterion (frequency response technique);

(g) use the root locus technique to examine the nature of a system as a particular system parameter is varied;

(h) understand the meaning and significance of the open loop characteristics of the closed loop system being examined. Application of the Nyquist stability criterion, and the root locus technique, are based on a system's open loop transfer function;

(i) obtain closed loop system frequency response characteristics directly from the system's Nyquist diagram or root locus plot.

Most of the work presented has been directed toward examining the performance characteristics of systems in which all parameters are given. A system as originally designed may prove to be inadequate due to one of the following factors:

(a) its stability condition — it may be unstable, or too oscillatory;

(b) its speed of response — it may be too slow or too fast;

(c) its accuracy — it may contain excessive steady-state errors between the actual and desired values of the controlled variable;

The effect on performance of varying the values of one or more system parameters has been introduced at several points; for example,

(1) the effect of damping ratio on the response of simple second-order systems was discussed;

(2) the effect on system stability of varying a system constant was examined with both the Routh and Nyquist criteria;

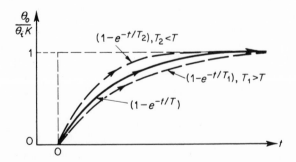

Fig. 9.1 Response of the system $\theta_o/\theta_i = K/(1 + T D)$ to step change in θ_i, for several values of T.

(3) the root locus technique requires that at least one system parameter (commonly the open loop sensitivity) be varied, implying that one has a choice of the value of this constant.

Figure 9.1 shows how the response of a simple first-order system to step input can be adjusted by changing the value of the time constant. Note that the response curve is changed in magnitude but that its nature remains unaltered.

It is common that practical reasons dictate limits to the possibilities of improving system performance by changing time or gain constants. Practical limitations include the range, size, and cost of available stock components. Also, it may be necessary to significantly change the nature of the system to achieve the desired quality of performance. Such change can be made by introducing a different or additional control component into the closed loop system. Improving the performance of a system by adding to it a component which affects the nature of the system is called **compensation.** Essentially, additional terms which cause the desired improvement in performance are added to the system's transfer function. Compensation is a widely used and effective technique. It is possible to utilize physically simple and inexpensive devices to achieve substantial changes in the nature of a feedback control system. The remainder of this chapter will be devoted to the description and utilization of common compensating devices.

Changes in the nature of a system due to added compensating devices can be examined with frequency response and/or root locus techniques. Use of both techniques will be demonstrated.

9.2 COMPENSATION

The process of improving the performance of a control system by compensation is creative rather than formal. Only considerable practice can give the feel and insight necessary to achieve good compensation.

Consider the general system block diagram of Fig. 9.2. The regulator

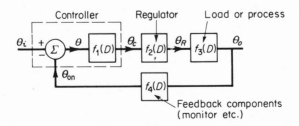

Fig. 9.2 General feedback control system.

and the process being controlled are normally designed to fit specified requirements which are more or less independent of the automatic control features. For example, the fuel regulating valve and the turbo-alternator of an electricity generating set are designed to provide a specified rate of electrical energy, while the automatic control of the plant is a secondary requirement. The controller and the response monitoring devices of Fig. 9.2 are the added automatic control elements. It is apparent that changes in the control system dynamics are best sought through adjustments in the control elements, rather than in the plant. For example, it is common for commercial controllers to contain several simple adjustments, with which the controller transfer function $\theta_c/\theta = f_1(D)$ can be changed significantly.

Compensation made by altering or adding a transfer function in the forward feed loop, Fig. 9.3(a), is called **series compensation.** Compen-

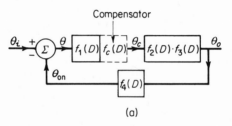

(a)

Series compensation, adding $f_c(D)$

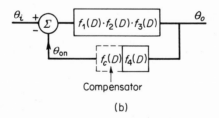

(b)

Parallel compensation, adding $f_c(D)$

Fig. 9.3 Series and parallel compensation.

sation achieved by affecting the feedback transfer function, Fig. 9.3 (b), is called **parallel compensation.**

A particular compensator transfer function results in the same open loop transfer function, whether it is placed in series or parallel. For example,

$$\frac{\theta_{on}}{\theta} = f_o(D) \cdot f_c(D)$$

where $f_o(D) = f_1(D) \cdot f_2(D) \cdot f_3(D) \cdot f_4(D)$, for both cases of Fig. 9.3.

Thus the system's Nyquist plot and its root locus plot, both of which are constructed by utilizing the open loop transfer function, are independent of where the compensation is applied. However, it should be appreciated that the system transfer function, and hence the performance of the closed loop system, is affected by the location of the compensation. For example,

$$\frac{\theta_o}{\theta_i} = \frac{f_f(D) \cdot f_c(D)}{1 + f_o(D) \cdot f_c(D)} \quad \text{(for Fig. 9.3a)}$$

$$\frac{\theta_o}{\theta_i} = \frac{f_f(D)}{1 + f_o(D) \cdot f_c(D)} \quad \text{(for Fig. 9.3b)}$$

where $f_f(D) = f_1(D) \cdot f_2(D) \cdot f_3(D)$; $f_o(D) = f_f(D) \cdot f_4(D)$.
This apparent paradox is explained by both systems having the same characteristic equation.

9.3 CONTROLLER ACTIONS

9.3.1 Introduction

Feedback control systems contain a component known as the controller, which measures the error (or deviation) between the signals representing the actual and desired values of the controlled variable. The controller generates a signal to the regulator which depends on the state of the error. The controller component is identified in Fig. 9.2. The following relationship is known as the **controller action**:

$$\frac{\theta_c}{\theta} = f_1(D)$$

where θ is the error $(\theta_i - \theta_{on})$; θ_c is the output signal of the controller.

A number of different controller characteristics can be obtained. It is common for commercial controllers to have simple adjustments with which a variety of controller action transfer functions can be utilized as required. These factors make the controller a favorite point of compensation.

The basic dynamic characteristics which can be utilized in controller actions are

Proportional action

$$\frac{\theta_c}{\theta} = K \quad \text{or} \quad \theta_c = K\theta$$

where K is a constant, i.e., the action θ_c of the controller is proportional to the error θ.

Integral action

$$\frac{\theta_c}{\theta} = \frac{K}{D} \quad \text{or} \quad \theta_c = K \frac{\theta}{D} = K \int \theta \, dt$$

i.e., the action θ_c is proportional to the time integral of error. By differentiating the expression $\theta_c = K\theta/D$, we get

$$D\theta_c = K\theta$$

which means that the rate of change of the action, $D\theta_c$, is proportional to the error θ.

Derivative action

$$\frac{\theta_c}{\theta} = K D \quad \text{or} \quad \theta_c = K D\theta$$

i.e., the action θ_c is proportional to the rate of change of the error θ.

Methods for physically realizing these controller actions will be demonstrated in Section 9.3.2. It will be shown that each of the three basic actions have undesirable characteristics when used alone. However, the desirable characteristics of each can be utilized by combining them. The most used combinations are:

Proportional plus integral action

$$\frac{\theta_c}{\theta} = K_1 + \frac{K_2}{D} \quad \text{or} \quad \theta_c = \left(K_1 + \frac{K_2}{D}\right)\theta$$

in which the action θ_c is proportional to both the error and the time integral of the error.

Proportional plus derivative action

$$\frac{\theta_c}{\theta} = K_1 + K_3 D \quad \text{or} \quad \theta_c = (K_1 + K_3 D)\theta$$

in which the action θ_c is proportional to both the error and its rate of change.

Proportional plus integral plus derivative action

$$\frac{\theta_c}{\theta} = K_1 + \frac{K_2}{D} + K_3 D \quad \text{or} \quad \theta_c = \left(K_1 + \frac{K_2}{D} + K_3 D\right)\theta$$

This is the general three-term controller, in which the action is proportional to the error, its time integral, and its rate of change.

With the multiple action controller the degree of each effect (proportional, integral, derivative) on the total action depends on the relationships between the proportionality constants (K_1, K_2, K_3).

9.3.2 Realization of Controller Actions

Proportional action

Figure 9.4(a) shows a simple tank system in which it is desired to hold the actual head h_o to a desired value h_i, in the face of an external flow disturbance q_e. The float detects any change in h_o, and hence any move-

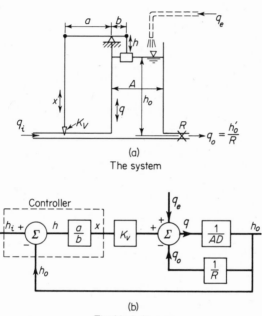

(a)

The system

(b)

The block diagram
(all variables are changes from their
steady-state values)

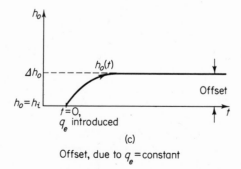

(c)

Offset, due to q_e = constant

Fig. 9.4 Proportional control of a simple tank system.

ment h of the float represents the error $(h_i - h_o)$. The float is directly connected to the flow regulator valve through a lever arm and link. Figure 9.4(b) shows the block diagram of this system. It is apparent that the float movement and lever arm comprise the controller and that the controller action is

$$\frac{x}{h} = \frac{a}{b}$$

which is a constant, indicating proportional controller action.

The general characteristics of proportional controller action are indicated in Fig. 9.4. These include

(a) the direct and physically simple connection between error and action, which produces a fast and stable action;
(b) the rigid connection between the error sensor (the float) and the regulator (the inflow valve). The regulator cannot be adjusted to allow for external disturbances, without a corresponding change in the position of the float. Imagine the tank to be in equilibrium such that

$$h_o = h_i; \quad q_i = q_o; \quad \text{and} \quad q_e = 0$$

when the external disturbance q_e is introduced. Then, the flow q_e causes the head to start to rise, the float to rise, and the regulator valve starts to close. In effect, the control action is causing q_i to be reduced to offset the effect of q_e. The system will seek a new equilibrium condition,

$$q_i' + q_e = q_o'$$

Because q_i has to change to q_i' the regulator valve position also has to remain changed. Consequently, the float position has to remain changed. That is, the new equilibrium head h_o' is not the same as the original value h_o. A steady-state error $(h_o' - h_o)$ or $(h_o' - h_i)$ has to be accepted. The error is known as **offset** and is an undesirable characteristic of proportional control action. Figure 9.4(c) shows the effect of offset when the present system is subjected to a step input flow rate q_e = constant.

Because of its simplicity and stability, proportional controller action is often used where a degree of offset can be accepted. Good design can minimize offset.

Integral action

Figure 9.5(a) shows the tank system with a hydraulic valve-ram component included between the float and regulator.

If a disturbance q_e is introduced the float starts to rise, lifting the spool valve and causing the ram to start closing the regulator valve. Thus the inflow q_i is reduced to counter the effect of q_e.

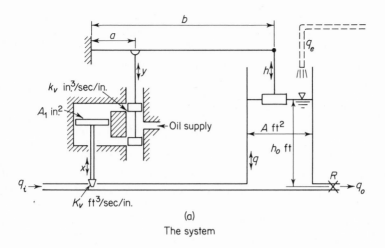

(a)

The system

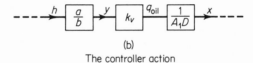

(b)

The controller action

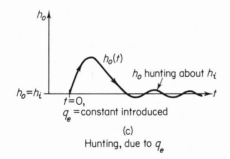

(c)

Hunting, due to q_e

Fig. 9.5   Integral control of a simple tank system.

Figure 9.5(b) shows part of the block diagram of the system. The remaining parts of the diagram are the same as in Fig. 9.4(b). It should be apparent that

$$\frac{x}{h} = \frac{a}{b} \cdot \frac{k_v}{A_1} \cdot \frac{1}{D} = \frac{K_2}{D}$$

is integral controller action.

The regulator valve will remain in motion until the spool returns to its central position, where both ports to the ram are blocked. The spool and float are directly connected and the system is adjusted so that the spool is in its equilibrium position when the float is at the desired head position. Hence control action will continue until the head in the tank is at the desired value. That is, only when

$$h_o = h_i \quad \text{and} \quad h = 0$$

can action cease. Hence integral action does not permit offset. Note that the regulator valve and the float are not directly tied together. Elimination of offset is the major advantage of integral control action.

Integral action, when used alone, has several serious disadvantages. It is relatively slow in action, due to the "soft" connection between the error-sensing float and the error-correcting regulator. Also, the spool tends to overshoot its mid-position when the controller is acting to offset a disturbance, due to the time delays in the ram unit and in the tank process itself. This overcorrection causes oscillation of the controlled variable about its desired value. This effect, known as **hunting,** is illustrated in Fig. 9.5(c).

Derivative action

Figure 9.6(a) shows the tank system with a viscous dashpot placed in the link between the float lever and the regulator valve. The disturbance flow q_e would act to cause the float to rise from its initial equilibrium position. The dashpot piston is forced downward (y) by the lever action. The dashpot cylinder, to which the regulator spindle is fixed, is also driven downward (x), closing the regulator as required. However, leakage past the dashpot piston ensures that the displacements x and y are not equal. In fact,

$$x = y - z$$

where z is the relative displacement of the piston in the cylinder. Also the spring action on the dashpot cylinder ensures that in due time the cylinder returns to its original equilibrium position, dragging the regulator valve with it.

Figure 9.6(b) shows part of the block diagram of the system, the remaining parts being similar to Fig. 9.4(b). It is apparent that

$$\frac{x}{h} = \frac{a/b}{1 + k/c\,D}$$

If the device is designed so that $k/c\,D \gg 1$, then

$$\frac{x}{h} \approx \frac{a/b}{k/c\,D} = \frac{ac}{bk}\cdot D = K_3\,D$$

which is derivative controller action.

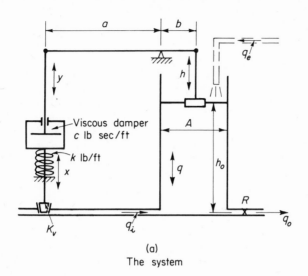

(a)

The system

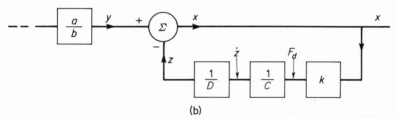

(b)

The controller action

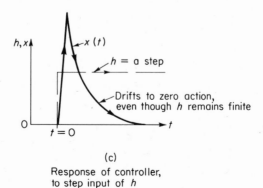

(c)

Response of controller,
to step input of h

Fig. 9.6   Derivative control of simple tank system.

The advantages and disadvantages of derivative controller actions are indicated in Fig. 9.6(a). If error h is changing fast, the dashpot acts as a "hard" component in the linkage (i.e., z is small relative to y), and the inflow rate q_i is rapidly adjusted to effect the desired control. For example, for a step change in h, Dh approaches infinity, and x is very large. However, if h is changing very slowly, such that the dashpot leakage causes $z = y$, regulator displacement x can be zero. Thus tank head could drift slowly without any corrective action from the controller. Derivative action alone is never used, due to its inability to sense and counter **drift.**

Figure 9.6(c) shows the nature of the response of a derivatively controlled system to step input. Note the large and rapid initial action, followed by the eventual decay to zero action.

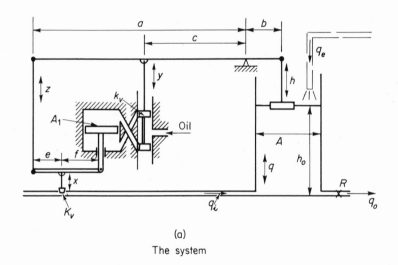

(a)

The system

(b)

The controller action

Fig. 9.7   Proportional plus integral control of a simple tank system.

Proportional plus integral action

Figure 9.7(a) shows the tank system with a combination of direct lever action (h to z to x_1) and hydraulic spool-ram action (h to y to x_2). Using the idea of superposition, applicable to linear systems, the two component actions x_1 and x_2 can be assessed separately and added to give the total action. For example, consider the spool spindle detached from the main lever $(a + b)$, and the lower lever point 0_1 fixed. Then, the action due to a change in h is

$$x_1 = h \cdot \frac{a}{b} \cdot \frac{f}{e + f} = K_1 h$$

Similarly, if the lever link is disconnected, and the lower lever point 0_2 held fixed, the action would be

$$x_2 = h \cdot \frac{c}{b} \cdot \frac{k_v}{A_1 D} \cdot \frac{e}{e + f} = \frac{K_2 h}{D}$$

Then, the total action is

$$x = x_1 + x_2 = \left(K_1 + \frac{K_2}{D} \right) h$$

which is proportional plus integral action.

Figure 9.7(b) shows part of the system's block diagram, formed following the superpositioning procedure outlined above. The diagram is easily reduced to obtain the above controller action.

Proportional plus integral action is widely used, as it provides some of the directness and simplicity of proportional action while the integral component eliminates offset. It is apparent in Fig. 9.7(a) that the spool must be in its mid-position for equilibrium, and that this occurs only when error h is zero.

Proportional plus derivative action

Figure 9.8(a) shows the tank system with a combination of direct lever and dashpot actions. Using the approach of superpositioning, the block diagram, Fig. 9.8(b), of the action can be formed. The diagram reduces to yield

$$x = (K_1 + K_3 D)h$$

where

$$K_1 = \frac{ae}{b(e + f)}; \qquad K_3 = \frac{df}{b(e + f)} \cdot \frac{c}{k}$$

which is proportional plus derivative action. It can be seen in Fig. 9.8(a) that a large degree of action takes place if float position h suddenly changes. Both ends of the lower lever $0_1 0_2$ would be forced downward if the float position changed upward. However, if h changed slowly, the dashpot effect

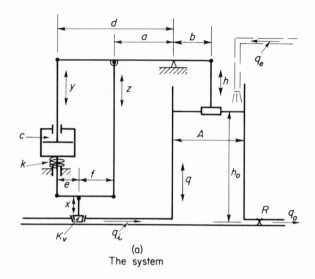

(a)

The system

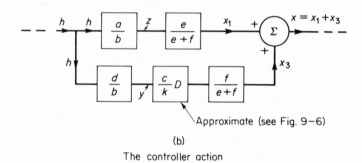

Approximate (see Fig. 9–6)

(b)

The controller action

Fig. 9.8 Proportional plus derivative control of a simple tank system.

would ensure a slower degree of action x. Also, the direct lever (proportional) component of the action ensures that the system will not drift if h changes very slowly. Thus the action attains the desirable characteristics of both proportional and derivative actions, without retaining the derivative action's susceptibility to drift. However, the action allows offset, the undesirable feature of proportional action.

Proportional plus integral plus derivative action

Figure 9.9(a) shows the tank system with a combination of direct linkage, spool-ram linkage, and dashpot linkage of the float to the regulator

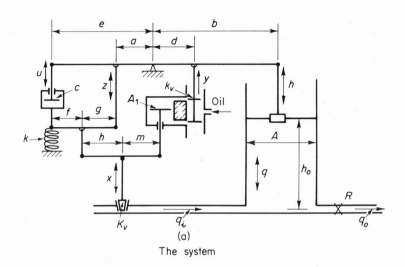

(a)

The system

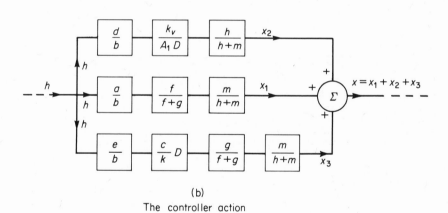

(b)

The controller action

Fig. 9.9 Proportional plus integral plus derivative control of a simple tank system.

valve. Again using the principle of superposition, the block diagram of Fig. 9.9(b) can be derived. The diagram yields

$$x = \left(K_1 + \frac{K_2}{D} + K_3 D\right)h$$

where

$$K_1 = \frac{afm}{b(f+g)(h+m)}; \quad K_2 = \frac{dh\,k_v}{b(h+m)A_1}; \quad K_3 = \frac{egm}{b(f+g)(h+m)} \cdot \frac{c}{k}$$

which is proportional plus integral plus derivative action. It should be apparent in Fig. 9.9(a) that the action combines the directness of proportional connection, the additional response of derivative action to rapid changes in h, and the elimination of offset by the integral connection.

9.3.3 Some Multiple-Action Controllers

(a) A Pneumatic Controller: Figure 9.10 illustrates a three-term low pressure pneumatic controller, which can be used anywhere where

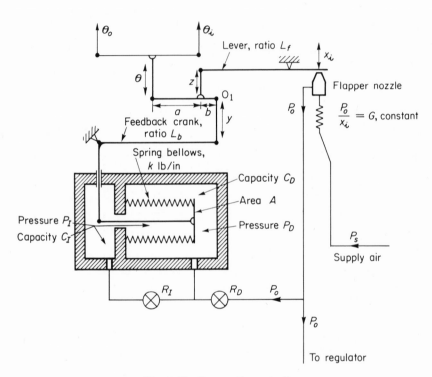

Fig. 9.10   Pneumatic controller.

(a) the controlled variable (speed, voltage, temperature, pressure, etc.) can be transduced to a displacement θ_o;

(b) the desired values of the controlled variable can be represented as a displacement on a scale θ_i;

(c) the controller output air pressure P_o can be used to control the system's regulator. An air-motor valve (Example 3.6) is a typical pressure controlled regulator.

The basic operation of the unit is as follows:

(1) θ_i is set to the desired value;

(2) $\theta_o = \theta_i$ is the required condition of the system for which error $\theta = 0$;

(3) if $\theta_o \neq \theta_i$, error θ is finite and acts through the lever linkage a, b, L_f, to cause displacement of the flapper x_i;

(4) displacement x_i causes the nozzle output pressure P_o to change.

Thus a change in θ_o causes a change in pressure P_o which can be used to adjust the system's regulator in a manner to bring θ_o back to its desired value θ_i. The relationship

$$\frac{P_o}{\theta} = f(D)$$

describes the action of the controller.

If the valve R_D is shut, the pressure inside and around the spring bellows unit will be unaffected by changes in the output pressure P_o. Hence the bellows will remain stationary and the pivot point 0_1 on the forward linkage a, b will be fixed.

If the valve R_D is fully or partly open, the changes in pressure P_o are felt by the spring bellows. If valve R_I is shut, the effect is felt only on the outside of the bellows. If R_I is open, the effect is felt inside and outside of the bellows. In either case, the bellows can be deflected by changes in P_o. Deflection of the bellows is transmitted via the lever linkage L_b to 0_1. Thus, the net displacement of the flapper x_i is affected both by the forward displacement due to θ and by the feedback action y due to the bellows unit.

Any of four controller actions can be obtained by adjustments to the two valves R_D and R_I. The following analysis assumes that (1) the air is incompressible; (2) the valves R_D and R_I have infinite resistance to flow when shut, zero resistance to flow when fully open, and offer a linear resistance to flow $q = P/R$ when partly open; (3) the air lines in the unit offer zero resistance to air flow. These assumptions are valid for the low pressure, slow response, small changes-in-pressure situations for which the controller is intended.

Proportional action

Valve R_D is shut and valve R_I open (optional) so that the bellows unit remains fixed in the face of changes in pressure P_o. It follows that the controller action (Fig. 9.11a) is

$$P'_o = \left(\frac{b}{a+b}\cdot L_f\cdot G\right)\theta$$

(i.e., imagine a change θ and its effect on the unit) which is proportional action).

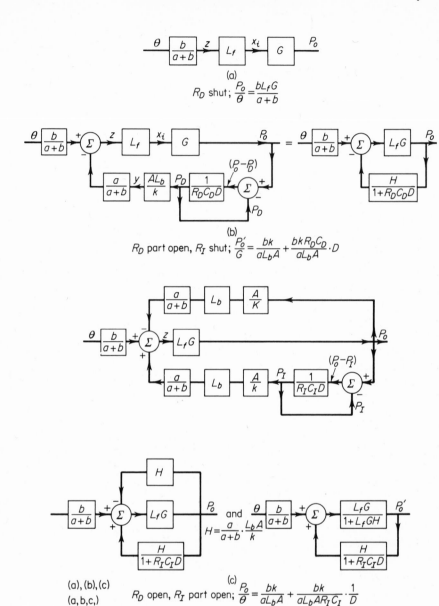

Fig. 9.11 The several actions of the three-term controller of Fig. 9.10—*continued on facing page.*

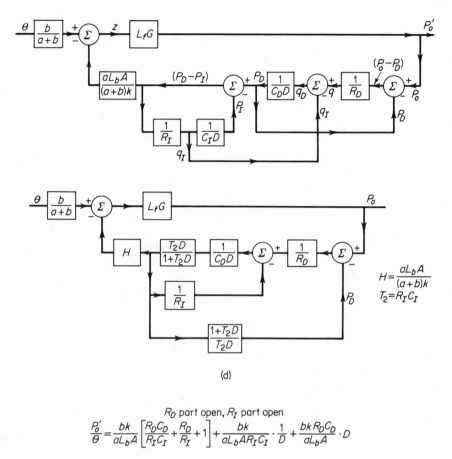

$$R_D \text{ part open, } R_I \text{ part open}$$

$$\frac{P_o'}{\theta} = \frac{bk}{aL_b A}\left[\frac{R_D C_D}{R_I C_I} + \frac{R_D}{R_I} + 1\right] + \frac{bk}{aL_b A R_I C_I}\cdot\frac{1}{D} + \frac{bk R_D C_D}{aL_b A}\cdot D$$

Fig. 9.11 *Continued.*

Proportional plus derivative action

Valve R_D is partly open so that it offers resistance R_D lb sec in.$^{-5}$ to flow. Valve R_I is shut. The initial operating equilibrium condition of the unit requires that

$$\theta = 0; \quad P_o = P_D \quad \text{(pressure in chamber } C_D\text{)}$$

Imagine θ to be changed in the upward sense in Fig. 9.10. The response pressure P_o will change by $P_o'(t)$, as for the previous case. However, P_o' also bleeds through R_D to build up the pressure P_D in chamber C_D by the amount $P_D'(t)$, causing a time displacement of the bellows and a consequent feedback displacement of the linkage and flapper. The equations of action are illustrated in the block diagram of Fig. 9.11(b), which can be reduced to yield

$$\frac{P'_o}{\theta} = \frac{b/(a+b)}{\dfrac{1}{L_fG} + \dfrac{a}{(a+b)} \cdot \dfrac{AL_b}{k} \cdot \dfrac{1}{1+R_DC_D\,D}} \approx \frac{b/(a+b)}{\dfrac{a}{a+b} \cdot \dfrac{AL_b}{k(1+R_DC_D\,D)}}$$

as $1/(L_fG) \to 0$ because G is very large (10^4 to 10^5 lb/in.^{2}/in.).

$$\frac{P'_o}{\theta} = \frac{bk(1+R_DC_D\,D)}{aAL_b} = K_1 + K_3\,D$$

where $K_1 = bk/aAL_b$ and $K_3 = bkR_DC_D/aAL_b$), which is proportional plus derivative action.

Proportional plus integral action

Valve R_D is fully open, and valve R_I is partially open. With $R_D = 0$, any pressure change P'_o is instantly felt in chamber C_D. With R_I partly open to offer resistance R_I to flow through it, pressure change P'_o bleeds into the chamber C_I, which includes the inside of the bellows. The resulting action can be derived by imagining a change θ, and forming the resulting equations of action. Figure 9.11(c) shows the block diagram which represents these equations. The diagram can be reduced as illustrated to yield

$$\frac{P'_o}{\theta} = \frac{b/(a+b)}{\dfrac{1+L_fGH}{L_fG} - \dfrac{H}{R_IC_I\,D+1}}$$

where $H = [a/(a+b)] \times L_b \times A/k$

$$\frac{P'_o}{\theta} = \frac{b(a+b)}{\dfrac{1}{L_fG} + H - \dfrac{H}{R_IC_I\,D+1}} \approx \frac{b/(a+b)}{H - \dfrac{H}{R_IC_I\,D+1}}$$

as $1/L_fG \to 0$ because G is large.

$$\therefore \frac{P'_o}{\theta} = \frac{b/(a+b)\cdot(R_IC_I\,D+1)}{H(R_IC_I\,D+1) - H} = \frac{b/(a+b)\cdot(R_IC_I\,D+1)}{HR_IC_I\,D}$$

$$= \frac{b}{(a+b)H} + \frac{b}{(a+b)HR_IC_I\,D} = K_1 + \frac{K_2}{D}$$

where $K_1 = bk/aL_bA$ and $K_2 = bk/aL_bA\,R_IC_I$, which is proportional plus integral action.

Proportional plus integral plus derivative actions

Valves R_D and R_I are both partly open, so that pressure change P'_o is felt in both chambers C_D and C_I. The equations of action following a disturbance θ can be expressed in the block diagram form of Fig. 9.11(d). The diagram can be reduced as illustrated to yield

$$\frac{P_o'}{\theta} = \frac{bk}{aL_bA}\left(\frac{R_DC_D}{R_IC_I} + \frac{R_D}{R_I}\right) + \frac{bk}{aL_bAR_IC_I}\cdot\frac{1}{D} + \frac{bkR_DC_D}{aL_bA}\cdot D$$

which is of the form $K_1 + K_2/D + K_3\,D$, proportional plus integral plus derivative action.

(b) An Engine Speed Governor: Figure 9.12(a) illustrates an engine speed governor in which the engine speed is sensed by the centripetal

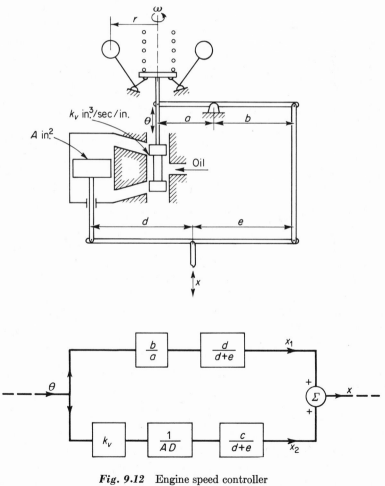

Fig. 9.12 Engine speed controller

$$\frac{x}{\theta} = \frac{bd}{a(d+e)} + \frac{e}{d+e}\cdot\frac{k_v}{AD}$$

governor action of the rotating masses. For any one speed, the mass path radius is a particular value. If the speed changes, the masses are displaced radially, causing the following:

(1) the spool is displaced from its mid-position (closed ports), thus driving the ram to adjust the regulator valve;
(2) the lever linkage is displaced, thus adjusting the position of the regulator valve.

Figure 9.12(b) shows the block diagram which describes the action of the unit. The action is described by

$$\frac{x}{\theta} = K_1 + \frac{K_2}{D}$$

where

$$K_1 = \frac{bd}{a(d+e)}; \quad K_2 = \frac{e}{d+e} \cdot \frac{k_v}{A}$$

which is proportional plus integral action.

9.3.4 Summary of Controller Actions

There are three basic controller actions, each having both good and undesirable characteristics. These are the following:

(a) Proportional action, in which the action is proportional to the error. The action is simple, stable, and direct, but causes offset. Offset can be described as the steady-state error associated with the response of a system to a step input disturbance.
(b) Integral action, in which the rate of change of the action is proportional to the error. Integral action eliminates offset, but is a "soft" action which permits hunting (oscillation) of a system's response, about its steady-state condition.
(c) Derivative action, in which the action is proportional to the rate of change of the error. Derivative action gives a rapid response to counter the effect of rapidly changing errors, but is insensitive to slowly changing error and hence allows drift.

Because of their unfavorable characteristics, integral and derivative actions are never used alone. The three basic actions can be combined in several ways to achieve the desirable characteristics of each, while eliminating the undesirable characteristics. The four controller actions which are realizable are the following:

(d) Proportional action, as discussed in (a).

(e) Proportional plus integral action, in which the proportional component provides the directness and stability, while the integral component eliminates offset. The action tends to be somewhat oscillatory.

(f) Proportional plus derivative action, in which the proportional action provides the stability and eliminates drift, while the derivative action provides the surge of action necessary to counter rapidly changing disturbances to the system being controlled. This action still causes offset.

(g) Proportional plus integral plus derivative action, which provides the stability of proportional action, eliminates offset with the integral action, and provides rapid action with the derivative action, which also provides the damping necessary to eliminate hunting.

Figure 9.13 illustrates qualitatively the characteristics of each action by showing the response to step input of a system having each control action in turn.

The four useful controller actions can be expressed in the conventional time constant forms:

(h) Proportional:

$$\frac{\theta_c}{\theta} = K_1$$

(i) Proportional plus integral:

$$\frac{\theta_c}{\theta} = K_1 + \frac{K_2}{D} = K_1 \left(1 + \frac{1}{T_I D}\right) = \frac{K_2(1 + T_I D)}{D}$$

where $T_I = K_1/K_2$ is called the integral time constant.

(j) Proportional plus derivative:

$$\frac{\theta_c}{\theta} = K_1 + K_3 D = K_1 (1 + T_D D)$$

where $T_D = K_3/K_1$ is called the derivative time constant.

(k) Proportional plus integral plus derivative:

$$\frac{\theta_c}{\theta} = K_1 + K_2 D + K_3 D = K_1 \left(1 + \frac{1}{T_I D} + T_D D\right)$$

$$= K_1 \left(\frac{T_I D + 1 + T_I T_D D^2}{T_I D}\right) = \frac{K_2(1 + T_I D + T_I T_D D^2)}{D}$$

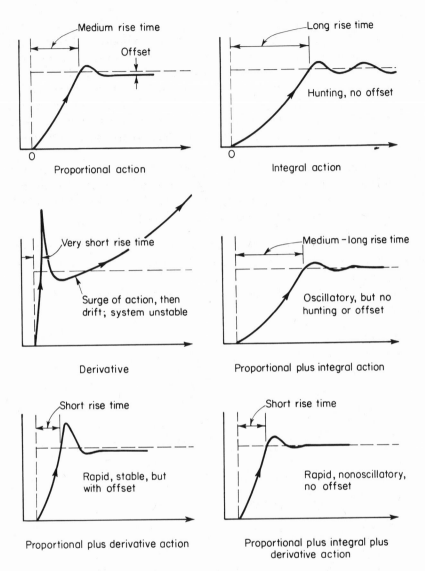

Fig. 9.13 The response to step input disturbance of a typical system, when it has various controller actions.

9.4 LAG AND LEAD ACTIONS

9.4.1 Introduction

As an alternative to (or in addition to) the controller actions discussed in Section 9.3, compensation to improve the performance of a system can be achieved by using so-called lag and lead devices. Several such devices will be illustrated in the present section. Such compensators can be used in either the forward feed or feedback loops of a system, as illustrated in previous Fig. 9.3, to provide the desired change in the system's transfer function.

The devices which will be discussed are defined as follows:

(a) First-order lag:

$$\frac{\theta_c}{\theta} = \frac{1 + T_n\,D}{1 + T_d\,D}$$

where $T_d > T_n$.

(b) First-order lead:

$$\frac{\theta_c}{\theta} = \frac{(T_d/T_n)(1 + T_nD)}{1 + T_d\,D}$$

where $T_n > T_d$.

(c) Second-order lag-lead:

$$\frac{\theta_c}{\theta} = \frac{1 + (T_1 + T_2)D + T_1 T_2\,D^2}{1 + (T_1 + T_2 + T_3)D + T_1 T_2\,D^2}$$

The meaning of lag and lead

The meaning of lag and lead is associated with the frequency response characteristics of the compensators. For example,

$$\frac{1 + T_n\,D}{1 + T_d\,D} = \frac{1 + j\omega T_n}{1 + j\omega T_d}$$

for frequency response, i.e.,

$$G = \left(\frac{1 + \omega^2 T_n^2}{1 + \omega^2 T_d^2}\right)^{1/2}; \qquad \phi = \tan^{-1}\omega T_n - \tan^{-1}\omega T_d$$

If $T_d > T_n$, then $\tan^{-1}\omega T_d > \tan^{-1}\omega T_n$, and ϕ is negative. That is,

$$\frac{1 + T_n\,D}{1 + T_d\,D}$$

where $T_d > T_n$, is a phase lag term. If, however, $T_d < T_n$, then $\tan^{-1}\omega T_n > \tan^{-1}\omega T_d$, and phase ϕ is positive. That is,

$$\frac{1 + T_n\,D}{1 + T_d\,D}$$

where $T_d < T_n$, is a phase lead term.

It will be shown in Section 9.5 that the second-order lag-lead compensator provides lag for low values of frequency, and lead for high values of frequency.

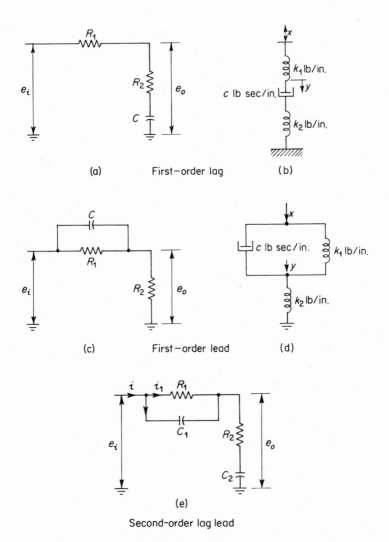

(a)   First−order lag   **(b)**

(c)   First−order lead   **(d)**

(e)

Second-order lag lead

Fig. 9.14   Some lag and lead action generators.

It should be appreciated that there are many other useful compensator transfer functions.

9.4.2 Realization of Lag and Lead

Figure 9.14(a) shows an electrical circuit. To derive its transfer function, imagine the circuit to be in equilibrium when the voltage e_i is applied. The resulting relationship between e_i and the response voltage e_o is

$$e_i - e_o = iR_1; \quad e_o = iR_2 + \frac{i}{C\,D} = i\left(R_2 + \frac{1}{C\,D}\right)$$

$$\therefore e_i - e_o = \frac{e_o R_1}{R_2 + 1/C\,D} = \frac{e_o R_1 C\,D}{R_2 C\,D + 1}$$

$$\therefore e_i = e_o\left(1 + \frac{R_1 C\,D}{R_2 C\,D + 1}\right) = e_o\left(\frac{R_2 C\,D + 1 + R_1 C\,D}{R_2 C\,D + 1}\right)$$

and

$$\frac{e_o}{e_i} = \frac{R_2 C\,D + 1}{(R_2 C + R_1 C)D + 1} = \frac{1 + T_n\,D}{1 + T_d\,D}$$

where $T_n = R_2 C$ and $T_d = (R_1 C + T_n)$. Thus $T_d > T_n$ and the circuit yields the defined characteristic of a first-order lag component.

Figure 9.14(b) shows a mechanical system in which it is required to dynamically relate the displacements x and y. If the system is in equilibrium when a displacement x is introduced, the resulting equations of action are as follows:

$$(x - y)\,k_1 = F_d \quad \text{(the force experienced in the dashpot)}$$
$$F_d = c\dot{z} = c\,Dz$$

where z is the displacement of the dashpot piston in its cylinder;

$$z = (y - u)$$

where u is the displacement of the dashpot cylinder;

$$u k_2 = F_d \quad \text{(the force in the spring and in the dashpot)}$$

Hence $(x - y)\,k_1 = C\,Dz = C\,D(y - u) = CD(y - F_d/k_2) = C\,D[y - (x - y)\,k_1/k_2]$.

$$x\left(1 + \frac{c}{k_2}\,D\right) = y\left(1 + \frac{c}{k_1}\,D + \frac{c}{k_2}\,D\right)$$

$$\frac{y}{x} = \frac{1 + (c/k_2)\,D}{1 + (c/k_1 + c/k_2)\,D} = \frac{1 + T_n\,D}{1 + T_d\,D}$$

where $T_n = c/k_2$ and $T_d = T_n + c/k_1$. Thus $T_d > T_n$ and the system yields the characteristic of a first-order lag component.

Figure 9.14(c) shows an electrical circuit whose dynamic characteristics are readily shown to be

$$\frac{e_o}{e_i} = \frac{(T_d/T_n)(1 + T_n\,D)}{1 + T_d\,D}$$

where $T_n = R_1C$ and $T_d = [R_1/(R_1 + R_2)] \cdot T_n$. Thus $T_n > T_d$, and the device provides the defined characteristic of a first-order lead action.

Figure 9.14(d) shows a mechanical system in which the dynamic relationship between displacements x and y is readily shown to be

$$\frac{y}{x} = \frac{(T_d/T_n)(1 + T_nD)}{1 + T_dD}$$

where $T_n = c/k_1$ and $T_d = [c/(k_1 + k_2)]T_n$. Thus $T_n > T_d$ and the device provides first-order lead action.

Figure 9.14(e) shows a voltage system in which the input voltage e_i and the output voltage e_o can be related by combining the basic dynamic equations:

$$e_i - e_o = i_1R_1 = \frac{i_2}{C_1 D}$$

$$e_o = iR_2 + \frac{i}{C_2 D} = i\left(R_2 + \frac{1}{C_2 D}\right)$$

$$i = i_1 + i_2$$

Then,

$$e_i - e_o = (i - i_2)R_1 = \left[\frac{e_o}{R_2 + \dfrac{1}{C_2 D}} - C_1 D(e_i - e_o)\right]R_1$$

$$e_i(1 + R_1C_1 D) = e_o\left(1 + \frac{R_1}{R_2 + \dfrac{1}{C_2 D}} + R_1C_1 D\right)$$

from which

$$\frac{e_o}{e_i} = \frac{T_1T_2 D^2 + (T_1 + T_2)D + 1}{T_1T_2 D^2 + (T_1 + T_2 + T_3)D + 1}$$

where $T_1 = R_1C_1$; $T_2 = R_2C_2$; and $T_3 = R_1C_2$. Thus the circuit of Fig. 9.14(e) provides the defined second-order lag-lead characteristics.

Some further physical examples of compensators are included among the Problems.

9.5 USING FREQUENCY RESPONSE TECHNIQUES IN COMPENSATION

9.5.1 Introduction

Sections 9.1 through 9.4 introduced the idea of improving the performance of a closed loop system by changing its open loop transfer function. The required change can be made by adjusting or adding control components in the system. A number of physically realizable compensator transfer functions were established. To be able to select a suitable compensating transfer function, and to appreciate its effect on an original open loop transfer function, it is necessary to understand the dynamic natures of the compensators. Both frequency response and root locus techniques can be used for this purpose.

As previously discussed, series and parallel compensation have identical effects on a system's open loop transfer function. It should be kept in mind that a system's closed loop transfer function is affected by compensation and that the affect is dependent on whether series or parallel compensation is used.

In this section, frequency response techniques will be used to describe the nature of compensators and their effects on system characteristics. In Section 9.6, root locus techniques will be used.

9.5.2 Summary of Compensator Actions in Time Constant Form

The compensator actions discussed in the present chapter are

$$\frac{\theta_c}{\theta} = K_1 \quad \text{(proportional)}$$

$$\frac{\theta_c}{\theta} = \frac{K_2(1 + T_I D)}{D} \quad \text{(proportional + integral)}$$

$$\frac{\theta_c}{\theta} = K_1(1 + T_D D) \quad \text{(proportional + derivative)}$$

$$\frac{\theta_c}{\theta} = \frac{K_2(1 + T_I D + T_I T_D D^2)}{D} \quad \text{(proportional + integral + derivative)}$$

$$= \frac{K_2(1 + T_1 D)(1 + T_2 D)}{D} \quad \text{or} \quad \frac{K_2(1 + 2\xi T D + T^2 D^2)}{D}$$

depending on whether $(1 + T_I D + T_I T_D D^2)$ has real or complex roots, where T_1 and T_2, or ξ and T, can be defined in terms of T_I and T_D.

$$\frac{\theta_c}{\theta} = \frac{1 + T_n D}{1 + T_d D}, \quad T_d > T_n \quad \text{(first-order lag)}$$

$$= \frac{1 + T D}{1 + \alpha T D}, \quad \alpha > 1$$

where $T = T_n$ and $\alpha = T_d/T_n$.

$$\frac{\theta_c}{\theta} = \frac{(T_d/T_n)(1 + T_n D)}{1 + T_d D}, \quad T_n > T_d \quad \text{(first-order lead)}$$

$$= \frac{\beta(1 + T D)}{1 + \beta T D}, \quad \beta < 1$$

where $\beta = T_d/T_n$; $T = T_n$.

$$\frac{\theta_c}{\theta} = \frac{1 + (T_1 + T_2)D + T_1 T_2 D^2}{1 + (T_1 + T_2 + T_3)D + T_1 T_2 D^2} \quad \text{(second-order lag-lead)}$$

$$= \frac{(1 + T_1 D)(1 + T_2 D)}{(1 + T_A D)(1 + T_B D)} \quad \text{or} \quad \frac{(1 + T_1 D)(1 + T_2 D)}{1 + 2\xi T D + T^2 D^2}$$

where T_A and T_B, or T and ξ, are functions of T_1, T_2, and T_3. It should be appreciated that other useful forms of compensator transfer functions exist.

9.5.3 Frequency Response Characteristics of Compensators

Frequency response data is commonly plotted in one of the following:

(a) polar form;
(b) Bode diagram form;
(c) Nichols coordinate form (G, db–$\phi°$)

The magnitude ratio G_c and phase ϕ_c versus frequency expressions are obtained by substituting $j\omega$ for D in the compensator transfer functions. For example,

(1) Proportional plus integral:

$$\frac{\theta_c}{\theta} = \frac{K_2(1 + j\omega T_I)}{j\omega}$$

$$G_c = \frac{K_2(1 + \omega^2 T_I^2)^{1/2}}{\omega}; \quad \phi_c = -90° + \tan^{-1} \omega T_I$$

(2) Proportional plus derivative:

$$G_c = K_1(1 + \omega^2 T_D^2)^{1/2}; \quad \phi_c = \tan^{-1} \omega T_D$$

(3) Proportional plus integral plus derivative:

$$G_c = \frac{K_2[(1 - T_I T_D \omega^2)^2 + \omega^2 T_I^2]^{1/2}}{\omega}; \quad \phi_c = -90° + \tan^{-1} \frac{\omega T_I}{1 - T_I T_D \omega^2}$$

(4) First-order lag:

$$G_c = \left(\frac{1 + \omega^2 T_n^2}{1 + \omega^2 T_d^2}\right)^{1/2}; \quad \phi_c = \tan^{-1} \omega T_n - \tan^{-1} \omega T_d$$

where $T_d > T_n$, $G_c < 1$ and $\phi_c < 0$ for all ω.

(5) First-order lead:

$$G_c = \frac{(T_d/T_n)(1 + \omega^2 T_n^2)^{1/2}}{(1 + \omega^2 T_d^2)^{1/2}}; \quad \phi_c = \tan^{-1} \omega T_n - \tan^{-1} \omega T_d$$

where $T_n > T_d$; $G_c < 1$; $\phi_c > 0$ for all ω.

(6) Second order lag-lead:

$$G_c = \left[\frac{(1 - T_1 T_2 \omega^2)^2 + (T_1 + T_2)^2 \omega^2}{(1 - T_1 T_2 \omega^2)^2 + (T_1 + T_2 + T_3)^2 \omega^2} \right]^{1/2}$$

$$\phi_c = \tan^{-1} \frac{(T_1 + T_2)\omega}{1 - T_1 T_2 \omega} - \tan^{-1} \frac{(T_1 + T_2 + T_3)\omega}{1 - T_1 T_2 \omega^2}$$

The forms of the frequency response characteristics of each of these compensators is shown in Fig. 9.15 in polar, Bode, and Nichols coordinate forms. It should be appreciated that the second-order transfer functions could conceivably have complex roots instead of the real factors used in the illustrations.

It must be appreciated that the addition of any compensator action, whether it be series or parallel with the forward feed of the system, affects both the open loop magnitude ratio and phase.

9.5.4 Effect of Compensation on Open Loop Characteristics

If a system's original open loop magnitude ratio and phase lag are G_o and ϕ_o^*, then Fig. 9.15 illustrates that:

(a) At low frequencies $(\omega \to 0,\ \omega \ll 1/T,\ 1/T_1,\ 1/T_2,$ etc.$)$

proportional + integral action causes
G_o to be increased toward ∞ for $\omega \to \infty$, ϕ_o to be increased by $90°$;

proportional + derivative action causes
G_o to be multiplied by a constant K_1, ϕ_o to be unchanged;

proportional + integral + derivative action causes
G_o to be increased toward ∞ for $\omega \to 0$, ϕ_o to be increased by $90°$;

first-order lag action causes
G_o to be unaffected, ϕ_o to be unaffected;

first-order lead action causes
G_o to be multiplied by a constant $\beta < 1$, ϕ_o to be unaffected;

second-order lag-lead action causes
G_o to be unaffected, ϕ_o to be unaffected.

(b) At middle frequencies $(\omega \approx 1/T,\ 1/T_1,\ 1/T_2,$ etc.$)$

proportional + integral action causes
G_o to be decreasingly affected by G_c, ϕ_o to be decreasingly affected by ϕ_c;

proportional + derivative action causes
G_o to be increasingly affected by a coefficient $> K_1$, ϕ_o to be decreased;

proportional + integral + derivative action causes
G_o to be multiplied by a constant $\sqrt{2}\,K/T_1$, ϕ_o to be relatively unaffected.

*ϕ_o is defined here as a phase lag, instead of as a phase angle as previously.

Compensator action	Transfer function (time constant)	Frequency response characteristic		
		Polar form	Bode form	Nichols form
Proportional + integral	$\dfrac{K_2(1+T_I D)}{D}$	$\omega=\infty$ at $K_2 T_I$; Radius $K_2 T_I$ for large ω; $\omega_3,\ \omega_2,\ \omega_1$; $\omega=0$ at ∞	-20 db/dec; G_c, db; ϕ_c, degrees (0, -90); $\omega=1/T_I$	G_c, db; $\omega_1,\ \omega_2,\ \omega_3$; ϕ_c, degrees (-90, 0)
Proportional + derivative	$K_1(1+T_D D)$	to ∞, for $\omega=\infty$; $\omega_3,\ \omega_2,\ \omega_1$; G_c; ϕ_c; K_1, for $\omega=0$	-20 db/dec; ϕ_c; $-\omega$; G_c, db; K_1 db; ϕ_c, degrees (90, 0); $\omega=1/T_D$	G_c, db; K_1 db; $\omega_1,\ \omega_2,\ \omega_3$; ϕ_c, degrees (0, 90)
Proportional + integral + derivative	$\dfrac{K_2(1+T_I D+T_I T_D D^2)}{D}$ or $\dfrac{K_2(1+T_1 D)(1+T_2 D)}{D}$	ω_3; ω_2; ω_1	ϕ_c; -20 db/dec; 20 db/dec; G_c, db; $\dfrac{\sqrt{2}\,K_2}{T_1}$ db; ϕ_c, degrees (90, 0, -90); $\omega=1/T_1$ $\omega=1/T_2$	G_c, db; $\dfrac{\sqrt{2}\,K_2}{T_1}$ db; $\omega_1,\ \omega_2,\ \omega_3,\ \omega_4$; ϕ_c, degrees (-90, 0, 90)

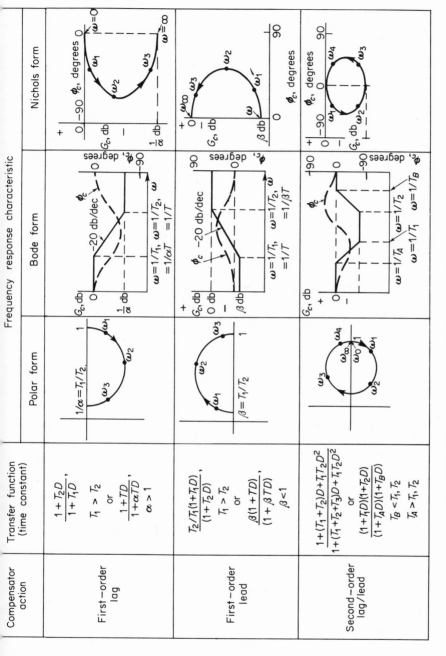

Fig. 9.15 Frequency response characteristics of various compensators.

first-order lag action causes	G_o to be attenuated,
	ϕ_o to be increased;
first-order lead action causes	G_o to be increasingly less affected by G_c,
	ϕ_o to be reduced;
second-order lag-lead action causes	G_o to be attenuated,
	ϕ_o to be increased, then decreased.

(c) At high frequencies ($\omega \gg 1/T, 1/T_1, 1/T_2$, etc., $\omega \to \infty$)

proportional + integral action causes	G_o to be multiplied by a constant $K_2 T_I$,
	ϕ_o to be unaffected;
proportional + derivative action causes	G_o to be increased toward ∞,
	ϕ_o to be decreased by 90°,
proportional + integral + derivative action causes	G_o to be increased towards ∞,
	ϕ_o to be decreased by 90°;
first-order lag action causes	G_o to be multiplied by a constant $G_c < 1$,
	ϕ_0 to be unaffected;
first-order lead action causes	G_o to be unaffected,
	ϕ_o to be unaffected;
second-order lag-lead action causes	G_o to be unaffected,
	ϕ_o to be unaffected.

9.5.5 Selection of Compensator Parameters

The need to compensate a system does not arise until the system's performance has been examined and found inadequate. Commonly, the system's stability condition, as defined by gain and phase margins, may be unsatisfactory. It is presupposed here that the principal components of the closed loop system are themselves satisfactory. To compensate the system toward having a satisfactory stability condition, the compensator characteristics must be matched with the original system's open loop characteristics to produce the desired performance conditions. The frequencies at which compensation must be most effective and the degree of compensation necessary will be apparent from a system's original frequency response curves. The foregoing frequencies also set the ranges of the compensator time constants $T = 1/\omega$. It is not possible to lay down rigid rules for selecting an optimum compensator. A degree of judgment and selective trial and error is usually necessary. The techniques of selecting compensator forms and parameters will be demonstrated in the examples in Section 9.5.6.

All of the compensator actions of Fig. 9.15 have at least two parameters (K or T). It is of interest to study the effects of various ratios of these parameters on the degree of compensation available. In each case, families of frequency response characteristics can be drawn, and then utilized when selecting compensation for a particular unsatisfactory system.

For example, Fig. 9.16(a) shows on Nichols coordinates the characteristics of first-order lag and lead actions, for several values of $\alpha = T_n/T_d$ and $\beta = T_n/T_d$ respectively. The characteristics can also be presented as

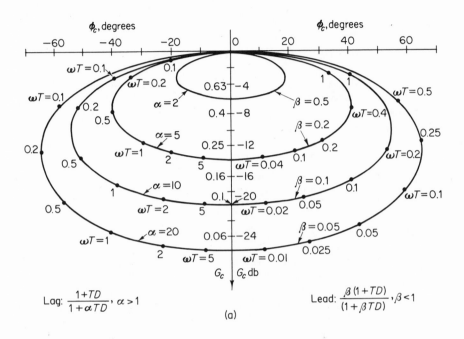

Lag: $\dfrac{1+TD}{1+\alpha TD}$, $\alpha > 1$

Lead: $\dfrac{\beta(1+TD)}{(1+\beta TD)}$, $\beta < 1$

(a)

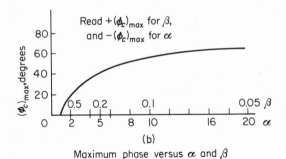

(b)

Maximum phase versus α and β

Fig. 9.16 The effect of α (lag) and β (lead) on first-order lag and lead compensator characteristics.

families of curves in polar and Bode diagram forms. Figure 9.16(b) shows the maximum compensating phase angle achieved for several values of α and β.

9.5.6 Examples

The following examples demonstrate the application of series compensation using frequency response techniques. Polar, Bode, and Nichols chart representations of open loop data will be used. The reader may develop his own preference for one type of plot. Because of the element of judgment and selective trial and error, the use of digital computer programming to obtain frequency response data is very effective.

Example 9.1: The initial design of a closed loop system results in the reduced block diagram shown in Fig. 9.17(a). It is required that the system have a gain margin of about 4 and a phase margin of about 30°, while the open loop gain constant is to be maintained at 30.

If the system does not satisfy these specifications, use first-order lag series compensation to achieve the desired improvement. Obtain the frequency response characteristics of the original system, and of the compensated system.

Solution: The original open loop transfer function is

$$\frac{\theta_{on}}{\theta} = \frac{30}{(1 + 0.5D)(1 + D)(1 + 10D)}$$

The original Nyquist plot is shown in Fig. 9.17(b); the original system is stable, with gain and phase margins

$$a = 1.12; \quad \phi_m = 4°$$

The margins of stability do not meet the performance specifications. First-order lag action is described by

$$\frac{\theta_c}{\theta} = \frac{1 + TD}{1 + \alpha T D}, \quad \alpha > 1$$

which increases the open loop lag at any particular frequency. To offset the destabilizing effect of increased open loop lag, the open loop magnitude ratio must be reduced to shrink the Nyquist plot away from enclosing $(-1, 0)$. Hence α and T must be chosen to produce a strong attenuation effect on G_o.

From Fig. 9.17(b), it can be seen that reshaping of the Nyquist plot should start from about the $\omega = 0.5$ rad/sec region. Hence select a compensator numerator time constant $T = 1/(\omega = 0.5) = 2$ sec. To get a pronounced attenuation effect from the compensator, select $\alpha = 10$.

Thus try the compensator $(1 + 2D)/(1 + 20D)$ (Fig. 9.17c). The compensated system's open loop transfer function is

$$\left(\frac{\theta_{on}}{\theta}\right)_c = \frac{30(1 + 2D)}{(1 + 20D)(1 + 0.5D)(1 + D)(1 + 10D)}$$

The new system's Nyquist plot is shown in Fig. 9.17(d). The gain and phase margins of the compensated system are $a = 4.7$, $\phi_m = 27°$, while the open loop gain is still $K_o = 30$.

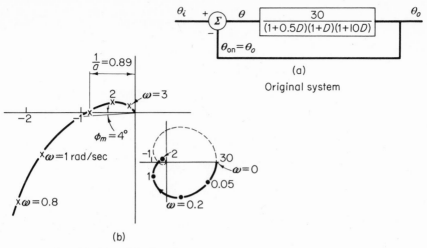

(a)
Original system

(b)
Nyquist plot, original system

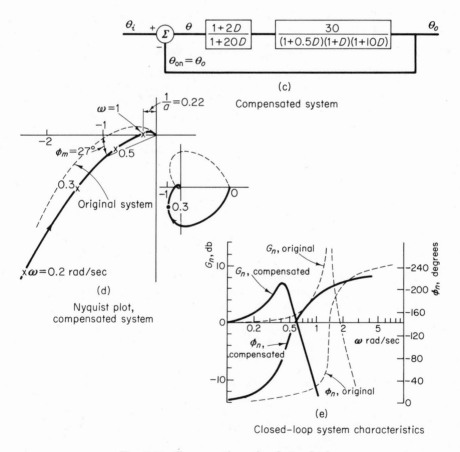

(c)
Compensated system

(d)
Nyquist plot,
compensated system

(e)
Closed-loop system characteristics

Fig. 9.17 Compensation using first-order lag.

The closed loop transfer functions of the original and compensated systems are respectively

$$\frac{\theta_o}{\theta_i} = \frac{0.97}{0.16D^3 + 0.5D^2 + 0.37D + 1} \quad \text{(original)}$$

$$\left(\frac{\theta_o}{\theta_i}\right)_c = \frac{0.97(1 + 2D)}{0.1D^4 + 0.33D^3 + 7.3D^2 + 1.08D + 1} \quad \text{(compensated)}$$

Figure 9.17(e) shows the frequency response characteristics of both systems. The data is most readily obtained using previously calculated open loop data on a Nichols chart. It can be seen that (a) the original system was very lightly damped; (b) the compensated system has more damping, but is still relatively lightly damped. The lag compensation has also reduced the resonant frequency and hence the natural undamped frequency of the system. This is an unfavorable aspect of lag compensation, as the useful frequency range of the system has been reduced.

Example 9.2: An original system has the open loop transfer function

$$\frac{\theta_{on}}{\theta} = \frac{25}{D(1 + \frac{1}{4}D)(1 + \frac{1}{16}D)}$$

It is required that this system's gain and phase margins exceed 1.5 and 15° respectively. Ascertain if the original system meets the specification. If not, compensate the system with first-order lead action. The open loop gain is to be maintained at 25 and an additional proportional amplifier can be used, if necessary, to achieve this.

Solution: Figure 9.18(a) shows the open loop Bode diagram for the original system. The gain and phase margins are

$$a, \text{db} = -2 \quad \text{and} \quad a = 0.8, \quad \phi_m = -6°$$

The system is unstable. The degree of instability is not large. First-order lead action

$$\frac{\beta(1 + T D)}{1 + \beta T D}, \quad \beta < 1$$

has the effect of reducing both phase lag and open loop gain at any particular frequency. We can concentrate the effect of the action on the region near $\phi_o = -180°$ by appropriate selection of T and β. Try $T = 1/(\omega = 5) = 0.2$, and $\beta = 0.2$ to give

$$\frac{\theta_c}{\theta} = \frac{0.2(1 + 0.2D)}{(1 + 0.04D)}; \quad \left(\frac{\theta_{on}}{\theta}\right)_c = \frac{5(1 + \frac{1}{5}D)}{D(1 + \frac{1}{25}D)(1 + \frac{1}{4}D)(1 + \frac{1}{16}D)}$$

The open loop gain constant has been reduced to 5, which in itself is sufficient to render the original system stable. However, it is specified that $K_o = 25$ is to be maintained. Hence a 5× amplifier must also be included in the forward loop (Fig. 9.18b), giving

$$\frac{\theta_{on}}{\theta} = \frac{25(1 + \frac{1}{5}D)}{D(1 + \frac{1}{25}D)(1 + \frac{1}{4}D)(1 + \frac{1}{16}D)}$$

Figure 9.18(b) shows the open loop Bode diagram of the compensated system. The gain and phase margins are

$$a, \text{db} = 4 \quad \text{and} \quad a = 1.6, \quad \phi_m = 15°$$

If larger gain and phase margins were required, a second choice of T_c and/or β could be made, with $T_c > 0.2$ and $\beta < 0.2$.

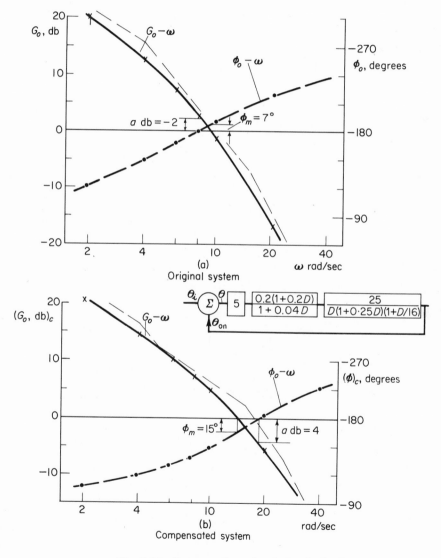

Fig. 9.18 Compensation using first-order lead.

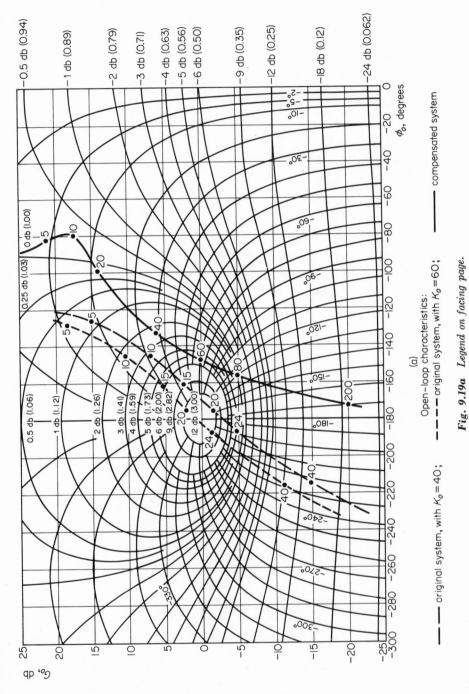

Fig. 9.19a *Legend on facing page.*

(a)

Open-loop characteristics:
— — — original system, with $K_0 = 40$;
— · — · — original system, with $K_0 = 60$;
———— compensated system

ϕ_0, degrees

G_0, db

344

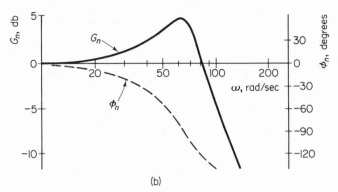

(b)

Closed–loop characteristics, compensated system

Fig. 9.19   Using 1.5 (1 + D/5) to compensate the system of Example 9.3:
(a), *on facing page*, open loop characteristics; (b) closed loop characteristics.

Example 9.3: A system has the open loop transfer function

$$\frac{\theta_{on}}{\theta} = \frac{40(1 + D/8)}{D(1 + D/4)(1 + D/16 + D^2/625)}$$

It is required to increase the open loop gain constant to 60 and to ensure that the system has an adequate margin of stability. Obtain the frequency response characteristic of the final system.

Solution: Figure 9.19(a) shows the original open loop characteristic on the Nichols chart. It is apparent that the system is barely stable, with stability margins

$$a,\, \mathrm{db} = 3 \quad \text{and} \quad a = 1.4, \quad \phi_m = 10°$$

If the open loop gain constant is increased to $K_o = 60$, the system becomes unstable $[(a,\, \mathrm{db}) \approx 0$ and $a \approx 1$, $\phi_m \approx 0°$, Fig. 9.19(a)].

Proportional plus derivative action, $K(1 + T D)$, provides strong lead action, i.e., reduces phase lag. Also, making $K = 1.5$ satisfies the need to increase K_o from 40 to 60. It is apparent from Fig. 9.19(a) that reshaping of the curve needs to start in the region $\omega = 5$ rad/sec. Hence try

$$\frac{\theta_c}{\theta} = 1.5\left(1 + \frac{D}{5}\right)$$

as a series compensator, giving

$$\left(\frac{\theta_{on}}{\theta}\right)_c = \frac{60(1 + D/8)(1 + D/5)}{D(1 + D/4)(1 + D/16 + D^2/625)}$$

Figure 9.19(a) shows the Nichols plot of this open loop transfer function. The compensated system is stable, with gain and phase margins

$$a,\, \mathrm{db} = \infty; \quad a = \infty; \quad \phi_m = 30°$$

These stability margins can be increased by selecting a larger value for the compensator time constant.

Figure 9.19(b) shows the closed loop system frequency response characteristics.

9.6 USING ROOT LOCUS TECHNIQUES IN COMPENSATION

9.6.1 Introduction

The root locus technique is as much a tool of synthesis as of analysis. The technique requires that at least one system constant be variable from zero to infinity, implying that the system being investigated has not been finalized.

It should be recalled that

(1) the root locus provides the path of all possible values of each root of a system characteristic equation;
(2) characteristics of the system's open loop transfer function are utilized to enable rapid construction of root locus diagrams;
(3) the branch root loci start at open loop poles and finish at open loop zeros (real or infinite).

The art of compensation to improve the performance of a system has been shown to require the judicial adding of $a + b\,D$ factors to the numerator and/or denominator of the open loop transfer function. In the pole-zero terminology used in root locus techniques,

$$1 + T\,D = T(D + 1/T)$$

and compensation becomes the art of adding suitable poles and/or zeros to a system's open loop transfer function.

Because of the need to use selective trial and error techniques in most compensation situations, use of the Spirule to aid root locus construction is strongly recommended.

9.6.2 The Effect of Adding an Open Loop Zero or Pole to a System

Figure 9.20(a) shows the block diagram and the root locus for the system

$$\frac{\theta_{on}}{\theta} = \frac{K_o}{D(T\,D + 1)} = \frac{K'_o}{D(D + 1/T)} \quad \text{(open loop)}$$

$$\frac{\theta_{on}}{\theta_i} = \frac{1}{(T/K_o)\,D^2 + (1/K_o)\,D + 1}$$

$$= \frac{K'_o}{D^2 + (1/T)\,D + K'_o} \quad \text{(closed loop)}$$

where $K'_o = K_o/T$.

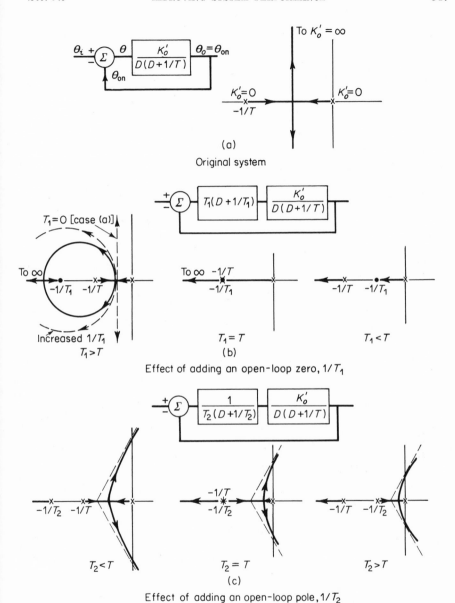

(a)

Original system

(b)

Effect of adding an open-loop zero, $1/T_1$

(c)

Effect of adding an open-loop pole, $1/T_2$

Fig. 9.20 The effect of adding an open loop pole or zero to a system.

Consider the case when a factor $1 + T_1 D = T_1(D + 1/T_1)$ is added into the forward feed (Fig. 9.20b), giving an additional open loop zero $-1/T_1$ and a new open loop sensitivity ($K'_{o1} = K'_o T_1$). The system transfer functions become

$$\frac{\theta_{on}}{\theta} = \frac{K'_{o1}(D + 1/T_1)}{D(D + 1/T)} \quad \text{(open loop)}$$

$$\frac{\theta_{on}}{\theta_i} = \frac{K'_{o1}(D + 1/T_1)}{D^2 + (1/T + K'_{o1})D + K'_{o1}/T_1} \quad \text{(closed loop)}$$

The added zero has one of three effects on the root locus:

(a) If $T_1 < T$ so that $1/T_1 > 1/T$, the new open loop zero $-1/T_1$ lies to the left of the open loop pole $-1/T$. The resulting root locus is shown in Fig. 9.20(b). The smaller that T_1 becomes, the larger $1/T_1$, and the less its effect on the original root locus. When $T_1 \to 0$, $1/T_1 \to \infty$ and $T_1 (D + 1/T_1) \to 1$, leaving the original root locus of Fig. 9.20(a).

(b) If $T_1 = T$ so that $1/T_1 = 1/T$, the added zero cancels the original pole, leaving the transfer functions

$$\frac{\theta_{on}}{\theta} = \frac{K'_{o1}}{D}; \quad \frac{\theta_{on}}{\theta_i} = \frac{K'_{o1}}{D + K'_{o1}}$$

the root locus of which is shown in Fig. 9.20(b).

(c) If $T_1 > T$ so that $1/T_1 < 1/T$, the new open loop zero lies to the right of the open loop pole $-1/T$, producing the root locus shown in Fig. 9.20(b). The smaller that $1/T_1$ becomes, the smaller the characteristic equation root represented by the righthand locus becomes.

Consider the case when a factor $(1/T_2)/(D + 1/T_2)$ is added into the forward feed (Fig. 9.20c), giving an additional open loop pole $-1/T_2$ and a new open loop sensitivity $K'_{o2} = K'_o/T_2$. The system transfer functions become

$$\frac{\theta_{on}}{\theta} = \frac{K'_{o2}}{D(D + 1/T)(D + 1/T_2)} \quad \text{(open loop)}$$

$$\frac{\theta_{on}}{\theta_i} = \frac{K'_{o2}}{D^3 + (1/T + 1/T_2)D^2 + (1/TT_2)\,D + K'_{o2}} \quad \text{(closed loop)}$$

Figure 9.20(c) shows the root locus diagram for each of the three possibilities:

$$T_2 < T; \quad T_2 = T; \quad T_2 > T$$

The shapes of the diagrams do not change dramatically with the value of T_2, but all are significantly varied from the shape of the original diagram of Fig. 9.20(a). The destabilizing effect of an additional open loop pole is clearly indicated by the entry of the loci into the righthand half plane for increasing K'_o. Note also that the $\pm 60°$ asymptotes move toward the right as T_2 increases, causing the branch loci to move closer to the region of unstable characteristic equation roots.

Figure 9.20 demonstrates the general tendency that

(a) adding open loop zeros acts to draw a root locus diagram to the left, away from the righthand half plane, and hence away from possible system instability;

(b) adding open loop poles acts to draw a root locus diagram to the right, toward the righthand half plane, and hence toward possible system instability.

9.6.3 Dominant Poles and Zeros

The stability condition of a linear system is associated with the solution of the system's homogeneous equation. The solution is of the form (Section 4.2)

$$\theta_{o2} = \sum_1^n (Be^{\alpha t})$$

where the α values are the roots of the characteristic equation.

If α is a large negative number, then $Be^{\alpha t}$ decays rapidly toward zero. If α is a small negative number, $Be^{\alpha t}$ decays slowly toward zero. That is, if the transient term of a system's response to a disturbance is

$$\theta_{o2}(t) = B_1 e^{-k_1 t} + B_2 e^{-k_2 t} + B_3 e^{-k_3 t} + \ldots + B_n e^{-k_n t}$$

where k is a positive number, then the smaller the number k, the more its contribution to $\theta_{o2}(t)$.

It follows that negative characteristic equation roots which are located near the imaginary axis (small roots) contribute significantly to a system's nature and performance, whereas roots which plot well to the left of the imaginary axis (large roots) have a less significant effect. The imaginary axis is of course the border line between positive and negative roots, and consequently between unstable and stable response; hence all positive roots are significant.

If a root locus exists near the imaginary axis, then small negative characteristic equation roots can exist. Such roots will dominate the effects of larger negative roots on the nature of the system. Commonly, loci adjacent to the imaginary axis are likely to result from open loop poles and/or zeros which are themselves close to the imaginary axis. This situation is demonstrated in Fig. 9.20(c), where increasing T_2, i.e., decreasing $1/T_2$, causes a shift of loci toward the imaginary axis.

It is common for negative open loop poles or zeros which are close to the imaginary axis to have a dominating effect on the performance of the system. Consequently, any compensation of the system should aim to reduce the effect of such poles or zeros.

It is possible to negate the effect of an undesired pole by adding an equal or near-equal zero, and vice versa.

9.6.4 Damping and Resonance Due to Complex Roots

If, for a particular sensitivity, the root locus indicates the presence of a pair of complex roots in a system characteristic equation, the system transfer function contains a quadratic of the form

$$\frac{\omega_n^2}{D^2 + 2\xi\omega_n D + \omega_n^2}$$

$$= \frac{\omega_n^2}{\{D + [\xi\omega_n + j\omega_n(1 - \xi^2)^{1/2}]\}\{D + [\xi\omega_n - j\omega_n(1 - \xi^2)^{1/2}]\}}$$

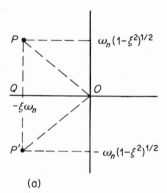

(a)

Location of complex roots P and P'

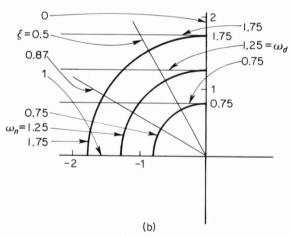

(b)

Contours of constant ω_n, ω_d, and ξ, for use with root locus diagrams

Fig. 9.21 The damping and resonance associated with a pair of complex roots of a system's characteristic equation.

where $\xi < 1$. ξ is the damping ratio and ω_n is the undamped natural frequency associated with the quadratic.

Figure 9.21(a) shows such a pair of roots, located by the real abscissa $-\xi\omega_n$ and the imaginary ordinates $\pm\omega_n(1 - \xi^2)^{1/2}$. The phasor OP which locates the roots has the magnitude $(OQ^2 + ON^2)^{1/2}$:

$$OP = \{(\xi\omega_n)^2 + [\omega_n(1 - \xi^2)^{1/2}]^2\}^{1/2} = [\xi^2\omega_n^2 + \omega_n^2(1 - \xi^2)]^{1/2} = \omega_n$$

The angle β between the phasor and the negative real axis is described by

$$\cos\beta = \frac{OQ}{OP} = \frac{\xi\omega_n}{w_n} = \xi$$

The term $\omega_n(1 - \xi^2)^{1/2}$ is often referred to as the damped natural frequency ω_d. Hence

(1) circles about the origin are lines of constant undamped natural frequency, and the radius of a circle equals ω_n;
(2) radial lines through the origin are lines of constant damping ratio, and $\xi = \cos\beta$ where β is the angle between a line and the negative real axis;
(3) lines parallel to the real axis are lines of constant damped natural frequency and their displacement from the real axis equals $\omega_d = \omega_n$ $(1 - \xi^2)^{1/2}$.

Figure 9.21(b) shows contours of ω_n, ω_d, and ξ. It is necessary only to use such contours in the quadrant shown.

Points to note

(a) Each pair of complex roots in a characteristic equation has its own damping ratio and undamped natural frequency.
(b) The larger the ratio of real part to imaginary part, the higher the damping ratio ξ, and the less the oscillatory effect on the response.
(c) The magnitude of the real part of a complex root dictates the transient rate of decay associated with the root, as discussed in Section 9.6.3.

9.6.5 The Pole-Zero Patterns of Compensators

Figure 9.22 shows the pole-zero patterns of the compensator actions previously discussed. Selection of the pole and zero values will depend on the system being compensated. The general approach to selection of these values has been discussed in the preceding sections. However, good judgment can only be achieved through the working of problems.

Action	θ_c/θ	Pole-zero pattern
$P+D$	$K/T(D+1/T)$ or $K'(D-z)$, $z=-1/T$	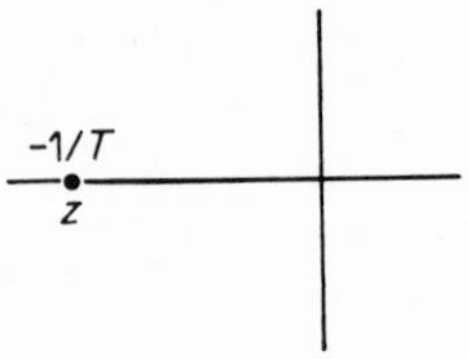 $\frac{-1/T}{z}$
$P+I$	$\dfrac{K/T(D+1/T)}{D}$ or $\dfrac{K'(D-z)}{D}$	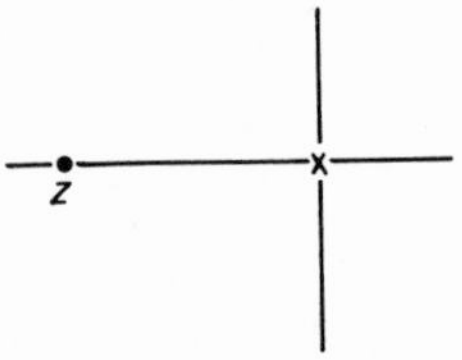 z
$P+D+I$	$\dfrac{K'(D-z_1)(D-z_2)}{D}$	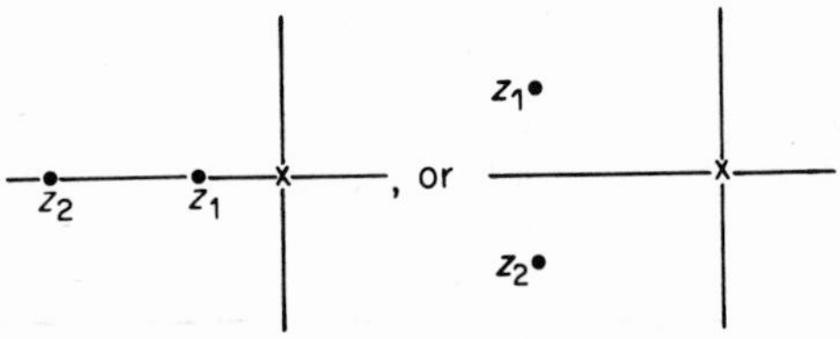 $z_2 \quad z_1$, or z_1 , z_2
First-order lag	$\dfrac{K'(D-z)}{(D-p)}$ $p<z$	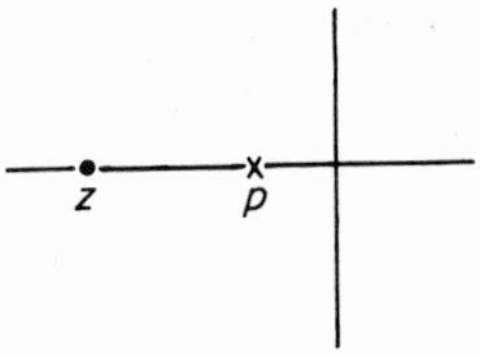 $z \quad p$
First-order lead	$\dfrac{K'(D-z)}{(D-p)}$ $p>z$	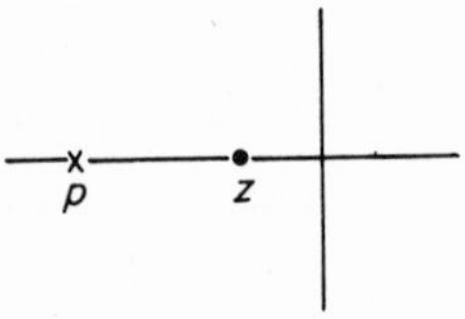 $p \quad z$
Second-order lag/lead	$\dfrac{K'(D-z_1)(D-z_2)}{(D-p_1)(D-p_2)}$	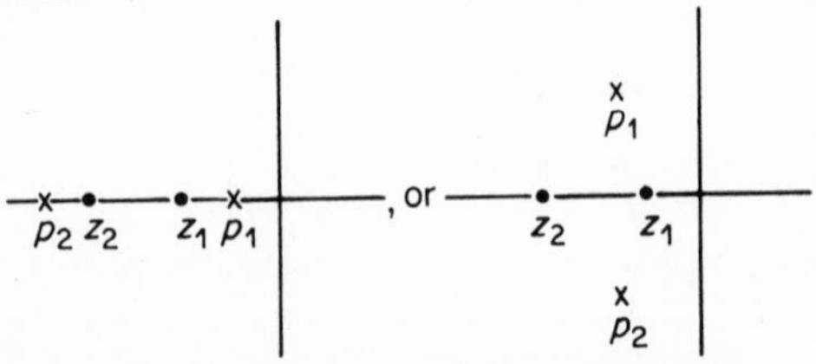 $p_2\,z_2 \quad z_1\,p_1$, or p_1 , $z_2 \quad z_1$, p_2

Fig. 9.22 Pole-zero patterns of common compensator actions.

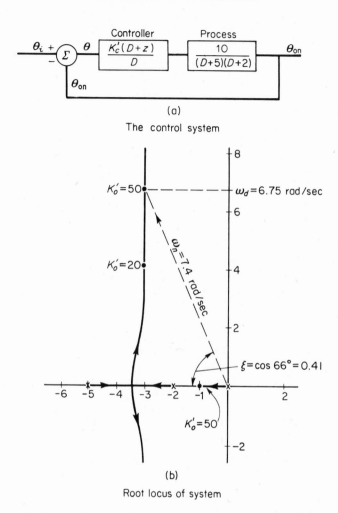

(a)

The control system

(b)

Root locus of system

Fig. 9.23 Fitting the controller to a process for automatic control, using root locus techniques.

9.6.6 Examples

Example 9.4: A process which is to be automatically controlled has the transfer function

$$\frac{10}{(D+5)(D+2)}$$

Specifications require that the controller used should include integral action to eliminate offset. The final system should have an open loop sensitivity of about 50 and a damping ratio of about 0.6. Select a controller action, examine the nature of your system by root locus methods, and make suggestions for any further adjustments to the compensator which will help to achieve the specifications.

Solution: Select proportional plus integral control action,

$$\frac{K(1 + T D)}{D} = \frac{KT(D + 1/T)}{D} = \frac{K'_c(D + z)}{D}$$

giving the system illustrated in Fig. 9.23(a). Select $z = 1$ for a first trial, giving the open loop transfer function

$$\frac{\theta_{on}}{\theta} = \frac{K'_o(D + 1)}{D(D + 5)(D + 2)}$$

Figure 9.23(b) shows the root locus of this system, from which the characteristic equation roots for $K'_o = 50$ are -0.92 and $-3.04 \pm j6.75$. For $\xi = 0.6$ ($\beta = \cos^{-1} 0.6 = 53°$), $K'_o = 20$. For $K'_o = 50$, $\xi = 0.41$. For a second trial, reduce z to 0.5.

The original open loop sensitivity was 10. When the compensator is added, $K'_o = 10K'_o$ is the new sensitivity. To give $K'_o = 50$, K'_c must be 5.

Note that the problem can also be solved by selecting a value of compensator sensitivity K'_c, and then seeking the value of the compensator zero which gives the specified damping ratio.

Example 9.5: A system has the open loop transfer function

$$\frac{\theta_{on}}{\theta} = \frac{40}{D(1 + \frac{1}{2}D)(1 + \frac{1}{4}D)}$$

It is to be compensated, using in series

$$\frac{\theta_c}{\theta} = \frac{(1 + 0.1D)0.1}{1 + 0.01D}$$

With reasonable accuracy, sketch the root loci of both the original and compensated systems.

Was the compensation necessary, and has it been effective?

Solution: In pole-zero form, the original open loop and compensator transfer functions are

$$\frac{\theta_{on}}{\theta} = \frac{320}{D(D + 2)(D + 4)}$$

$$\frac{\theta_c}{\theta} = \frac{D + 10}{D + 100}$$

$$\left(\frac{\theta_{on}}{\theta}\right)_c = \frac{320(D + 10)}{D(D + 2)(D + 4)(D + 100)}$$

Figure 9.24(a) shows the root locus of the original system, the critical locations being the following:

branches start at the open loop poles 0, -2, and -4;
high K_o' asymptotes have angles of $\alpha = n \times 180/(3 - 0) = \pm 60°$ and $180°$;
the asymptotes start at $\bar{x} = -(6 - 0)/(3 - 0) = -2$;
$K_o' = 48$ as branches cross imaginary axis.

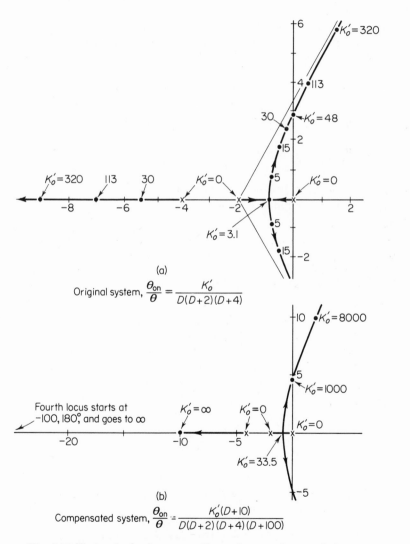

(a)

Original system, $\dfrac{\theta_{on}}{\theta} = \dfrac{K_o'}{D(D+2)(D+4)}$

(b)

Compensated system, $\dfrac{\theta_{on}}{\theta} = \dfrac{K_o'(D+10)}{D(D+2)(D+4)(D+100)}$

Fig. 9.24 First-order lead compensation, using root locus techniques.

Hence the system is unstable for the specified $K'_o = 320$ (check by finding the characteristic equation and using Routh's criteria).

Figure 9.24(b) shows the root locus of the compensated system, the critical locations being the following:

branches start at 0, -2, -4, and -100;

one branch ends at -10, the other three at ∞;

the three asymptotes have angles of $\pm 60°$ and $180°$;

the asymptotes intersect the negative real axis at $(106 - 10)/(4 - 1) = 32$. The effect of the lead action (zero dominant) has been to draw the complex branches to the left. The compensated system is stable for all values of $K'_o < 1002$.

The original system was unstable; hence compensation was necessary. The compensated system is stable; hence the compensation was effective.

Example 9.6: A system has the open loop transfer function

$$\frac{\theta_{on}}{\theta} = \frac{10(1 + 0.5D)}{D(1 + 1.2D + 0.2D^2)(1 + D)} \quad \text{(time constant form)}$$

$$= \frac{25(D + 2)}{D(D + 1)(D + 1)(D + 5)} \quad \text{(pole-zero form)}$$

It is desired that the system be stable, with a damping ratio of about 0.7 with the sensitivity maintained at $K'_o = 25$.

Solution: Figure 9.25(a) shows the root locus of the system. The system is unstable for $K'_o > 9$; whereas if $\xi = 0.7$ is to be achieved, K'_o would have to be about 0.7. It is necessary to compensate in order to achieve the specifications.

It is apparent that the complex root loci need to be drawn back into the lefthand half plane. Hence we need a dominant zero effect (corresponding to a lead effect with the frequency response method). Try a first-order lead action, of the form

$$\frac{\theta_c}{\theta} = \frac{K'(D + z)}{D + p}, \quad p > z$$

(Lead is

$$\frac{\theta_c}{\theta} = \frac{\beta(1 + T D)}{1 + \beta T D}, \quad \beta < 1$$

Hence

$$\frac{\theta_c}{\theta} = \frac{\beta T(D + 1/T)}{\beta T(D + 1/\beta T)}$$

$$= \frac{D + z}{D + p}$$

where $z = 1/T$ and $p = 1/\beta T = z/\beta$.)

Selecting $z = 1$ as the compensator zero causes cancellation of one of the $(D + 1)$ poles, and will provide a strong action to draw the original root locus to the left. Select $\beta = 0.1$ and hence $p = 10$ as the pole, so that it does not counter the effect of $z = 1$ too strongly. Consideration of the effect of large open loop poles on the sensitivity of any point on a root locus indicates that a large value of p will

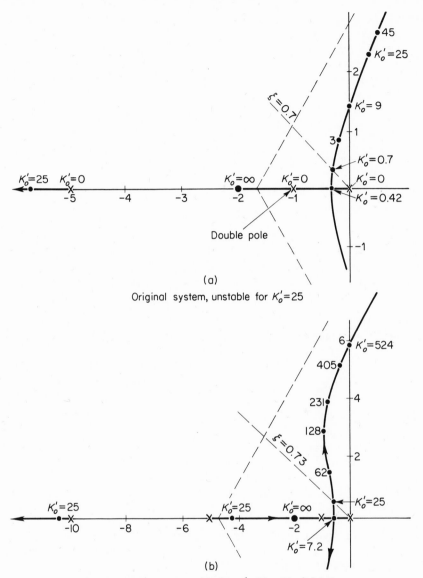

(a)

Original system, unstable for $K_o'=25$

(b)

Compensated system, stable for $K_o'=25$, with $\xi \doteq 0.7$

Fig. 9.25 Stabilizing the system

$$\frac{\theta_{on}}{\theta} = \frac{K_o'(D+2)}{D(D+1)^2(D+5)}$$

with the compensator $\dfrac{\theta_c}{\theta} = \dfrac{K(D+1)}{(D+10)}$

cause higher values of K'_o at a given location on the locus. This is desirable in the present case.

The open loop transfer function of the compensated system is

$$\left(\frac{\theta_{on}}{\theta}\right)_c = \frac{K'_o(D+2)(D+1)}{D(D+1)^2(D+5)(D+10)} = \frac{K'_o(D+2)}{D(D+1)(D+5)(D+10)}$$

The root locus is shown in Fig. 9.25(b). For $K'_o = 25$, the damping ratio (cos β) is $\xi = 0.73$. The natural frequencies of the system are $\omega_n = 0.9$ rad/sec (undamped), and $\omega_d = 0.6$ rad/sec (damped).

From the root locus, the system's characteristic equation for $K'_o = 25$ is

$$(D+10.4)(D+4.3)(D+0.65+j0.6)(D+0.65-j0.6) = 0$$

which reduces to

$$D^4 + 16D^3 + 65D^2 + 75D + 50 = 0$$

Note that the compensated system is stable for all values of K'_o up to 520, and that ξ decreases, ω_n increases, and ω_d increases as K'_o increases.

9.7 FEEDBACK COMPENSATION

The examples used in the preceding Sections 9.5 and 9.6 used series compensation, in which the compensator was placed in the forward feed. As discussed in Section 9.2, the compensating transfer function may be placed in the feedback loop (parallel compensation). It was shown that the resulting open loop transfer function, the Nyquist plot, the stability condition, the characteristics equation, and the root locus are all unaffected by the location of the compensator. Hence the techniques used in Sections 9.5 and 9.6 apply equally to series or parallel compensation, except for the transfer function and frequency response characteristics of the final closed loop system achieved. Both of these are dependent on the location of the compensator, as discussed in Section 6.5.2.

Location of a compensator in a real situation depends on such factors as the following:

(a) To which signals in the loop can compensator actions be physically applied? At what cost and convenience?
(b) Which location (series or parallel) has the most desirable effects on the closed loop system's performance characteristics?

9.8 SUMMARY

A basic approach to the synthesis (design) of a closed loop control system is

(a) to make a preliminary design of the system, including evaluation of the component and system transfer functions;

(b) to examine the proposed system's characteristics and performance against known specifications and criteria;

(c) to alter or adjust the control components if the performance is inadequate due to stability, speed of response, damping, natural frequencies, etc., in a manner such as to achieve the desired performance.

A number of physically achievable compensator actions have been examined. The compensator actions and their effects on system performance have been studied, using both frequency response and root locus techniques.

While few hard and fast rules for compensation have been offered, the desirable and undesirable effects of various compensator actions have been examined. The effect of a compensator action is highly dependent on the system itself, and good judgment in this area can only come with experience. The use of trial and error in applying compensation is reduced, as good criteria by which judgments can be made are achieved through knowledge of the compensator characteristics.

PROBLEMS

9.1 Show that the device shown in Fig. 9.26 (p. 360) yields a proportional plus derivative action between the input displacement x_i and the response pressure P_o:

$$K_p = \frac{P_o}{x} \text{ lb/in.}^2/\text{in.} \quad \text{is a large number}$$

$$L = \frac{x}{x_i} \quad \text{when pivot } O_1 \text{ is stationary}$$

$$M = \frac{x}{y} \quad \text{when pivot } O_2 \text{ is stationary}$$

Answer: $\frac{P_o}{x_i} \approx \frac{kL}{aM} (1 + T D)$, where $T = RC_b$.

9.2 A system has the open loop transfer function

$$\frac{10}{D(D + 1)(D/5 + 1)}$$

Establish the stability condition of the system, and use frequency response techniques to achieve gain and phase margins of 2 and 45° respectively, with first-order lag compensation.

9.3 Solve Problem 9.2 using first-order lead compensation.

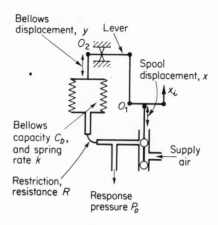

Bellows displacement, y Lever

O_2

Spool displacement, x

x_i

O_1

Bellows capacity C_b, and spring rate k

Restriction, resistance R

Response pressure P_o

Supply air

Fig. 9.26

9.4 A process has the transfer function

$$\frac{20}{(1 + D/4)(1 + D/16)}$$

It is desired to design an automatic control system for the process. It can be assumed that unity feedback of the system's response is achieved. Select a controller action which will approximately satisfy the following requirements:

(a) closed loop damping is to be greater than $\xi = 0.8$;
(b) closed loop natural undamped frequency is to be 10 rad/sec;
(c) open loop gain is to be about 100, to minimize steady-state errors.

9.5 A system has the open loop transfer function

$$\frac{\theta_{on}}{\theta} = \frac{40}{D(1 + \frac{1}{2}D)(1 + \frac{1}{4}D)}$$

It is to be compensated using, in series,

$$\frac{10(D^2 + 2D + 2)}{D}, \quad (P + I + D)$$

With reasonable accuracy, sketch the root loci of both the original and compensated systems. Was the compensation necessary and has it been effective? For what open loop sensitivity is the system damping ratio 0.3?

9.6 A system has the open loop transfer function

$$\frac{\theta_{on}}{\theta} = \frac{K_o' D(D + 0.56)}{(D + 4)(D + 10)(D^2 + 1.68D + 8.7)}$$

Sketch the root locus with sufficient accuracy to show that the system is highly oscillatory for values of $K_o' < 50$. Compensate the system to reduce its oscillatory nature, aiming for a damping ratio of about 0.6 and a natural undamped frequency of about 0.6 radian/sec for an open loop sensitivity of about $K_o' = 50$.

10 *Introduction to nonlinear analysis*

10.1 INTRODUCTION

For the purposes of the present text, a *linear engineering system* can be defined as one whose nature and behavior can be *adequately* described by one or more linear ordinary differential equations in time.

Conversely, a *nonlinear system* is one whose nature and behavior cannot be *adequately* described by differential equations without the inclusion of one or more nonlinear relationships.

Some common nonlinear relationships are discussed in Section 1.5 of Chapter 1 and in Appendix A.

The above definitions hinge on the word *adequately*. Most engineering situations are inherently nonlinear, and can be successfully linearized only for particular operating conditions which should be carefully specified and understood. For example, Fig. 10.1 shows a load-extension curve for a "linear" coil spring. Within its "working range," deflection is proportional to load, a linear relationship. However, if the load is increased beyond the maximum of the working range, the spring material starts to yield and permanently deforms the spring. The behavior of the spring is no longer described by $F = kx$. Also, if the spring is subjected to compression (negative load), it behaves linearly only up to the point at which it approaches the solidly compressed condition. Many engineering relation-

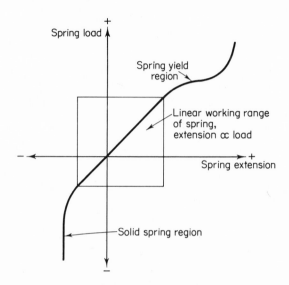

Fig. 10.1   Typical load-extension characteristic of a linear spring.

ships can be successfully linearized if the range of operation is clearly delineated. However, a considerable number of useful engineering relationships cannot be adequately linearized, i.e., a linear analysis of them produces gross errors in the correlation between the calculated performance and the real performance of the system.

The advantages of linearization and the consequent conventional linear analysis are very real. Linear analysis is general and straightforward. The advantages include the following:

(a) The system transfer function is independent of the size and shape of an input disturbance and of any initial values of the system variables. The transfer function is truly the mathematical model of the system.

(b) The principle of superposition holds. Thus the total response of the system to two inputs is the sum of its responses to the inputs taken one at a time. Also, the system's response to an input is doubled in magnitude if the input is doubled in size, etc.

(c) The solution of a linear transfer function to many forms of input is readily affected.

(d) The steady-state condition achieved by a stable system is of the same form as the input.

Nonlinear systems and nonlinear analysis have the following disadvantages:

(a) A nonlinear transfer function is in itself not descriptive of the nature of the system. The nature and response of a nonlinear system depends on both the type and the size of an input disturbance, and also on the initial values of the system variables. A nonlinear system which has been adjusted to give good response to a particular size of step input may respond quite badly — even to the point of being unstable — to a step input of different size, or to a ramp, or to a sine input.
(b) Superposition does not apply.
(c) There is no general technique for solving nonlinear equations. Particular nonlinearities have to be handled with particular techniques of analysis.
(d) The steady-state condition of the system following an input is not necessarily of the form of the input.

The requirements of analysis of nonlinear systems are identical with those of linear analysis. System stability is the primary condition to be examined. The stability of a linear system is a characteristic only of the system itself. The stability of a nonlinear system depends on the system, on the form and size of the input, and on the initial condition of the system when the input is introduced. The degree of oscillation in the response, the speed of response, the accuracy of response, and the transient behavior must also be investigated.

Good understanding of the nature of a system does not necessarily require that system equations be accurately solved for time responses. Even with linear analysis, the frequency response and root locus techniques give comprehensive data on the performance of a system, without requiring solution of equations. Most of the techniques which have been accepted for the analysis of nonlinear systems require studying the steady-state condition achieved by the system after it experiences an input. Studies of the transient regime of response have been relatively unsuccessful.

The advent of computers, both analog and digital, has provided the means for the solution of many nonlinear equations. In both cases, the real problem is simulated on the computer. The analog computer is limited by the number of nonlinear function generators which can be achieved and by the difficulties in scaling complex problems. The digital computer, which allows the use of numerical techniques (trial and error with converging approximations), has been used increasingly to solve nonlinear equations. Accuracy and computer time may raise difficulties.

The difficulty in predicting the behavior of nonlinear components and systems has led to a tendency to seek linear designs. It should not be inferred, however, that a nonlinear component or system is inherently inferior to its linear counterpart. Some nonlinear relationships have highly desirable characteristics which can be utilized to reduce the expense and increase the performance of engineering systems. Linearization, on the other hand, can be expensive and unnecessary. The discontinuous (on-off) tank level and refrigerator temperature control systems discussed in Chapter 1, Section 1.7, are examples of simple, effective, nonlinear systems.

Careful linearization and linear analysis of systems containing nonlinear relationships has been successful. The tools of linear analysis have been carefully extended so as to be useful in the analysis of certain nonlinear situations. However, nonlinear physical components and nonlinear equations have inherent characteristics which are different from linear components and equations. These very nonlinearities can be useful in obtaining superior hardware and performance. Hence, despite inherent difficulties, nonlinear analysis of systems, where appropriate, must be made. Finally, all analysis, whether linear or nonlinear, is entirely dependent on proper description of the actions which take place in the components which make up the system. A properly derived differential equation set will contain all of the fundamental information required to predict the physical behavior of the system.

10.2 SOME TYPES AND CLASSIFICATIONS OF ENGINEERING NONLINEARITIES

10.2.1 Types

(a) **Simple continuous nonlinear relationships** of the forms shown in Fig. 10.2(a) are common. For example:

(1) For turbulent flow through fluid restrictions,

$$q \propto \Delta p^{1/2}$$

where q is flow rate; Δp is pressure drop.

(2) For centripetal force on a revolving mass,

$$F_c \propto N^2$$

where F_c is centripetal force; N is speed, rpm.

(3) For a nonlinear spring,

$$F \propto x^n \quad (n \neq 1)$$

where F is the load and x the extension.

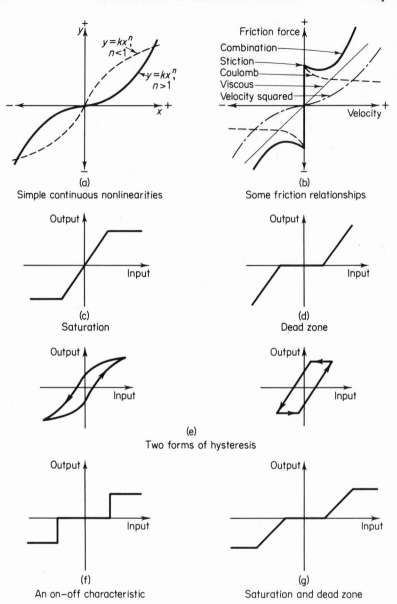

Fig. 10.2 Some common nonlinear relationships.

(4) In general,

$$\theta_o \propto \theta_i^n \quad (n \neq 1)$$

Simple exponential relationships are also of this type.

(b) **Friction** occurs in many forms and is generally nonlinear in nature. Viscous friction is the exception. Figure 10.2(b) shows several common forms of friction, including a composite curve of stiction plus coulomb plus viscous friction. The difficulty in describing actions with static and coulomb friction is apparent.

(c) **Saturation:** No physical component can generate a continually increasing quantity. The device reaches a physical limit, such as a mechanical stop or fuse, beyond which it will not operate. Figure 10.2(c) shows how even a linear relationship can reach this cutoff condition, known as *saturation*. The nonlinear relationships of Fig. 10.2(a) would also be subjected to saturation in any real physical situation.

(d) **Dead zone** describes a range of input for which the response is zero. Figure 10.2(d) describes this situation, which is also known as **threshold,** or **flat spot.**

(e) **Hysteresis,** a commonly occurring phenomena, is illustrated in Fig. 10.2(e). It is a complex form of dead zone for which the output can have many (random) values for a particular input condition. The curved form of hysteresis is found in electromagnetic circuits, due to residual magnetic action. The parallelogram form is associated with the backlash in mechanical gear systems, due to the inevitable clearance present.

(f) **On-off characteristics** of the type discussed in Chapter 1, Section 1.7, can be represented as in Fig. 10.2(f).

(g) **Combination:** It is likely that a real nonlinearity is composed of one or more of the preceding types, or other forms not discussed here. For example, Fig. 10.2(g) shows a combination of dead zone and saturation.

(h) **Sampled-data systems** operate in a continuous, intermittent manner. A switch on the sampler unit of the controller (Fig. 10.3) closes at preset discrete intervals to permit signal flow in the system. If error exists, action takes place to eliminate it. When the switch opens according to its preset program, the monitor holds the last value of error until the

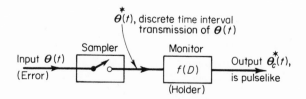

Fig. 10.3 Sampled-data controller unit.

sampler switch closes again. Thus the output from the monitor is a train of pulse-like signals, instead of the continuous signal of linear control. Complex modern systems which include digital computers as control components are usually linked up in sampled-data form so that the computer accepts information at discrete intervals and promotes the action necessary to restore the system condition to the programed requirement.

10.2.2 Classifications

An infinite variety of nonlinear relationships exist which makes general classification difficult. Some of the broader classification terms are introduced here.

(a) **Inherent** or **parasitic nonlinearities** are those the presence of which in a system, although undesirable, cannot be eliminated for practical reasons. These include backlash and friction in mechanical systems, and hysteresis in electromagnetic systems.

(b) **Intentional** or **essential nonlinearities** are deliberately built into a system either to improve its performance or, in some cases, to make the system work. Examples are nonlinear springs, nonlinear damping (velocity-squared friction), and semiconductors.

(c) **Large-value nonlinearities** are linear over large ranges of operation. In the overall sense, all linear engineering components, such as the linear spring in Fig. 10.1, fall into this category.

(d) **Small-value nonlinearities** are those the characteristic slopes of which change too rapidly, or have discontinuities, so that linearization is ineffective.

(e) **Continuous nonlinearities** are those of the type shown in Fig. 10.2(a), having smooth variations of the input-output relationship.

(f) **Discontinuous nonlinearities,** which include those shown in Figs. 10.2(c) and (d), have abrupt changes in the relationship between input and output.

(g) **Simple nonlinearities** have single-valued repeatable relationships between the input and response. Figures 10.2(a), (b), (c), and (d) all are of this form.

(h) **Complex nonlinearities** have multivalued possible relationships between the output and a particular input. Hysteresis, Fig. 10.2(e), is of this type. So too is the electric-motor torque-speed-current relationship shown in Fig. 10.4.

(i) **Single-variable nonlinearities** have only the input and the output as system variables. All of the previous cases are of this type.

(j) **Multi-variable nonlinearities** have the output as a function of more than one variable. Figure 10.4 shows the torque-speed-current rela-

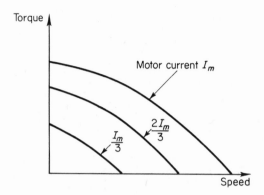

Fig. 10.4 Torque-speed-current characteristic of two-phase electric servo-motor.

tionships for an electric servomotor. The output torque is a nonlinear function of both speed and control current.

10.3 SOME TYPICAL BEHAVIOR PATTERNS

The behavior of linear systems is predictable and repeatable, even if the system is unstable. The behavior of nonlinear systems is much more complex, and in some cases can appear to be quite arbitrary. However, certain patterns of behavior are commonly experienced, and will be introduced here.

Typically, the behavior of a nonlinear system will depend on the form of an input, on the size of the input, and on the initial state of the system when the input is introduced. Figure 10.5(a) shows how one system might respond to step inputs of different size.

Some nonlinear systems develop a steady-state oscillation which persists after the transient response to an input, such as a step, decays to zero. The oscillation is usually periodic, but not necessarily sinusoidal. This self-excited or natural oscillation is called **limit cycle oscillation.** If of very small amplitude, such an oscillation is not always harmful, and is classified as "noise." Figure 10.5(b) shows how such a system might respond to a step input.

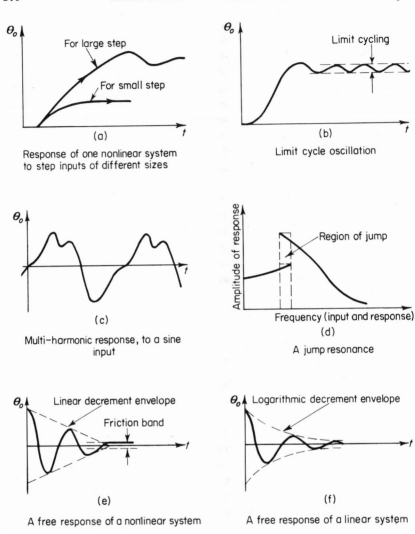

Fig. 10.5 Some response characteristics of nonlinear systems.

Other nonlinear systems subjected to a sine input develop a multi-frequency steady-rate response. The frequencies involved can be less than the input frequency (subharmonics) or greater than it (superharmonics or, simply, harmonics). Figure 10.5(c) shows a typical case. This condition is referred to as **harmonic oscillation.** With linear systems, the frequency of the steady-state response sinusoid is the same as the frequency of the input sine, even though both response amplitude and phase are affected by the input frequency.

Still other nonlinear systems have a smooth sinusoidal response to an input sine, and hence may be mistaken for linear systems. However, if a frequency response test is made, it is likely that discontinuities will appear in the amplitude ratio and phase-versus-frequency curves, as illustrated in Fig. 10.5(d). Such discontinuities are referred to as **jump resonances.**

Nonlinearities such as friction can cause a loss of **static accuracy,** which means a development of steady-state errors. A linear system with no inputs assumes a unique steady-state condition. A nonlinear system with no inputs may occupy any condition in an equilibrium range. Figure 10.5(e) shows a typical free response (i.e., motivation by an initial condition only) of a mechanical system with coulomb friction. Friction can cause the system to come to rest anywhere in the friction band.

It is well known that the free response of a lightly-damped linear system fits into an exponentially decaying envelope, as shown in Fig. 10.5(f). The exponential decay is called the **logarithmic decrement.** A nonlinearity in a system can be revealed if the envelope for free response is other than exponential. For example, Fig. 10.5(e) shows a **linear decrement,** the system of which must be nonlinear.

10.4 SOME TECHNIQUES OF ANALYSIS

10.4.1 Introduction

As already stated, there is no general approach to the solution of nonlinear equations. Solutions for some types of equations — usually not of engineering interest — have been developed. A variety of numerical and graphic techniques have been developed for handling particular types of nonlinear terms. The two most common of these, the phase plane and the describing function techniques, will be discussed in some detail.

It should be appreciated that only one term of an equation need be nonlinear to render the equation nonlinear. Commonly, an engineering system equation will contain both linear and nonlinear terms. For example, in the equation

$$M D^2x + c(Dx)^2 + kx = F_i$$

all the terms are linear except $c(Dx)^2$.

The idea of linearizing nonlinear relationships within narrow operating ranges has already been discussed. It is a most widely used technique and is often quite adequate for small inputs or perturbations in the narrow range of operation.

10.4.2 Stability

The stability of linear systems is very conveniently tied to the condition of the roots of the system's characteristic equation. Even so, several criteria of stability are in use, so it is not necessary to actually extract the roots of the high-order polynomials which are the characteristic equations of linear systems. The Routh and Nyquist stability criteria both reveal either the presence or absence of roots with positive real parts, without evaluating the roots.

Except for some special cases, the concept that stability is associated with the system's characteristic equation has no meaning with nonlinear equations. The stability of a nonlinear system can be dependent on the size and type of input experienced by the system or on the initial state of the system when a disturbance is introduced.

Stability of nonlinear systems is usually examined keeping in mind that if a small temporary input applied to the system when in equilibrium causes only a temporary change in the response, the system is stable. If this condition is satisfied, the system is stable only about the specified point of equilibrium. The same input applied when the system is in a different equilibrium state may evoke an unstable response, as illustrated in Fig. 10.6. Criteria have been developed whereby the conditions for

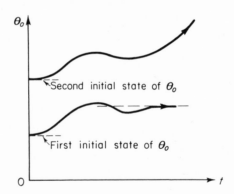

Fig. 10.6 Illustrating how initial state of system variables can affect response to a particular input.

stability for nonlinear systems can be established without requiring full solutions of equations. The Liapunov approaches are prominent among these, and allow establishment of the bounds of the system's variables for which the system will be inherently stable.

10.4.3 Describing Function Analysis

This technique, an extension of steady-state frequency response analysis, is used to investigate the stability of certain types of nonlinear systems. It is useful where the nonlinearities can be represented in one block of the block diagram of a negative feedback system, as illustrated in Fig. 10.7. The response of the nonlinear element to sinusoidal input must be

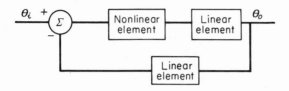

Fig. 10.7   Feedback system with only one nonlinear element.

periodic, although not necessarily sinusoidal, for the describing function technique to be useful. Figure 10.5(c) shows a typical periodic nonsinusoidal response.

A periodic function of the type illustrated in Fig. 10.5(c) can be described by the Fourrier series:

$$x(t) = B_1 \sin (\omega t + \phi_1) + B_2 \sin (2\omega t + \phi_2) + B_3 (3\omega t + \phi_3) \ldots \quad (10.1)$$

If the periodic response is due to an input

$$\theta_i = H \sin \omega t \quad (10.2)$$

then $\omega_1 = \omega$, and coefficients $B_1, B_2, \ldots$ and $\phi_1, \phi_2, \ldots$ are functions of the input amplitude H.

The first term of the expansion, $B_1 \sin (\omega_1 t + \phi_1)$, is called the **fundamental term** of the output $x(t)$. A **describing function** for the nonlinear element is defined as

$$\text{D.F.} = \frac{B_1}{H}, \quad \measuredangle \phi_1 \quad (10.3)$$

which, in terms of frequency response, is a phasor on the complex plane of magnitude B_1/H and angle ϕ_1. The describing function so defined can be regarded as an equivalent frequency response characteristic of the nonlinear element. It is an approximation only, as all of the other terms of Eq. 10.1 were neglected. With feedback systems, the error associated with this approximation is usually not great, for the high frequency effects are attenuated (filtered out) by the linear elements in the loop. This fact is demonstrated by the increasing attenuation at higher frequencies on the frequency response characteristics of systems investigated in Chapter 5. Note that the describing function is input-amplitude-dependent, thus retaining its essential nonlinearity.

Having established a describing function, the stability of the system can be examined by applying the Nyquist criterion. The Nyquist diagram is input-amplitude-dependent.

10.4.4 Phase-Plane Analysis

Phase-plane analysis is confined to second-order systems, and hence is of limited use. However, apart from its usefulness in allowing the handling of second-order nonlinear systems, the phase-plane technique is worthy of introduction as an introduction to the **phase-space** (more often called **state-space**) techniques with which high-order equations can be analyzed (introduced in Chapter 11).

Consider the second-order system equation

$$A\ddot{x} + B\dot{x} + Cx = y$$

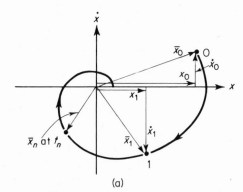

(a)

Phase–plane representation

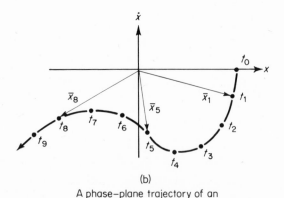

(b)

A phase–plane trajectory of an
unstable system

Fig. 10.8 Phase-plane trajectories, nonlinear second-order systems.

The state of this system as time varies can be ascertained if $x(t)$ and $\dot{x}(t)$ are established. The time-varying state of the system can be described graphically by plotting values of $x(t)$ and $\dot{x}(t)$ on the x, $\dot{x}$ coordinates shown in Fig. 10.8. Thus the initial values x_o and $\dot{x}_o$ at $t = 0$ are shown as point 0, whereas the values at t_1 (x_1 and $\dot{x}_1$) are shown at point 1. Note that the condition of x_n and $\dot{x}_n$ at any time t_n, and hence the state of the system, can be represented by the vector $\bar{x}_n = \overline{x_n + \dot{x}_n}$. Here x and $\dot{x}$ are called the **state variables** of the system, and $\bar{x}$ is the **state vector**. The path formed by discrete time interval evaluations of $\bar{x} = \overline{x + \dot{x}}$, giving all corresponding values of x and $\dot{x}$, is called the **phase-plane trajectory** of the system. With time as a parameter on it, the trajectory is a time history of the behavior of the system following an input. The value of phase-plane analysis is that the trajectory can be obtained even when the nonlinear equation itself cannot be directly solved to give $x(t)$. A family of trajectories, known as the **phase portrait** of the system, can be formed to completely describe the response behavior of a system for specific input and initial state conditions.

When such a trajectory is obtained, the stability condition of the system is apparent. In Fig. 10.8(a), the trajectory decreases in time toward zero, showing that response $\bar{x} = \overline{x + \dot{x}}$ decreases in time, the criterion for a stable system. In Fig. 10.8(b), the trajectory increases continually in time, indicating that the response $\bar{x} = \overline{x + \dot{x}}$ is increasing in time, the sign of instability.

It is possible to calculate $x(t)$ and $\dot{x}(t)$ for all linear and for some nonlinear second-order systems. However, for the general case of second-order nonlinear systems, the trajectory must be constructed by graphic methods, such as the isocline technique.

10.5 SUMMARY

The subject of nonlinear systems, their behavior, and methods of analysis has been qualitatively introduced. Nonlinear systems and equations are **inherently** different from their linear counterparts, and extensions of linear analysis to cover nonlinear systems are at best only partly successful. Nonlinear analysis can and must be made in the many real situations where linearizations and linear analysis do not adequately describe the behavior of the system.

BIBLIOGRAPHY

1. Cunningham, W. J., *Introduction to Non-linear Analysis*. New York: McGraw-Hill Book Company, 1958.
2. Graham, D. and McRuer, D., *Analysis of Non-linear Control Systems*. New York: John Wiley & Sons, Inc., 1961.

3. Struble, R. A., *Non-linear Differential Equations.* New York: McGraw-Hill Book Company, 1962.

4. Gibson, J. E., *Non-linear Automatic Control.* New York: McGraw-Hill Book Company, 1963.

5. Hahn, W., *Theory and Application of Liapunov's Direct Method.* Englewood Cliffs, New Jersey: Prentice-Hall, Inc., 1963.

6. Lefschetz, S., *Stability of Non-linear Control Systems.* New York: Academic Press, Inc., 1965.

11 Introduction to the state-variable method of analysis

11.1 INTRODUCTION

The present text has been so far primarily concerned with the analysis of relatively simple linear systems. The techniques described and developed are eminently suited to the task, and will continue to be the keystones of analysis of such systems. Basically, our approach has been to investigate the nature of a single system variable, designated the response, when the system is disturbed by a change (the input) in another unique system variable. Systems have been described by the dynamic relationship between the response and the input, commonly expressed as a single-input single-output transfer function.

Conventional linear analysis becomes inadequate if

(a) a system contains nonlinear relationships between its variables, which cannot be ignored as secondary or effectively linearized;

(b) it is desired to study simultaneously the response of more than one system variable;

(c) it is desired to subject the system to several simultaneous input disturbances;

(d) the system is highly complex: some modern systems are composed of several component subsystems, each having the complexity of the most complicated system discussed in this book.

The state-variable method of analysis provides a technique whereby systems can be represented concisely by a mathematical model which allows the ready inclusion of multiple inputs, multiple response variables, initial values of the system variables, and both linear and nonlinear relationships. The model has the potential to yield comprehensive information on the response of all significant system variables.

The ideas of the method are not new, being extensions of the classical representation and solution of time-domain differential equations. Well-established mathematical tools such as matrix and vector-matrix algebra are used to concisely describe and manipulate complicated and extensive mathematical relationships. The ability of the modern computer to rapidly evaluate vector-matrix relationships has provided the incentive for the current rapid development of the state-variable method of analysis.

As implied, the method has the most general applicability. However, it will be introduced using the relatively simple linear systems associated with the previous work of the present text.

11.2 OUTLINE OF THE STATE-VARIABLE METHOD

The object of the dynamic analysis of an engineering system is to predict the future state of a system from knowledge of its present state, and of the input disturbances experienced by the system during the time period considered. For complete analysis, it is desirable that the mathematical representation of the dynamic state of a system allow determination of the values at any instant of all of the variables which together describe the state of the system. The state-variable analysis technique enables a set of significant system variables, known as the **state variables,** to be defined and to be described as functions of time.

This chapter describes methods for selecting a significant set of state variables and for forming a system model in vector-matrix form which relates the state variables (including their initial values), the system inputs (which are independent of the system), and the characteristic parameters of the system itself. Sufficient matrix algebra is included in Appendix D to enable the reader to comprehend the methods of forming the vector-matrix system model. However, techniques for solving the vector-matrix equations require extensive understanding of the manipulation of vector-matrices and, most conveniently, use of the digital computer, and are considered to be beyond the scope of the present chapter.

Briefly, the state-variable technique requires the following:

(a) that the system and its inputs be represented by a set of normal-form first-order ordinary differential equations (remember that a high-order transfer function is formed by combining a set of simultaneous low-order relationships which describe the action of the system);

(b) that the set of first-order equations, known as the state equations, contain sufficient information on the initial state of the system and of the inputs to enable the future state to be predicted;

(c) that the dependent variable of each state equation be assigned to be a state variable of the system, whose time history following inputs to the system is required for full comprehension of the behavior of the system;

(d) that the first-order state equations be represented in vector-matrix form, known as the state model, in order to concisely contain the information required for analysis of the state variables;

(e) that the vector-matrix state model be solved to yield the time histories of the state variables due to the operation of the inputs. For systems where it is worthwhile using the state-variable technique, solution will require use of a digital computer.

11.3 THE STATE VARIABLES OF A SIMPLE SYSTEM

Example 11.1:

(a) Figure 11.1(a) shows the simple damped-spring-mass system of Examples 3.8 and 3.14. The system equation is

$$M\, D^2 y + c\, Dy + ky = F(t)$$

It is apparent that

$$Dy = \dot{y} \quad \text{and} \quad M\, D\dot{y} + c\dot{y} + ky = F(t)$$

which can be written

$$Dx_1 = x_2 \quad \text{and} \quad M\, Dx_2 + cx_2 + kx_1 = F(t)$$

where $x_1 = y$ and $x_2 = \dot{y}$.

Rearrangement yields

$$Dx_1 = x_2 \quad \text{and} \quad Dx_2 = \frac{-kx_1 - cx_2 + F(t)}{M}$$

which are two normal-form first-order differential equations which describe the system; $x_1 = y$ and $x_2 = \dot{y}$ are the dependent variables of the respective equations, and are therefore the state variables of the system. Thus the displacement and the velocity of the mass are the state variables of the damped-spring-mass system. It is no coincidence that the second-order system has two state variables.

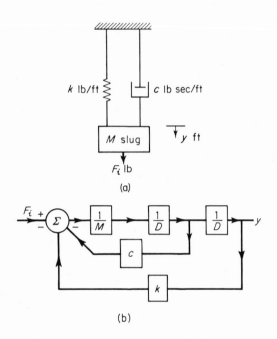

(a)

(b)

Fig. 11.1   (a) Damped-spring-mass system.   (b) Block diagram of system.

(b) Figure 11.1(b) shows the block diagram of the damped-spring-mass system. The equation associated with the righthand integration is

$$\dot{y}\frac{1}{D} = y \quad \text{or} \quad Dy = \dot{y}$$

The equation associated with the lefthand integration is

$$\left(\frac{F(t)}{M} - \frac{k}{M}y - \frac{c}{M}\dot{y}\right)\frac{1}{D} = \dot{y} \quad \text{or} \quad D\dot{y} = \frac{F(t)}{M} - \frac{cy}{M} - \frac{k}{M}y$$

Letting $y = x_1$ and $\dot{y} = x_2$ yields

$$Dx_1 = x_2 \quad \text{and} \quad Dx_2 = \frac{F(t) - cx_2 - kx_1}{M}$$

Thus the state variables of the systems, x_1 and x_2, are the outputs of the integrations present in the system's block diagram. This is a most useful general rule for selecting a useful set of state variables for a system.

Other signal-flow diagrams, such as signal-flow graphs or analog computer diagrams, can be used to select the state variables of a system. In each case, the output of each integration in the diagram is a state variable.

11.4 THE STATE VARIABLES OF A SYSTEM — GENERAL

(a) A single-input single-output system of nth order, in which no time derivatives of the input exist, has n state variables consisting of

(1) the selected output variable y,
(2) the derivatives of this variable: $\dot{y}$, $\ddot{y}$,..., up to the $(n-1)$th derivative. Thus the damped-spring-mass of Example 11.1 has state-variables y and $\dot{y}$, referred to as x_1 and x_2 respectively.

(b) A single-input single-output system of nth order which contains derivatives of the input, i.e., has zeros in the transfer function, contains n state variables. However, the state variables will not be defined as in (a). The basic premise of defining as the state variables the dependent variables of the n normal-form first-order differential equations, which together produce the transfer function, must be adhered to. Selection of the state variables may be made directly as the outputs of the integrations of the system's block diagram or of its analog computer diagram.

Example 11.2: Figure 11.2 shows the block diagram of a system whose transfer function is

$$\frac{\theta_o}{\theta_i} = \frac{(1+D)}{D^2 + aD + b}$$

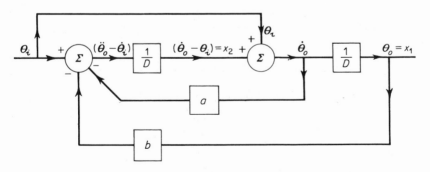

Fig. 11.2   Block diagram of the system:

$$\frac{\theta_o}{\theta_i} = \frac{1+D}{D^2 + aD + b}$$

The system is of second order, and will require two state variables. The state variables of the system are the integrator outputs

$$x_1 = \theta_o \quad \text{and} \quad x_2 = (\dot{\theta}_o - \theta_i)$$

(c) Multiple-input multiple-output systems will have a number of state variables equal to the total number of integrations required to reduce the system equations in order to yield the output variables.

Example 11.3: A system which is described by the two simultaneous equations

$$\ddot{y}_1 + 3\dot{y}_1 + 2y_2 = u_1 \quad \text{and} \quad \ddot{y}_2 + \dot{y}_1 + y_2 = u_2$$

has two inputs u_1 and u_2 and two outputs y_1 and y_2. Jointly, the equations contain four derivative orders ($\ddot{y}_1$ is of second order, $\ddot{y}_2$ is of second order). Hence the system has four state variables. This fact is clearly demonstrated by the block diagram representation of the system equations, Fig. 11.3, which contains four integrations. Clearly, the state variables are

$$x_1 = y_1; \quad x_2 = \dot{y}_1; \quad x_3 = y_2; \quad x_4 = \dot{y}_2$$

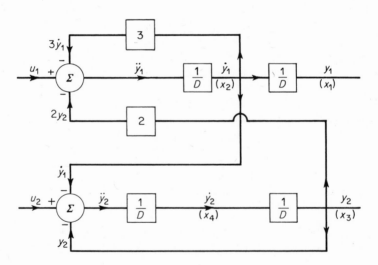

Fig. 11.3 Block diagram of the equations:

$$\ddot{y}_1 + 3\dot{y}_1 + 2y_2 = u_1$$
$$\ddot{y}_2 + \dot{y}_1 + y_2 = u_2$$

The state variables can be seen directly as the outputs of the integrations in Fig. 11.3, or could be selected by using the idea expressed in (a). As in (b), the state variables would not follow the above pattern if derivatives of the inputs ($\dot{u}_1$, $\dot{u}_2$, etc.) had been present.

11.5 THE STATE VECTOR

The damped-spring-mass system of Example 11.1 has the state equations

$$Dx_1 = x_2 \quad \text{and} \quad Dx_2 = -\frac{k}{M} x_1 - \frac{c}{M} x_2 + \frac{F(t)}{M}$$

which must be solved for $x_1(t)$ and $x_2(t)$ to yield the state of the system at any time.

Solutions for x_1 and x_2 at particular times can be plotted on the x_1, x_2 coordinates shown in Fig. 11.4(a). The starting point for the plot is the $t = 0$ values of x_1 and x_2. At $t = t_1$, $x_1(t)$ and $x_2(t)$ locate a point as shown. Thus the state of the system at t_1 can be expressed by the vector relationship

$$\bar{x}(t) = \bar{x}_1(t) + \bar{x}_2(t)$$

or simply $\bar{x} = \bar{x}_1 + \bar{x}_2$

The motion of the system under the influence of input $F(t)$ can be described by the path formed on the x_1, x_2 plane by $\bar{x} = \bar{x}_1 + \bar{x}_2$, as time increases from $t = 0$, the instant the response solution is started.

Thus the state of the system can be described by a vector $\bar{x}$, known as the **state vector,** which is the vector sum of the state variables. The path described by the head of the state vector as time increases is called the **state path** or **state trajectory.**

The two-dimensional state plane of Fig. 11.4(a) is commonly referred to as the phase-plane, and phase-plane analysis of second-order systems, i.e., having two state variables, is widely used, especially for the analysis of nonlinear second-order systems.

The idea of the state vector and state path is readily extended to three-dimensional coordinates. Figure 11.4(b) shows three-dimensional space coordinates used to describe the three state variables of a third-order system. At time $t = t_1$,

$$\bar{x} = \bar{x}_1 + \bar{x}_2 + \bar{x}_3$$

is the state vector, describing a single point in space, which describes the instant state of the system. The state of the system as time increases can be visualized as a path in space, each point of which describes an instantaneous state of the system.

The idea can be extended to nth-order systems by accepting the abstract notion of n-dimensional state-space, such that

$$\bar{x} = \bar{x}_1 + \bar{x}_2 + \bar{x}_3 + \ldots + \bar{x}_n$$

is the state vector which describes the instant values of all of the state variables.

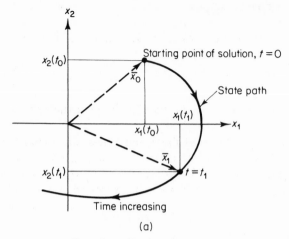

(a)

Two–dimensional state vector

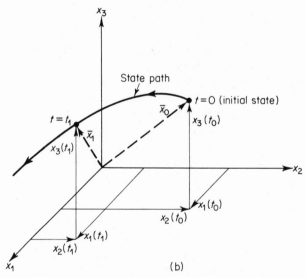

(b)

Three–dimensional state vector

Fig. 11.4 Representing state vectors and state paths.

The phase-plane, Fig. 11.4(a), is merely the two-dimensional case of state-space.

Using the column-matrix notation given in Appendix D, the state vector $\bar{x}$ can be represented by the set

$$\bar{x} = \begin{bmatrix} x_1 \\ x_2 \\ \cdot \\ \cdot \\ \cdot \\ x_n \end{bmatrix} \tag{11.1}$$

which is a convenient way of expressing the state variables $(x_1, x_2, \ldots, x_n)$.

Thus for the damped-spring-mass system, Example 11.1,

$$\bar{x} = \begin{bmatrix} x_1 \\ x_2 \end{bmatrix} \tag{11.2}$$

(where $x_1 = y$, $x_2 = \dot{y}$) is the state vector, in both conventional and matrix forms.

For Example 11.2 of Section 11.4(b), the state vector is

$$\bar{x} = \begin{bmatrix} x_1 \\ x_2 \end{bmatrix} \tag{11.3}$$

where $x_1 = \theta_o$; $x_2 = (\dot{\theta}_o - \dot{\theta}_i)$.

For Example 11.3 of Section 11.4(c), the state vector is

$$\bar{x} = \begin{bmatrix} x_1 \\ x_2 \\ x_3 \\ x_4 \end{bmatrix} \tag{11.4}$$

where $x_1 = y_1$; $x_2 = \dot{y}_1$; $x_3 = y_2$; and $x_4 = \dot{y}_2$.

The input vector

Utilizing the ideas expressed above, the inputs can be grouped together and expressed as the input vector,

$$\bar{u} = \begin{bmatrix} u_1 \\ u_2 \\ \cdot \\ \cdot \\ \cdot \\ u_m \end{bmatrix} \tag{11.5}$$

which means that the total input $\bar{u}$ is the vector sum of all component inputs u_1, u_2, etc.

Thus

$$\bar{u} = \begin{bmatrix} F(t) \end{bmatrix}, \quad \begin{bmatrix} \theta_i \end{bmatrix}, \quad \text{and} \quad \begin{bmatrix} u_1 \\ u_2 \end{bmatrix}$$

respectively, for the three examples discussed above.

The output vector

Similarly, those variables chosen as the primary response variables, denoted as outputs, can be expressed by the output vector

$$\bar{y} = \begin{bmatrix} y_1 \\ \cdot \\ \cdot \\ \cdot \\ y_p \end{bmatrix} \tag{11.6}$$

For the three examples under discussion,

$$\bar{y} = \begin{bmatrix} y = x_1 \end{bmatrix}, \quad \begin{bmatrix} \theta_o = x_1 \end{bmatrix}, \quad \text{and} \quad \begin{bmatrix} y_1 = x_1 \\ y_2 = x_3 \end{bmatrix}$$

respectively.

Commonly, but not necessarily, the outputs will consist of several of the system's state variables.

11.6 THE STATE MODEL

11.6.1 The State Equations in Normal Form

In general, the normal-form first-order state equations of a system are expressed as follows:

$$Dx_1 = f_1(x_1, x_2, \ldots, x_n; \quad u_1, u_2, \ldots, u_m) \tag{11.7a}$$

$$Dx_2 = f_2(x_1, x_2, \ldots, x_n; \quad u_1, u_2, \ldots, u_m) \tag{11.7b}$$

$$\cdot \qquad \qquad \cdot$$
$$\cdot \qquad \qquad \cdot$$
$$\cdot \qquad \qquad \cdot$$

$$Dx_n = f_n(x_1, x_2, \ldots, x_n; \quad u_1, u_2, \ldots, u_m) \tag{11.7n}$$

where $x_1, x_2, \ldots, x_n$ are the system's state variables; $u_1, u_2, \ldots, u_m$ are the external inputs experienced by the system.

For real systems, all x and u variables will not appear in every $f(x, u)$ function, as a number of the coefficient will be zero. Example 11.1 (Section 11.3) has the state equations

$$Dx_1 = x_2 \quad \text{and} \quad Dx_2 = -\frac{k}{M}x_1 - \frac{c}{M}x_2 - \frac{F(t)}{M}$$

which are of the above form. In $Dx_1 = x_2$, the coefficient of x_1 and $F(t)$ are zero. $F(t) = u_1$ is the only input present in this case.

Example 11.2 (Section 11.4b) has the state equations

$$Dx_1 = x_2 + \theta_i$$
$$Dx_2 = -bx_1 - ax_2 + (1 - a)\theta_i$$

found by writing the equations around each integration in turn. The input to each integration becomes the righthand side of a state equation, after it is expressed in terms of state variables, inputs, and system constants only. For example, from Fig. 11.3 it is apparent that

$$\dot{\theta}_o \frac{1}{D} = \theta_o \quad \text{or} \quad \dot{\theta}_o = D\theta_o = Dx_1$$

But

$$\dot{\theta}_o = x_2 + \theta_i$$
$$\therefore x_2 + \theta_i = Dx_1$$

which is a state equation. Also, the equation across the lefthand integration is

$$(\ddot{\theta}_o - \dot{\theta}_i)\frac{1}{D} = x_2 \quad \text{or} \quad Dx_2 = \ddot{\theta}_o - \dot{\theta}_i$$

now

$$\ddot{\theta}_o - \dot{\theta}_i = \theta_i - bx_1 - a\dot{\theta}_o = \theta_i - bx_1 - a(x_2 + \theta_i)$$

and

$$Dx_2 = -bx_1 - ax_2 + \theta_i - a\theta_i$$

is a state equation.

Example 11.3 (Section 11.4c), has the state equations

$$Dx_1 = x_2$$
$$Dx_2 = -3x_2 - 2x_3 + u_1$$
$$Dx_3 = x_4$$
$$Dx_4 = -x_2 - x_3 + u_2$$

found by writing in turn the equations across each integration, eliminating all variables except x and u by substitution.

11.6.2 The State Equations in Vector–Matrix Form

Using the idea of the state vector and input vector, the state Eqs. 11.7 can be expressed concisely:

$$D\bar{x} = f(\bar{x}, \bar{u}) \tag{11.8}$$

For linear systems, this vector state equation can be expanded to the form

$$D\bar{x} = \mathbf{A}\bar{x} + \mathbf{B}\bar{u} \tag{11.9}$$

where $\bar{x}$ and $\bar{u}$ are the state and input vectors respectively; $\mathbf{A}$ is the system matrix, containing the coefficients and parameters of the system in an ordered manner; $\mathbf{B}$ is the distribution matrix, containing those system coefficients experienced by inputs $\bar{u}$, in an ordered manner. $\mathbf{A}$ and $\mathbf{B}$ are arranged such that Eq. 11.9 represents the normal-form state equations of the system.

For example, for the damped-spring-mass system of Example 11.1, Eq. 11.9 becomes

$$D\bar{x} = D\begin{bmatrix} x_1 \\ x_2 \end{bmatrix} = \begin{bmatrix} 0 & 1 \\ -k/M & -c/M \end{bmatrix}\begin{bmatrix} x_1 \\ x_2 \end{bmatrix} + \begin{bmatrix} 0 \\ 1/M \end{bmatrix}\begin{bmatrix} F(t) \end{bmatrix} \tag{11.10}$$

$$\mathbf{A} = \begin{bmatrix} 0 & 1 \\ -k/M & -c/M \end{bmatrix} \quad \text{and} \quad \mathbf{B} = \begin{bmatrix} 0 \\ 1/M \end{bmatrix}$$

Check by performing the matrix operations (reviewed in Appendix D)

$$Dx_1 = 0x_1 + 1x_2 + 0F(t) = x_2$$

$$Dx_2 = -\frac{k}{M}x_1 - \frac{c}{M}x_2 + \frac{1}{M}F(t)$$

which were obtained previously in Section 11.3.

Note the significance of the state Eq. 11.9. The rate of change of the state of the system $D\bar{x}$ is related to the present state $\mathbf{A}\bar{x}$ and the input effects $\mathbf{B}\bar{u}$.

Note also that the two matrix products $\mathbf{A}\bar{x}$ and $\mathbf{B}\bar{u}$ must be *conformable*. That is, $\bar{x}$ must have the same number of rows as $\mathbf{A}$ has columns, and $\bar{u}$ must have the same number of rows as $\mathbf{B}$ has columns.

The relationship of the $\mathbf{A}$ and $\mathbf{B}$ matrices to the state equations is readily seen from the above example. The first row of the $\mathbf{A}$ matrix is formed from the coefficients of the state variables in the first state equation, taken in order (0 for x_1 and 1 for x_2). The second row is similarly obtained from the second state equation ($-k/M$ for x_1 and $-c/M$ for x_2). The entries in the $\mathbf{B}$ matrix are similarly formed from the state equations, taking coefficients of $F(t)$ in order from each state equation [0 for $F(t)$ in row 1 of B, $1/M$ for $F(t)$ in row 2].

The state Eq. 11.9 is an abbreviation for the general relationship

$$
D\begin{bmatrix} x_1 \\ x_2 \\ \cdot \\ \cdot \\ \cdot \\ x_n \end{bmatrix} = \begin{bmatrix} a_{11} & a_{12} & \cdots & a_{1n} \\ a_{21} & a_{22} & \cdots & a_{2n} \\ \cdot & \cdot & & \cdot \\ \cdot & \cdot & & \cdot \\ \cdot & \cdot & & \cdot \\ a_{n1} & a_{n2} & \cdots & a_{nn} \end{bmatrix}\begin{bmatrix} x_1 \\ x_2 \\ \cdot \\ \cdot \\ \cdot \\ x_n \end{bmatrix} + \begin{bmatrix} b_{11} & \cdots & b_{1m} \\ b_{21} & \cdots & b_{2m} \\ \cdot & & \cdot \\ \cdot & & \cdot \\ \cdot & & \cdot \\ b_{n1} & \cdots & b_{nm} \end{bmatrix}\begin{bmatrix} u_1 \\ u_2 \\ \cdot \\ \cdot \\ \cdot \\ u_m \end{bmatrix} \quad (11.11)
$$

where

$$
\bar{x} = \begin{bmatrix} x_1 \\ x_2 \\ \cdot \\ \cdot \\ \cdot \\ x_n \end{bmatrix}
$$

is the state vector containing the set of state variables;

$$
D\bar{x} = D\begin{bmatrix} x_1 \\ x_2 \\ \cdot \\ \cdot \\ \cdot \\ x_n \end{bmatrix} = \begin{bmatrix} Dx_1 \\ Dx_2 \\ \cdot \\ \cdot \\ \cdot \\ Dx_n \end{bmatrix} = \begin{bmatrix} \dot{x}_1 \\ \dot{x}_2 \\ \cdot \\ \cdot \\ \cdot \\ x_n \end{bmatrix}
$$

describes the rate of change of the state variables;

$$
\mathbf{A} = \begin{bmatrix} a_{11} & \cdots & a_{1n} \\ \cdot & & \cdot \\ \cdot & & \cdot \\ \cdot & & \cdot \\ a_{n1} & \cdots & a_{nn} \end{bmatrix}
$$

is the system matrix, an $n \times n$ square matrix,* formed so that the entries in the ith row are the coefficients of the state variables in the ith state equation, taken in order.

$$
\mathbf{B} = \begin{bmatrix} b_{11} & \cdots & b_{1m} \\ \cdot & & \cdot \\ \cdot & & \cdot \\ \cdot & & \cdot \\ b_{n1} & \cdots & b_{nm} \end{bmatrix}
$$

*n columns, to be conformable with $\bar{x}$; n rows, to be conformable with $D\bar{x}$.

is the distribution matrix, an $n \times m$ rectangular matrix*, formed so that the entries in the ith row are the coefficients of the inputs in the ith state equation, taken in order.

$$\bar{u} = \begin{bmatrix} u_1 \\ u_2 \\ \cdot \\ \cdot \\ \cdot \\ u_m \end{bmatrix}$$

is the input vector containing the set of inputs.

The vector matrix Eq. 11.11 can be expanded to give

$$Dx_1 = a_{11}x_1 + a_{12}x_2 + \ldots + a_{1n}x_n + b_{11}u_1 + b_{12}u_2 + \ldots + b_{1m}u_m$$

$$Dx_2 = a_{21}x_1 + a_{22}x_2 + \ldots + a_{2n}x_n + b_{21}u_1 + \ldots + b_{2m}u_m$$

$$Dx_n = a_{n1}x_1 + a_{n2}x_2 + \ldots + a_{nn}x_n + b_{n1}u_1 + \ldots + b_{nm}u_m$$

which are the normal-form first-order state equations, each having a state variable as its dependent variable.

Example 11.4: Form the vector-matrix state equation for the system whose normal-form state equations are

$$Dx_1 = 7x_1 + 3x_2 + u_1$$

$$Dx_2 = 4x_2 + 2u_1 + u_2$$

$$Dx_3 = 3x_2 + u_2$$

Solution: The state vector is

$$\bar{x} = \begin{bmatrix} x_1 \\ x_2 \\ x_3 \end{bmatrix}$$

The input vector is

$$\begin{bmatrix} u_1 \\ u_2 \end{bmatrix}$$

$D\bar{x} = \mathbf{A}\bar{x} + \mathbf{B}\bar{u}$ yields

$$D\begin{bmatrix} x_1 \\ x_2 \\ x_3 \end{bmatrix} = \begin{bmatrix} 7 & 3 & 0 \\ 0 & 4 & 0 \\ 0 & 3 & 0 \end{bmatrix} \begin{bmatrix} x_1 \\ x_2 \\ x_3 \end{bmatrix} + \begin{bmatrix} 1 & 0 \\ 2 & 1 \\ 0 & 1 \end{bmatrix} \begin{bmatrix} u_1 \\ u_2 \end{bmatrix}$$

*m columns, to be conformable with $\bar{u}$; n rows, to be conformable with $D\bar{x}$.

Thus the first rows of **A** and **B** were formed by taking in order the coefficients of x and u from the first state equation.

Check by performing the matrix products

$$Dx_1 = 7x_1 + 3x_2 + 0x_3 + 1u_1 + 0u_2 = 7x_1 + 3x_2 + u_1$$

etc.

11.6.3 The Output Equation

It is common to choose certain system variables as outputs whose condition is of primary importance to the analyst. Often, though not necessarily, the outputs will be the lowest-order terms among a system's state variables. Thus, for the damped-spring-mass of Example 11.1, the output is the mass displacement y.

The condition of system outputs will depend on system parameters and on inputs. This interrelationship can be expressed by the vector-matrix equation

$$\bar{y} = \mathbf{P}\bar{x} + \mathbf{Q}\bar{u} \tag{11.12}$$

where

$$\bar{y} = \begin{bmatrix} y_1 \\ y_2 \\ \cdot \\ \cdot \\ \cdot \\ y_p \end{bmatrix}$$

is the output vector, discussed in Section 11.5; y_1, y_2, etc. are the chosen outputs; $\bar{x}$ and $\bar{u}$ are the state and input vectors respectively; **P** is the output system matrix; **Q** is the output distribution matrix, formed so that Eq. 11.12 describes the appropriate relationship between $\bar{y}$, $\bar{x}$, and $\bar{u}$.

For Example 11.1, with displacement y selected as the only output,

$$\bar{y} = \begin{bmatrix} y \end{bmatrix} = \begin{bmatrix} 1 & 0 \end{bmatrix}\begin{bmatrix} x_1 \\ x_2 \end{bmatrix} + \begin{bmatrix} 0 \end{bmatrix}\begin{bmatrix} F(t) \end{bmatrix}$$

which means $y = x_1$.

For Example 11.2, with θ_o as the only output,

$$\bar{y} = \begin{bmatrix} \theta_o \end{bmatrix} = \begin{bmatrix} 1 & 0 \end{bmatrix}\begin{bmatrix} x_1 \\ x_2 \end{bmatrix} + \begin{bmatrix} 0 \end{bmatrix}\begin{bmatrix} \theta_i \end{bmatrix}$$

For Example 11.3, with y_1 and y_2 chosen as the outputs (Fig. 11.3),

$$\bar{y} = \begin{bmatrix} y_1 \\ y_2 \end{bmatrix} = \begin{bmatrix} 1 & 0 & 0 & 0 \\ 0 & 0 & 1 & 0 \end{bmatrix}\begin{bmatrix} x_1 \\ x_2 \\ x_3 \\ x_4 \end{bmatrix} + \begin{bmatrix} 0 & 0 \\ 0 & 0 \end{bmatrix}\begin{bmatrix} u_1 \\ u_2 \end{bmatrix}$$

which expresses the normal-form relationships

$$y_1 = x_1$$

$$y_2 = x_3$$

For Example 11.4, with x_1 and x_3 chosen as the outputs,

$$\bar{y} = \begin{bmatrix} x_1 \\ x_3 \end{bmatrix} = \begin{bmatrix} 1 & 0 & 0 \\ 0 & 0 & 1 \end{bmatrix} \begin{bmatrix} x_1 \\ x_2 \\ x_3 \end{bmatrix} + \begin{bmatrix} 0 & 0 \\ 0 & 0 \end{bmatrix} \begin{bmatrix} u_1 \\ u_2 \end{bmatrix}$$

11.6.4 The State Model

The vector-matrix dynamic model of a system is comprised of the appropriate state equation and output equation.

Thus

$$\begin{aligned} D\bar{x} &= \mathbf{A}\bar{x} + \mathbf{B}\bar{u} \\ \bar{y} &= \mathbf{P}\bar{x} + \mathbf{Q}\bar{u} \end{aligned} \Bigg\} \tag{11.13}$$

describes the system, its inputs, and its responses. The pair of equations is called the **state model** of the system.

The state model corresponds to the conventional transfer function of a single-input single-output system.

11.7 DERIVING STATE MODELS

11.7.1 Summary of the Procedure

The procedure for forming state models of physical systems has been introduced in the previous sections. It can be summarized:

(a) Select a system of state variables, either by writing the normal-form state equations, or by forming a signal-flow diagram of the system. In both cases, the result of each integration is a state variable. Express the state variable as the state vector $\bar{x}$. The form of the state vector is independent of system inputs or initial values.
(b) Choose the system inputs and express them as the input vector $\bar{u}$.
(c) Form the system matrix $\mathbf{A}$ and the distribution matrix $\mathbf{B}$ of system coefficients such that

$$D\bar{x} = \mathbf{A}\bar{x} + \mathbf{B}\bar{u}$$

describes the normal-form state equations of the system.
(d) Select the variables required to be the primary response variables, and express them as the output vector $\bar{y}$.

(e) Form the output system matrix **P** and the output distribution matrix **Q** such that

$$\bar{y} = \mathbf{P}\bar{x} + \mathbf{Q}\bar{u}$$

describes the relationships between $\bar{y}$, $\bar{x}$, and $\bar{u}$.

The formation of **A**, **B**, **P**, and **Q** from the normal-form state equations has been thoroughly discussed.

In summary,

(f) The ith row of **A** is formed from the coefficients, taken in order, of state variables $x_1, x_2, \ldots, x_n$ in the ith state equation.

(g) The ith row of **B** is formed from the coefficients, taken in order, of the inputs $u_1, u_2, \ldots, u_m$ in the ith state equation.

(h) The ith row of **P** and of **Q** is chosen so that y_i is correctly expressed in terms of x and u functions only.

11.7.2 Using Signal-Flow Diagrams

It was demonstrated in Sections 11.3 and 11.4 that the state variables of a system can be read directly from a block diagram of the system, as the outputs of each integration present. The block diagram is an extremely useful link between a physical system and its mathematical model. The **A**, **B**, **P** and **Q** matrices can be formed directly from a completed block diagram.

The output of the ith integration is the state variable x_i. Hence the input to the ith integration is $Dx_i = \dot{x}_i$, which is the lefthand side of the ith state equation

$$Dx_i = a_{i1}x_1 + a_{i2}x_2 + \ldots + a_{in}x_n + b_{i1}u_1 + \ldots + b_{im}u_m$$

To form the ith row of the **A** matrix from the block diagram, do the following:

(a) Locate the ith integration, in the sense that the first integrator is that one the output of which is x_1, the second integrator is the one the output of which is x_2, etc.;

(b) a_{i1}, the first entry in the ith row of A, describes the *direct-path* relationship (if any) between x_1, and the ith integrator;

(c) a_{in}, the nth entry in row i, describes the *direct-path* relationship between the nth state variable x_n and the ith integrator.

A *direct path* is a path going in the direction in which the signals are flowing in the block diagram and which contains no intermediate integrations. A direct path can pass through a summing junction.

For example, Fig. 11.1(b) shows the block diagram of the damped-spring-mass system. The outputs of the two integrations y and $\dot{y}$ are the state variables x_1 and x_2 respectively. To form the first entry in the first row of $\mathbf{A}$, a_{11}, consider the first state variable x_1: x_1 has a path to the No. 1 integrator (the righthand integrator, as its output is x_1) by going around the feedback loop, through the summer, and then along the forward feed. However, it is *not* a *direct path*, due to the presence of the No. 2 integrator (the one whose output is $x_2 = \dot{y}$). Hence there is no direct relationship between x_1 and the input to No. 1 integrator, and the a_{11} entry in $\mathbf{A}$ is zero, as shown in Eq. 11.10.

For the entry a_{12}, consider the existence of a direct path between x_2 and the No. 1 integrator. In fact, the input to the No. 1 integrator is x_2 in this case, and hence the path relationship is 1. Enter $a_{12} = 1$ in $\mathbf{A}$.

For the a_{21} entry in $\mathbf{A}$, consider the path between x_1 and the No. 2 integrator; x_1 has a *direct path* to the No. 2 integrator, via the blocks k and $1/M$, with negative passage through the summer. Hence the a_{21} entry in A is $-k/M$, which means that $-X_1 k/M$ is a component of Dx_2, the input to the No. 2 integration.

For the a_{22} entry in $\mathbf{A}$, consider the existence of a path between x_2 and the input to the No. 2 integrator. Such a path exists through the upper feedback loop via c, through the summing unit negatively, and through $1/M$ in the forward feed. Thus, the a_{22} entry in $\mathbf{A}$ is $-c/M$.

With this procedure $\mathbf{A}$ is completed (Eq. 11.10)

The distribution matrix $\mathbf{B}$ is formed in the same way, by seeking *direct-path* relationships between the inputs and the integrations. For Example 11.1, Fig. 11.1(b), $F(t)$ is the only input. The b_{11} entry in $\mathbf{B}$ describes the direct path between $F(t)$ and the No. 1 integrator. No direct path exists, and b_{11} is zero. The b_{21} entry describes the direct path between $F(t)$ and the No. 2 integrator. The path contains $1/M$ only, and hence b_{21} is $1/M$, and $\mathbf{B}$ is as shown previously in Eq. 11.10.

When utilizing a block diagram,

(a) the sign of summing junctions must be heeded;
(b) all direct paths between state variables and integrators must be considered;
(c) only *direct paths* affect the matrix entries — a direct path has no intermediate integration;
(d) only paths flowing in the direction of real signal flow are considered.

Finally, analogue computer diagrams or signal-flow graphs can be utilized just as effectively as can block diagrams. It should be appreciated that all signal flow diagrams are only graphical representations of the state equations governing the system.

11.7.3 Examples

Example 11.5: Derive the vector-matrix state equation for the system shown in Fig. 11.5.

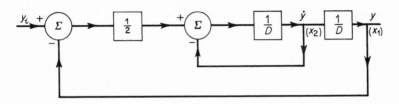

Fig. 11.5   Block diagram for Example 11.5.

Solution: The system has two integrations and hence has two state variables. These, the outputs of the integrations, are

$$x_1 = y \quad \text{and} \quad x_2 = \dot{y}$$

The state vector is

$$\bar{x} = \begin{bmatrix} x_1 \\ x_2 \end{bmatrix}$$

The system matrix is

$$\mathbf{A} = \begin{bmatrix} 0 & 1 \\ \frac{1}{2} & -1 \end{bmatrix}$$

formed by examining the direct-path connections between the state variables and the integrators. That is,

(a) x_1 has no *direct* link with the input to No. 1 integrator, and hence $a_{11} = 0$;

(b) x_2 is fed directly into the No. 1 integrator, and hence $a_{21} = 1$;

(c) x_1 is fed back through -1 at the summing junction, and then is fed forward through $\frac{1}{2}$, positively through the internal summing junction, and into the No. 2 integrator; hence $a_{21} = -\frac{1}{2}$;

(d) x_2 is fed back via the internal feedback loop, negatively through the summing junction, and then into the No. 2 integration; hence $a_{22} = -1$; y_1 is the only input, and hence $\bar{u} = y_i$.

The distribution matrix is

$$\mathbf{B} = \begin{bmatrix} 0 \\ \frac{1}{2} \end{bmatrix}$$

formed by describing the direct path from y_i to the No. 1 integrator (b_{11}) and No. 2 integrator (b_{21}) respectively.

Thus the state equation is

$$\begin{bmatrix} \dot{x}_1 \\ \dot{x}_2 \end{bmatrix} = \begin{bmatrix} 0 & 1 \\ -\frac{1}{2} & -1 \end{bmatrix} \begin{bmatrix} x_1 \\ x_2 \end{bmatrix} + \begin{bmatrix} 0 \\ \frac{1}{2} \end{bmatrix} [y_i]$$

where $x_1 = y$; $x_2 = \dot{y}$.

Example 11.6: Describe in vector-matrix form the system whose transfer function is

$$\frac{\theta_o}{\theta_i} = \frac{K}{D^4 + a_3 D^3 + a_2 D^2 + a_1 D + a_o}$$

Solution: The system is of fourth order, and hence has four state variables. No derivatives of the input θ_i exist, hence the state variables are $x_1 = \theta_o$, $x_2 = \dot{\theta}_o$, $x_3 = \ddot{\theta}_o$, $x_4 = \dddot{\theta}_o$.
Hence

$$\bar{x} = \begin{bmatrix} x_1 \\ x_2 \\ x_3 \\ x_4 \end{bmatrix}$$

is the state vector.

It is apparent by inspection that

$$Dx_1 = x_2 \tag{a}$$

$$Dx_2 = x_3 \tag{b}$$

$$Dx_3 = x_4 \tag{c}$$

From the transfer function

$$D^4\theta_o + a_3 D^3\theta_o + a_2 D^2\theta_o + a_1 D\theta_o + a_o\theta_o = K\theta_i$$

which, in terms of the defined state variables, becomes

$$Dx_4 + a_3 Dx_3 + a_2 Dx_2 + a_1 Dx_1 + a_o x_1 = K\theta_i$$

which, using Eqs. (a), (b), and (c), yields

$$Dx_4 = -a_3 x_4 - a_2 x_3 - a_1 x_2 - a_o x_1 + K\theta_i \tag{d}$$

Equations (a) through (d) are the state equations, whose coefficients taken in order provide the entries of the **A** and **B** matrices. Hence

$$\mathbf{A} = \begin{bmatrix} 0 & 1 & 0 & 0 \\ 0 & 0 & 1 & 0 \\ 0 & 0 & 0 & 1 \\ -a_o & -a_1 & -a_2 & -a_3 \end{bmatrix}$$

in which row 1 describes in order the coefficients of x_1, x_2, x_3, and x_4 in the first state equation, Eq. (a), etc.

Similarly,

$$\mathbf{B} = \begin{bmatrix} 0 \\ 0 \\ 0 \\ K \end{bmatrix}$$

in which the entries are the coefficients of θ_i as they appear in the state equations taken in order.

Hence the state equation in vector-matrix form is

$$\begin{bmatrix} \dot{x}_1 \\ \dot{x}_2 \\ \dot{x}_3 \\ \dot{x}_4 \end{bmatrix} = \begin{bmatrix} 0 & 1 & 0 & 0 \\ 0 & 0 & 1 & 0 \\ 0 & 0 & 0 & 1 \\ -a_o & -a_1 & -a_2 & -a_3 \end{bmatrix} \begin{bmatrix} x_1 \\ x_2 \\ x_3 \\ x_4 \end{bmatrix} + \begin{bmatrix} 0 \\ 0 \\ 0 \\ K \end{bmatrix} [\theta_i]$$

Example 11.7: Figure 11.2 shows the block diagram of the system whose dynamic performance is described by

$$D^2\theta_o + a\,D\theta_o + b\theta_o = \theta_i + D\theta_i$$

Derive the vector-matrix state equation for the system, direct from the diagram.

Solution: The two state variables are $x_1 = \theta_o$, $x_2 = \dot{\theta}_o - \theta_i$; the one input is $u_1 = \theta_i$; the system matrix is

$$\mathbf{A} = \begin{bmatrix} 0 & 1 \\ -b & -a \end{bmatrix}$$

where $a_{11} = 0$ describes the *direct* path from x_1 to the No. 1 integrator; $a_{12} = 1$ describes the *direct* path from x_2 to the No. 1 integrator; $a_{21} = -b$ describes the *direct* path from x_1 to the No. 2 integrator; $a_{22} = -a$ describes the *direct* path from x_2 to the No. 2 integrator.

The distribution matrix is

$$\mathbf{B} = \begin{bmatrix} 1 \\ (1-a) \end{bmatrix}$$

where b_{11} describes the direct path between θ_i and the No. 1 integrator; b_{21} describes the direct path between θ_i and the No. 2 integrator.

The **A** entries are fairly obvious, but the **B** entries may be vague to the inexperienced reader. Consider b_{11}: θ_i has one direct path to the No. 1 integrator, via the forward feed upper loop, and carries a factor of 1. Thus $b_{11} = 1$. Consider b_{21}: input θ_i has direct access in the forward feed to the No. 2 integrator, thus contributing $+1$ to b_{21}; θ_i also has access to the No. 2 integrator via the forward feed upper loop, through the inner summing junction, back via a in the inner negative feedback loop, and negatively through the left summing junction, thus contributing $-a$ to b_{21}. Thus $b_{21} = 1 - a$.

Hence

$$\begin{bmatrix} \dot{x}_1 \\ \dot{x}_2 \end{bmatrix} = \begin{bmatrix} 0 & 1 \\ -b & -a \end{bmatrix} \begin{bmatrix} x_1 \\ x_2 \end{bmatrix} + \begin{bmatrix} 1 \\ (1-a) \end{bmatrix} [u_1]$$

where $x_1 = \theta_o$; $x_2 = \dot{\theta}_o - \theta_i$; $u_1 = \theta_i$.

The result can be compared with Example 11.2 discussed in Sections 11.2 and 11.6.1.

Example 11.8: Form the vector-matrix model of the system the dynamic performance of which is described by the equations

$$3\ddot{y}_1 + 5\ddot{y}_1 + 2\dot{y}_2 + y_2 = 7u_1$$

$$4\ddot{y}_2 + 6\dot{y}_2 + 3y_1 = u_2 + 3\dot{u}_2$$

Solution: There are two inputs u_1 and u_2. In addition, a derivative $\dot{u}_2$ of u_2 exists. Select y_1 and y_2 as the output variables. There are five derivative orders present ($\ddot{y}_1$, $\ddot{y}_1$, $\dot{y}_1$, $\ddot{y}_2$, and $\dot{y}_2$), and hence five state variables are required. To help in forming the state model, form a block diagram for the system.

Form the diagram so that the inputs u_1 and u_2 are projecting from its left side, and the outputs y_1 and y_2 project from its right (Fig. 11.6).

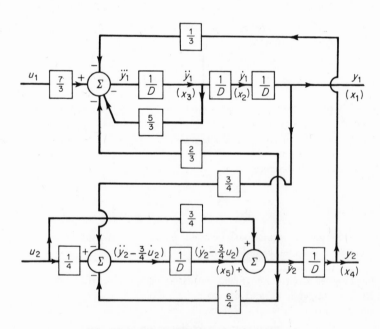

Fig. 11.6   Block diagram representation of:

$$3\ddot{y}_1 + 5\ddot{y}_1 + 2\dot{y}_2 + \ y_2 = 7u_1$$
$$4\ddot{y}_2 + 6\dot{y}_2 + 3y_1 = u_2 + 3\dot{u}_2$$

Form the upper summing junction on Fig. 11.6 so that it describes the first equation in the form

$$\ddot{y}_1 = \frac{7}{3} u_1 - \frac{5}{3} \ddot{y}_1 - \frac{2}{3} \dot{y}_2 - \frac{y_2}{3}$$

Form the lower summing junction on Fig. 11.6 so that it describes the second equation in the form

$$(\ddot{y}_2 - \tfrac{3}{4}\ddot{u}_2) = \tfrac{1}{4}u_2 - \tfrac{6}{4}\dot{y}_2 - \tfrac{3}{4}y_1$$

Complete the block diagram so that it describes the equations.
Pick the set of state variables (the outputs of the integrations)

$$x_1 = y_1; \quad x_2 = \dot{y}_1; \quad x_3 = \ddot{y}_1; \quad x_4 = y_2; \quad x_5 = \dot{y}_2 - \tfrac{3}{4}u_2$$

Form **A** and **B** using the direct path technique, getting

$$\begin{bmatrix} \dot{x}_1 \\ \dot{x}_2 \\ \dot{x}_3 \\ \dot{x}_4 \\ \dot{x}_5 \end{bmatrix} = \begin{bmatrix} 0 & 1 & 0 & 0 & 0 \\ 0 & 0 & 1 & 0 & 0 \\ 0 & 0 & -\frac{5}{3} & -\frac{1}{3} & -\frac{2}{3} \\ 0 & 0 & 0 & 0 & 1 \\ -\frac{3}{4} & 0 & 0 & 0 & -\frac{6}{4} \end{bmatrix} \begin{bmatrix} x_1 \\ x_2 \\ x_3 \\ x_4 \\ x_5 \end{bmatrix} + \begin{bmatrix} 0 & 0 \\ 0 & 0 \\ \frac{7}{3} & -\frac{1}{2} \\ 0 & \frac{3}{4} \\ 0 & \frac{7}{8} \end{bmatrix} \begin{bmatrix} u_1 \\ u_2 \end{bmatrix}$$

which is the state equation. The output expressions are

$$y_1 = x_1 \quad \text{and} \quad y_2 = x_4$$

which are readily put into the form $y = \mathbf{P}\bar{x} + \mathbf{Q}\bar{u}$.

Example 11.9: Obtain a vector-matrix dynamic model of the system shown in Fig. 11.7(a). F_1 and F_2 are separate input disturbances; y_1 and y_2 are the outputs.

Solution: Figure 11.7(b), shows the block diagram formed to describe the action of the system.

The state vector is

$$\bar{x} = [x_1 \quad x_2 \quad x_3 \quad x_4]^T,$$

The input vector is

$$\bar{u} = [F_1 \quad F_2]^T$$

The output vector is

$$\bar{y} = [y_1 \quad y_2]^T$$

where $x_1 = y_1$; $x_2 = \dot{y}_1$; $x_3 = y_2$; $x_4 = \dot{y}_2$.
Tracing the direct paths between the state variables and the integrators, in

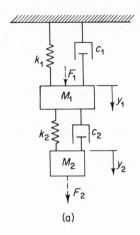

(a)

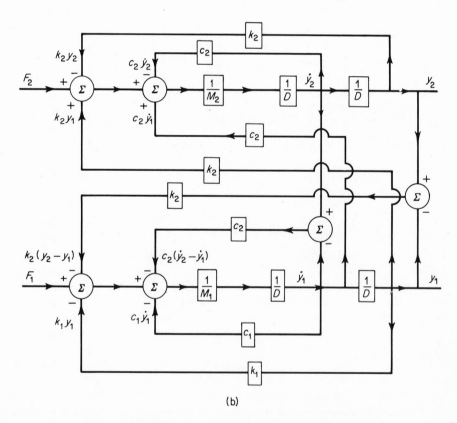

(b)

Fig. 11.7 (a) System and (b) block diagram for Example 11.9.

the ordered manner described in Section 11.7.2, the system and distribution matrices are formed, and the state equation is

$$
\begin{bmatrix} \dot{x}_1 \\ \dot{x}_2 \\ \dot{x}_3 \\ \dot{x}_4 \end{bmatrix} =
\begin{bmatrix}
0 & 1 & 0 & 0 \\
-k_2/M_2 & -c_2/M_2 & k_2/M_2 & c_2/M_2 \\
0 & 0 & 0 & 1 \\
k_2/M_1 & c_2/M_1 & -(k_2+k_1)/M_1 & -(c_2+c_1)/M_1
\end{bmatrix}
\begin{bmatrix} x_1 \\ x_2 \\ x_3 \\ x_4 \end{bmatrix}
$$

$$
+ \begin{bmatrix}
0 & 0 \\
1/M_2 & 0 \\
0 & 0 \\
0 & 1/M_1
\end{bmatrix}
\begin{bmatrix} F_2(t) \\ F_1(t) \end{bmatrix}
$$

The corresponding output equation is,

$$
\begin{bmatrix} y_1 \\ y_2 \end{bmatrix} =
\begin{bmatrix} 1 & 0 & 0 & 0 \\ 0 & 0 & 1 & 0 \end{bmatrix}
\begin{bmatrix} x_1 \\ x_2 \\ x_3 \\ x_4 \end{bmatrix}
+ \begin{bmatrix} 0 & 0 \\ 0 & 0 \end{bmatrix}
\begin{bmatrix} F_2(t) \\ F_1(t) \end{bmatrix}
$$

11.8 SUMMARY

The state-variable technique for the analysis of dynamic systems includes methods for concisely expressing the dynamic relationship between the system itself, the several inputs it may experience, and the chosen response variables. The intention is that the state-variable model can yield the time histories of a group of significant system variables, known as the state variables, which provide comprehensive understanding of the state of the system.

This chapter has concentrated on the selection of a significant set of state variables, and the linking of these with chosen input and response variables to provide a state model of the system in vector-matrix form. Having obtained a transfer function of a single-input single-output linear system, it is a relatively short step to obtain response solutions to specified inputs. The reader can appreciate that having obtained a state model of a multi-input multi-output system, solutions of the model can be affected for specified inputs and initial values, by standard procedures. Generally, for systems where state-variable analysis is used, such solutions are made by computer.

Linear-state models were used as a demonstration vehicle. However, the technique is quite general, and nonlinear terms and time-varying coefficients can be included. Also, system relationships can be manipulated to enable selection of state variables different to the set chosen by the direct technique discussed herein.

A thorough understanding of matrix manipulations is necessary for full understanding and development of the state-variable technique.

The Bibliography at the end of this chapter contains a number of texts which treat the state variable techniques more fully.

PROBLEMS

11.1 Establish the vector-matrix state model of the system of Example 11.3 directly from the system's block diagram, Fig. 11.3.

Answer: See Section 11.6.1.

11.2 Obtain the state model of the system illustrated in Fig. 11.8.

$$\textbf{Answer:} \begin{bmatrix} \dot{x}_1 \\ \dot{x}_2 \\ \dot{x}_3 \end{bmatrix} = \begin{bmatrix} 0 & 1 & 0 \\ 0 & 0 & 1 \\ 0 & -12 & -7 \end{bmatrix} \begin{bmatrix} x_1 \\ x_2 \\ x_3 \end{bmatrix} + \begin{bmatrix} 0 \\ 0 \\ 1 \end{bmatrix} [u]$$

$$y = [2 \quad 3 \quad 1] \begin{bmatrix} x_1 \\ x_2 \\ x_3 \end{bmatrix} + [0][u]$$

where x_1, x_2, x_3, and y are defined in Fig. 11.8.

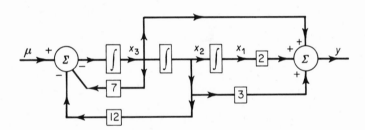

Fig. 11.8 Block diagram for Problem 11.2.

11.3 Figure 11.9 shows a schematic and a block diagram of a hydraulic positioner driving a damped-spring-mass. The system has two inputs, displacement y_i applied to the lever and force F_i applied to the mass. The chosen output is the mass position y_o; K_p, K_b, and V are oil compressibility parameters. Derive the vector-matrix state model of the system.

$$\textbf{Answer:} \begin{bmatrix} \dot{x}_1 \\ \dot{x}_2 \\ \dot{x}_3 \end{bmatrix} = \begin{bmatrix} 0 & 1 & 0 \\ -k/M & -c/M & A/M \\ (-a/b)(K_V K_B/V) & -A K_B/V & -K_P K_B/V \end{bmatrix} \begin{bmatrix} x_1 \\ x_2 \\ x_3 \end{bmatrix}$$

$$+ \begin{bmatrix} 0 & 0 \\ 0 & 1/M \\ [(a-b)/a] \cdot (K_V K_B/V) & 0 \end{bmatrix} \begin{bmatrix} y_i \\ F_i \end{bmatrix}$$

where $x_1 = y_o$; $x_2 = \dot{y}_o$; $x_3 =$ pressure on piston.

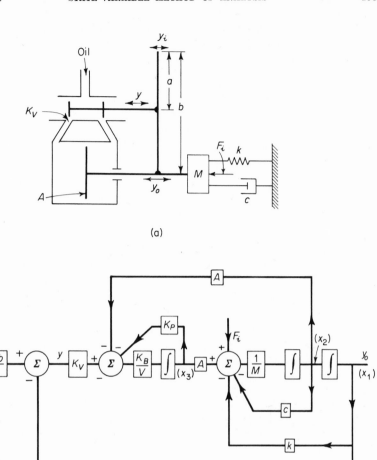

(a)

(b)

Fig. 11.9 (a) The system and (b) its block diagram for Problem 11.3.

11.4 Express the equation

$$D^4\theta + 2ab\,D^3\theta + b^2\,D^2\theta = kTb^2u(t)$$

where $u(t)$ is a forcing function (input); θ is the dependent variable (response); a, b, k, and T are constants; all in vector-matrix form.

Answer:
$$
\begin{bmatrix} \dot{x}_1 \\ \dot{x}_2 \\ \dot{x}_3 \\ \dot{x}_4 \end{bmatrix}
=
\begin{bmatrix}
0 & 1 & 0 & 0 \\
0 & 0 & 1 & 0 \\
0 & 0 & 0 & 1 \\
0 & 0 & -b^2 & -2ab
\end{bmatrix}
\begin{bmatrix} x_1 \\ x_2 \\ x_3 \\ x_4 \end{bmatrix}
+
\begin{bmatrix} 0 \\ 0 \\ 0 \\ kTb^2 \end{bmatrix}
[u(t)]
$$

11.5 An automobile suspension system can be modeled by the diagram shown in Fig. 11.10. Derive the vector-matrix model of the system when it is subjected to an input force F_i applied to the wheels.

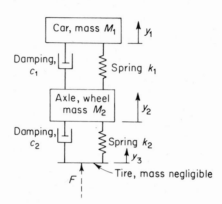

Fig. 11.10 Dynamic model of car suspension (Problem 11.5).

Answer:

$$\begin{bmatrix} \dot{x}_1 \\ \dot{x}_2 \\ \dot{x}_3 \\ \dot{x}_4 \\ \dot{x}_5 \end{bmatrix} = \begin{bmatrix} 0 & 0 & 0 & 0 & 1 \\ 0 & 0 & 0 & 1 & 0 \\ 0 & k_2/c_2 & -k_2/c_2 & 1 & 0 \\ k_1/M_2 & -k_1/M_2 & 0 & -c_1/M_2 & c_1/M_2 \\ -k_1/M_1 & k_1/M_1 & 0 & c_1/M_1 & -c_1/M_1 \end{bmatrix} \begin{bmatrix} x_1 \\ x_2 \\ x_3 \\ x_4 \\ x_5 \end{bmatrix}$$

$$+ \begin{bmatrix} 0 \\ 0 \\ 1/c_2 \\ 1/M_2 \\ 0 \end{bmatrix} [F_i]$$

where $x_1 = y_1$; $x_2 = y_2$; $x_3 = y_3$; $x_4 = \dot{y}_2$; $x_5 = \dot{y}_1$.

11.6 Figure 11.11 shows the block diagram of a system which is subjected to three input disturbances. Obtain a vector-matrix model of the system.

Answer:

$$\begin{bmatrix} \dot{x}_1 \\ \dot{x}_2 \\ \dot{x}_3 \end{bmatrix} = \begin{bmatrix} 0 & 1 & 0 \\ -k & -1 & k \\ 0 & 0 & -a \end{bmatrix} \begin{bmatrix} x_1 \\ x_2 \\ x_3 \end{bmatrix} + \begin{bmatrix} 0 & 0 & 1 \\ 0 & 1 & 0 \\ 1 & 0 & 0 \end{bmatrix} \begin{bmatrix} u_1 \\ u_2 \\ u_3 \end{bmatrix}$$

$$[y] = [1 \quad 0 \quad 0] \begin{bmatrix} x_1 \\ x_2 \\ x_3 \end{bmatrix} + [0 \quad 0 \quad 0] \begin{bmatrix} u_1 \\ u_2 \\ u_3 \end{bmatrix}$$

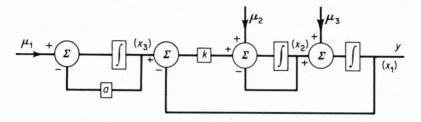

Fig. 11.11   System of Problem 11.6.

BIBLIOGRAPHY

1. Zadeh, L. A., and Desoer, C. A., *Linear System Theory: The State-Space Approach* New York: McGraw-Hill Book Company, 1963.
2. Tou, J., *Modern Control Theory*. New York: McGraw-Hill Book Company, 1964.
3. Dorf, R. C., *Time-Domain Analysis and Design of Control Systems*. Reading, Mass.: Addison-Wesley Publishing Co., Inc., 1965.
4. DeRusso, P. M., Roy, R. J., and Close, C. M., *State Variables for Engineers*. New York: John Wiley & Sons, Inc., 1965.
5. Athans, M., and Falb, P. L., *Optimal Control: An Introduction to the Theory and its Applications*. New York: McGraw-Hill Book Company, 1966.
6. Elgerd, O. I., *Control Systems Theory*. New York: McGraw-Hill Book Company, 1967.
7. Kuo, B., *Automatic Control Systems*, 2nd ed. Englewood Cliffs, N.J.: Prentice-Hall, Inc., 1967.

Classification of
differential
equations

The focal point of the present text is the formation and solution of linear ordinary differential equations which have constant coefficients and have time as the independent variable.

A mathematical equation shows the relationships between the variables appearing in it. The variables can be classified as dependent variables and independent variables. An independent variable does not depend in any way upon the state of any other variable. Thus time is an independent variable. A quantity is a dependent variable if its state is affected by other variables present in the equation or set of equations being considered. The displacement x of a mass acted upon by a force F varies both in time and according to the applied force. Hence x is a function of F and time, and is a dependent variable, denoted by $x = f(F,t)$.

The rate of change of a variable x with regard to another variable y, denoted dx/dy, is called the first derivative of x with respect to y. The rate of change of the first derivative with respect to y, denoted d/dy of $(dx/dy) = d^2x/dy^2$, is called the second derivative of x with respect to y. Thus a derivative term is said to have an **order**: dx/dy is a first-order term, d^3x/dy^3 is a third-order term, etc.

A differential equation shows the relationship between dependent variables, independent variables, and derivatives of the dependent variables with respect to other variables present in the equation. Thus

$$\frac{d^2y}{dt^2} + 3\frac{dy}{dt} + 10y = F(t) \tag{A-1}$$

is a differential equation with $y = f(t)$ as the dependent variable and t as the independent variable. The equation relates y and t.

Each algebraic or derivative term of an equation has a **degree** described by the exponent associated with the term. Thus $x = x^1$ is of first degree, x^2 is of second degree, x^n is of the nth degree. The terms dx/dy and $d^n x/dy^n$ are both of first degree, even though the latter is of nth order. The terms $(dx/dy)^2$ and $(d^n x/dy^n)^m$ are of second and mth degree respectively. Thus derivative terms have both order and degree.

The coefficients of the derivative terms of a differential equation can be constant, or can be dependent on one or more of the equation variables. Thus the term $6d^2x/dt^2$ has the constant coefficient 6, whereas $4t^2 dx/dt$ has the time varying coefficient $4t^2$.

A differential equation is **ordinary** if it contains *one* independent variable and all of the derivatives are with respect to this variable. If an equation contains derivatives with respect to more than one variable, it is **partial.** Equation A-2 is ordinary, and Eq. A-3 is partial. The partial derivative $\partial P/\partial y$ denotes the rate at which P is changing relative to y if all other variables (t in the present case) are held constant:

$$4\frac{d^2x}{dt^2} + 2\frac{dx}{dt} + x = 0 \tag{A-2}$$

$[x = f(t)$ is dependent, t independent],

$$3\frac{\partial^2 P}{\partial t^2} + 2\frac{\partial P}{\partial y} + y = 3t + 6 \tag{A-3}$$

$[P = f(y,t)$ and $y = f(P,t)$ are dependent variables, t is an independent variable].

A differential equation is **homogeneous** if it contains no **forcing functions,** and is **nonhomogeneous** if forcing functions are present. A forcing function (known also as a driving, disturbing, or input function) is any term which does not contain any of the equation's dependent variables. Equation A-2 is homogeneous, and A-3 is nonhomogeneous with $(3t + 6)$ as the forcing function.

The *order* of a differential equation is the order of the highest derivative term present. The *degree* of the equation is the power to which the highest-order term is raised. Thus Eq. A-2 is of second order and first degree, and Eq. A-6 is of third order and second degree.

A differential equation is **linear** if it contains only first-degree terms. If it contains one or more terms of degree other than one, the equation is **nonlinear.** Thus Eq. A-5 is linear, and Eq. A-6 is nonlinear due to the presence of the second-degree terms $(d^3x/dt^3)^2$ and x^2.

EXAMPLES OF DIFFERENTIAL EQUATIONS

$$\frac{dx}{dy} + 2x = 0 \qquad\qquad \text{(A-4)}$$

(y is an independent variable),

$$6\frac{d^2y}{dt^2} + 3\frac{dy}{dt} + 4y = 7 \qquad\qquad \text{(A-5)}$$

$$a\left(\frac{d^3x}{dt^3}\right)^2 + b\frac{d^2x}{dt^2} + ct\frac{dx}{dt} + ex^2 = 5t \qquad\qquad \text{(A-6)}$$

$$\frac{\partial}{\partial x}\left(\frac{h^3}{\mu}\cdot\frac{\partial P}{\partial x}\right) + \frac{\partial}{\partial y}\left(\frac{h^3}{\mu}\cdot\frac{\partial P}{\partial y}\right) = 0 \qquad\qquad \text{(A-7)}$$

(x, y, are independent; P, h, μ are dependent),

$$\frac{dy}{dt} + 3y = 5; \qquad 4\frac{dz}{dt} + z = 2y \qquad\qquad \text{(A-8)}$$

(y and z dependent),

$$\frac{d^3y}{dx^3} + \left(\frac{dy}{dx}\right)^{1/2} = 0 \qquad\qquad \text{(A-9)}$$

(y dependent, x independent).

Equation A-4 is linear (all terms are of first degree); ordinary (contains derivatives with respect to y only); has constant coefficients (1 for dx/dy, 2 for x); is homogeneous (has zero forcing functions); and is of first order (dx/dy, the highest-order term, is a first derivative). The equation contains x as the dependent variable, y as the independent variable.

Equation A-5 is of second order, of first degree, is linear and has constant coefficients, and is nonhomogeneous with the forcing function 7.

Equation A-6 is of third order, is of second degree and hence nonlinear, is ordinary (all derivatives with respect to t), has a nonconstant coefficient (ct associated with dx/dt), and is nonhomogeneous due to the presence of the forcing function $5t$. Note that the x term is also nonlinear (second-degree). The equation has one dependent variable x, and one independent variable t.

Equation A-7 is a partial differential equation (derivatives with regard to both x and y). It is of second order, for $[\partial/\partial x][(h^3/\mu)\cdot(\partial P/\partial x)]$ yields a term containing $\partial^2 P/\partial x^2$, is of first degree (no terms raised to powers other than 1), is homogeneous (no forcing functions), and has nonconstant coefficients $[h(x, y), \mu(x, y)]$.

Equations A-8 are a pair of simultaneous differential equations with y and z as the dependent variables, and time t as the independent variable. The equations are first-degree, linear, ordinary, nonhomogeneous, and have constant coefficients. They can be readily combined into a single second-order equation by substituting $y = 2\, dz/dt + z/2$ into the first equation to yield

$$2\frac{d^2z}{dt^2} + 6.5\frac{dz}{dt} + 1.5z = 5 \tag{A-10}$$

Equation A-9 must be rationalized before classification. Squaring the equation yields

$$\left(\frac{d^3y}{dx^3}\right)^2 - \frac{dy}{dx} = 0 \tag{A-9a}$$

which is nonlinear, ordinary, and homogeneous, of third order and second degree, and with constant coefficients.

SCOPE OF THE PRESENT TEXT

The text is primarily concerned with ordinary linear differential equations with constant coefficients, both homogeneous and nonhomogeneous. The equations contain a single dependent variable which is a function of time, time as the independent variable, and, at most, time-dependent forcing functions. The following examples are typical of the equations to be met in the text:

$$5\frac{d^2\theta}{dt^2} + 2\frac{d\theta}{dt} + \theta = 8 \tag{A-11}$$

$$\frac{d^3\theta}{dt^3} + 5\frac{d^2\theta}{dt^2} + 2\frac{d\theta}{dt} + 6\theta = 4\sin 3t \tag{A-12}$$

where the dependent variable θ is a function of time t. Such equations can be expressed in operational form as a ratio of the dependent variable to the forcing function,

$$\frac{\theta}{8} = \frac{1}{5D^2 + 2D + 1} \tag{A-11a}$$

$$\frac{\theta}{4\sin \omega t} = \frac{1}{D^3 + 5D^2 + 2D + 6} \tag{A-12b}$$

where operator $D = d/dt$ is treated algebraically. Cross-multiplication of

Eqs. A-11(a) and A-12(b) respectively yield Eqs. A-11 and A-12 respectively. The operator $D = d/dt$ is such that

$$Dx = \frac{dx}{dt}; \qquad D^n x = \frac{d^n x}{dt^n}$$

and

$$\frac{1}{D} x = \frac{x}{D} = \int_0^t x \, dt$$

(x/D^n is the nth time integration of x, where x is a function of time).

Methods of solving ordinary linear differential equations with constant coefficients are given in Chapter 3.

B

Complex numbers

An **imaginary number** occurs when the square root is taken of a negative real number. Thus

$$-4^{1/2} = (-1 \times 4)^{1/2} = -1^{1/2} \times 4^{1/2} = j2$$

where $j = -1^{1/2}$ is the imaginary operator and $j2$ is an imaginary number.

A **complex number** is one containing both real and imaginary parts; $3 + j4 = 3 + (-4)^{1/2}$ is an example. It is common for roots of polynomial equations to be complex.

Imaginary and complex numbers can be represented on normal coordinates denoted as the real axis and the imaginary axis (see Fig. B.1). Thus real numbers plot on the real axis, imaginary numbers plot on the imaginary axis, and complex numbers plot in the regions between the axes. The complex number $3 + j4$ is shown in Fig. B.1. Note that both 3 and $j4$ are treated as vectors when finding their sum.

The point $3 + j4$ can also be described in polar notation by the length OP and the angle ϕ. Note that the magnitude of OP is $(3^2 + 4^2)^{1/2}$ and that the angle ϕ is $\tan^{-1}(4/3)$.

The point $3 + j4$ can also be described by the exponential expression

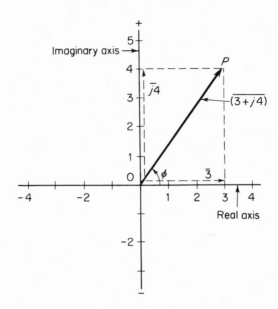

Fig. B.1

$Ae^{j\phi}$, where $A = (3^2 + 4^2)^{1/2}$ describes the length OP, and ϕ is $\tan^{-1}(4/3)$ expressed in radians; $e^{j\phi} = (\cos\phi + j\sin\phi)$ by definition. Hence

$$Ae^{j\phi} = A\cos\phi + j\,A\sin\phi$$

$$A\cos\phi = OP\cos\phi = 3; \qquad A\sin\phi = OP\sin\phi = 4$$

$$\therefore Ae^{j\phi} = 3 + j4$$

for the present case.

In general, the complex number $a + jb$, where a and b are real numbers and $j = -1^{1/2}$, can be represented by

(a) the vector relationship $a + jb$, where a denotes the magnitude a on the real axis, and jb denotes the magnitude b on the imaginary axis, which is normal to the real axis;

(b) the polar designation A, $\measuredangle\phi$, where $A = (a^2 + b^2)^{1/2}$, and $\phi = \tan^{-1}(b/a)$;

(c) the exponential $Ae^{j\phi}$, where A and ϕ are as defined in (b).

It should be appreciated that both a and b can be positive or negative. Note that

$$A = [(\text{magnitude of real part})^2 + (\text{magnitude of imaginary part})^2]^{1/2}$$

$$\phi = \tan^{-1} \frac{\text{algebraic magnitude of imaginary part}}{\text{algebraic magnitude of real part}}$$

Example: Describe in polar and exponential forms, the complex numbers

(a) $3 - j2$, (b) $-3 - j4$.

(a) $A = (3^2 + 2^2)^{1/2} = 13^{1/2}$,

$\phi = \tan^{-1} \dfrac{-2}{3} = 326° = 5.7$ radian.

Hence $(3 - j2) = 13^{1/2}; 326° = 13^{1/2}e^{j5.7}$

(b) $A = (3^2 + 4^2)^{1/2} = 5$;

$\phi = \tan^{-1} \dfrac{-3}{-4} = 217° = 3.8$ radian.

Hence $(-3 - j4) = 5; 217° = 5e^{j3.8}$

ADDITION AND SUBTRACTION

Addition and subtraction of complex numbers is readily achieved in the rectangular form by algebraic addition of the real and the complex parts. For example,

(a) $(a + jb) + (c + jd) = (a + c) + j(b + d)$

(b) $(a + jb) - (c + jd) = (a - c) + j(b - d)$

(c) $(2 + 3j) + (3 + j) - (1 + 2j) = 4 + 2j$

(d) $(7 + 2j) + (3 - 4j) + (-8 + j) - (-2 + 3j) = 4 - j4$

MULTIPLICATION

Multiplication of complex numbers is readily achieved in the polar or exponential forms. The product is the product of the magnitudes and the algebraic sum of the angles. For example,

(a) $(5, \angle 45°)(6, \angle 75°) = 30, \angle 120°$

(b) $(5, \angle 45°)(6, \angle -110°) = 30, \angle -65°$

(c) $(2, \angle 30°)(3, \angle 75°)(4, \angle 120°) = 24, \angle 225°$

(d) $5e^{j2} \cdot 6e^{j3} = 30e^{j5}$

(e) $3e^{j2} \cdot 2e^{-j} = 6e^{j}$

and in general,

$$(A_1, \angle\phi_1)(A_2, \angle\phi_2)\ldots(A_n, \angle\phi_n) = A_1A_2\ldots A_n, \angle(\phi_1 + \phi_2 + \ldots + \phi_n)$$

or

$$A_1e^{j\phi_1}\cdot A_2e^{j\phi_2}\cdot\ldots\cdot A_ne^{j\phi_n} = (A_1A_2\ldots A_n)e^{j(\phi_1+\phi_2+\ldots+\phi_n)}$$

DIVISION

Division is similar in principle to multiplication. Magnitudes are divided and denominator phase angles are subtracted algebraically from numerator angles. For example,

(a) $(6, \angle60°)/(3, \angle45°)\quad = 2, \angle15°$

(b) $(10, \angle160°)/(2, \angle250°) = 5, \angle-90°$

(c) $6e^{j2}/3e^{j}\qquad\qquad\quad = 2e^{j}$

(d) $15e^{J3}/30e^{J5}\qquad\qquad = 0.5e^{-j2}$

and in general,

$$\frac{A_1, \angle\phi_1}{A_2, \angle\phi_2} = \left(\frac{A_1}{A_2}\right),\quad \phi_1 - \phi_2$$

or

$$\frac{A_1e^{j\phi_1}}{A_2e^{j\phi_2}} = \left(\frac{A_1}{A_2}\right)e^{j(\phi_1-\phi_2)}$$

RAISING TO A POWER

Raising a complex number to a power is a special form of multiplication. For example,

$$(a + jb)^2 = \left[(a^2 + b^2)^{1/2}, \angle \tan^{-1}\frac{b}{a}\right]\left[(a^2 + b^2)^{1/2}, \angle \tan^{-1}\frac{b}{a}\right]$$

$$= (a^2 + b^2), \angle2\tan^{-1}\frac{b}{a}$$

which is simply the magnitude of $(a + jb)$ squared, and twice the angle of $(a + jb)$. In general,

$$(A, \angle\phi)^n = A^n, \angle n\phi$$

or

$$(Ae^{j\phi})^n = A^ne^{jn\phi}$$

For example,

$$\text{(a)} \quad (1 + j2) \quad = 5^{1/2}, \; \measuredangle 60° = 5^{1/2}e^{j1.05}$$

$$\text{(b)} \quad (1 + j2)^2 \; = 5, \; \measuredangle 120° \; = 5e^{j2.1}$$

$$\text{(c)} \quad (1 + j2)^{1/2} = 5^{1/4}, \; \measuredangle 30° = e^{j0.52}$$

That is, express the complex number in its polar or exponential form. Raise the magnitude to the power specified and multiply the angle by the power.

SUMMARY

Note that real numbers and imaginary numbers are only special cases of complex numbers. A real number is a complex number with the imaginary part equal to zero. Thus in polar and exponential forms, a real number a becomes

$$a = (a + j0) = a, \; \measuredangle 0° = ae^{j0} = a$$

An imaginary number jb is a complex number with the real part equal to zero. Thus

$$jb = (0 + jb) = b, \; \measuredangle 90° = be^{j\pi/2}$$

The significance of the imaginary operator $j = -1^{1/2}$ is that the number associated with it is $\pm 90°$ out of phase (depending on signs) with the corresponding real number.

C

Conversion tables

DECIBEL CONVERSION TABLE

G	.00	.01	.02	.03	.04	.05	.06	.07	.08	.09
					Second decimal of G (first for $G > 2$)					
					G, db $= 20 \log_{10} G$					
0.0	∞	-40.00	-33.98	-30.46	-27.96	-26.02	-24.44	-23.10	-21.94	-20.92
0.1	-20.00	-19.17	-18.42	-17.72	-17.08	-16.48	-15.92	-15.39	-14.89	-14.42
0.2	-13.98	-13.56	-13.15	-12.77	-12.40	-12.04	-11.70	-11.37	-11.06	-10.75
0.3	-10.46	-10.17	-9.90	-9.63	-9.37	-9.12	-8.87	-8.64	-8.40	-8.18
0.4	-7.96	-7.74	-7.54	-7.33	-7.13	-6.94	-6.74	-6.56	-6.38	-6.20
0.5	-6.02	-5.85	-5.68	-5.51	-5.35	-5.19	-5.04	-4.88	-4.73	-4.58
0.6	-4.44	-4.29	-4.15	-4.01	-3.88	-3.74	-3.61	-3.48	-3.35	-3.22
0.7	-3.10	-2.97	-2.85	-2.73	-2.62	-2.50	-2.38	-2.27	-2.16	-2.05
0.8	-1.94	-1.83	-1.72	-1.62	-1.51	-1.41	-1.31	-1.21	-1.11	-1.01
0.9	-0.92	-0.82	-0.72	-0.63	-0.54	-0.45	-0.35	-0.26	-0.18	-0.09
1.0	0.00	0.09	0.17	0.26	0.34	0.42	0.51	0.59	0.67	0.75
1.1	0.83	0.91	0.98	1.06	1.14	1.21	1.29	1.36	1.44	1.51
1.2	1.58	1.66	1.73	1.80	1.87	1.94	2.01	2.08	2.14	2.21
1.3	2.28	2.35	2.41	2.48	2.54	2.61	2.67	2.73	2.80	2.86
1.4	2.92	2.98	3.05	3.11	3.17	3.23	3.29	3.35	3.41	3.46
1.5	3.52	3.58	3.64	3.69	3.75	3.81	3.86	3.92	3.97	4.03
1.6	4.08	4.14	4.19	4.24	4.30	4.35	4.40	4.45	4.51	4.56
1.7	4.61	4.66	4.71	4.76	4.81	4.86	4.91	4.96	5.01	5.06
1.8	5.11	5.15	5.20	5.25	5.30	5.34	5.39	5.44	5.48	5.53
1.9	5.58	5.62	5.67	5.71	5.76	5.80	5.85	5.89	5.93	5.98
2.	6.02	6.44	6.85	7.23	7.60	7.96	8.30	8.63	8.94	9.25
3.	9.54	9.83	10.10	10.37	10.63	10.88	11.13	11.36	11.60	11.82
4.	12.04	12.26	12.46	12.67	12.87	13.06	13.26	13.44	13.62	13.80
5.	13.98	14.15	14.32	14.49	14.65	14.81	14.96	15.12	15.27	15.42
6.	15.56	15.71	15.85	15.99	16.12	16.26	16.39	16.52	16.65	16.78
7.	16.90	17.03	17.15	17.27	17.38	17.50	17.62	17.73	17.84	17.95
8.	18.06	18.17	18.28	18.38	18.49	18.59	18.69	18.79	18.89	18.99
9.	19.08	19.18	19.28	19.37	19.46	19.55	19.65	19.74	19.82	19.91

TABLE: *G and ϕ Values for* $(1 + j\omega T)$

ωT	G	ϕ	ωT	G	ϕ	ωT	G	ϕ
0.05	1.00	2.9	2.30	2.51	66.5	6.1	6.18	80.7
0.10	1.00	5.7	2.35	2.55	66.9	6.2	6.28	80.8
0.15	1.01	8.5	2.40	2.60	67.4	6.3	6.38	81.0
0.20	1.02	11.3	2.45	2.65	67.8	6.4	6.48	81.1
0.25	1.03	14.0	2.50	2.69	68.2	6.5	6.58	81.3
0.30	1.04	16.7	2.55	2.74	68.6	6.6	6.68	81.4
0.35	1.06	19.3	2.60	2.79	69.0	6.7	6.77	81.5
0.40	1.08	21.8	2.65	2.83	69.3	6.8	6.87	81.6
0.45	1.10	24.2	2.70	2.88	69.7	6.9	6.97	81.8
0.50	1.12	26.6	2.75	2.93	70.0	7.0	7.07	81.9
0.55	1.14	28.8	2.80	2.97	70.3	7.1	7.17	82.0
0.60	1.17	31.0	2.85	3.02	70.7	7.2	7.27	82.1
0.65	1.19	33.0	2.90	3.07	71.0	7.3	7.37	82.2
0.70	1.22	35.0	2.95	3.11	71.3	7.4	7.47	82.3
0.75	1.25	36.9	3.00	3.16	71.6	7.5	7.57	82.4
0.80	1.28	38.7	3.1	3.26	72.1	7.6	7.67	82.5
0.85	1.31	40.4	3.2	3.35	72.6	7.7	7.76	82.6
0.90	1.35	42.0	3.3	3.45	73.1	7.8	7.86	82.7
0.95	1.38	43.5	3.4	3.54	73.6	7.9	7.96	82.8
1.00	1.41	45.0	3.5	3.64	74.1	8.0	8.06	82.9
1.05	1.45	46.4	3.6	3.74	74.5	8.1	8.16	83.0
1.10	1.49	47.7	3.7	3.83	74.9	8.2	8.26	83.0
1.15	1.52	49.0	3.8	3.93	75.3	8.3	8.36	83.1
1.20	1.56	50.2	3.9	4.03	75.6	8.4	8.46	83.2
1.25	1.60	51.3	4.0	4.12	76.0	8.5	8.56	83.3
1.30	1.64	52.4	4.1	4.22	76.3	8.6	8.66	83.4
1.35	1.68	53.5	4.2	4.32	76.6	8.7	8.76	83.4
1.40	1.72	54.5	4.3	4.41	76.9	8.8	8.86	83.5
1.45	1.76	55.4	4.4	4.51	77.2	8.9	8.96	83.6
1.50	1.80	56.3	4.5	4.61	77.5	9.0	9.06	83.7
1.55	1.84	57.2	4.6	4.71	77.7	9.1	9.15	83.7
1.60	1.89	58.0	4.7	4.81	78.0	9.2	9.25	83.8
1.65	1.93	58.8	4.8	4.90	78.2	9.3	9.35	83.9
1.70	1.97	59.5	4.9	5.00	78.5	9.4	9.45	83.9
1.75	2.02	60.3	5.0	5.10	78.7	9.5	9.55	84.0
1.80	2.06	60.9	5.1	5.20	78.9	9.6	9.65	84.1
1.85	2.10	61.6	5.2	5.30	79.1	9.7	9.75	84.1
1.90	2.15	62.2	5.3	5.39	79.3	9.8	9.85	84.2
1.95	2.19	62.9	5.4	5.49	79.5	9.9	9.95	84.2
2.00	2.24	63.4	5.5	5.59	79.7	10.0	10.05	84.3
2.05	2.28	64.0	5.6	5.69	79.9	12.0	12.04	85.2
2.10	2.33	64.5	5.7	5.79	80.0	14.0	14.04	85.9
2.15	2.37	65.1	5.8	5.89	80.2	16.0	16.03	86.4
2.20	2.42	65.6	5.9	5.98	80.4	18.0	18.03	86.8
2.25	2.46	66.0	6.0	6.08	80.5	20.0	20.02	87.1

Example: For $G = 0.85$, G, db $= -1.41$.

Extrapolation of table for $G > 10$:

$$G = G'(10)^n$$

where $G' = G/10^n$ and n is selected so that $G' < 10$. Then,

$$G, \text{db} = G', \text{db} + 20n$$

Example: For $G = 60$,

$$G = 60 = 6 \times 10^1$$

$$G, \text{db} = 6, \text{db} + 20 \times 1 = 15.56 + 20 = 35.56$$

Example: Get G and ϕ of $(1 + 6D)$ for $\omega = 3$ rad/sec;

$$(1 + 6D)_{j\omega} = (1 + j\omega 6)_{\omega=3} = (1 + j18)$$

For $\omega T = 18$, table gives $G = 18.03$, $\phi^\circ = 86.8$.

D   *Matrices: some matrix operations*

DEFINITION OF A MATRIX

A **matrix** is an array of numbers which are arranged in rows and columns and which obey predetermined rules of addition and multiplication. The numbers, known as entries, can be real or complex. The array is enclosed in brackets to indicate that it comprises a matrix.

PURPOSE OF MATRIX

Matrices allow a compact representation of extensive sets of simultaneous relationships, algebraic and/or differential. In essence, a matrix is a scheme of detached coefficients considered as algebraic operators.

BASIC MATRIX FORMS

Rectangular Matrix (general form) of order $m \times n$ has m rows and n columns:

$$[a] = \begin{bmatrix} a_{11} & a_{12} & \cdots & a_n \\ a_{21} & a_{22} & \cdots & a_{2n} \\ \cdot & \cdot & & \cdot \\ \cdot & \cdot & & \cdot \\ \cdot & \cdot & & \cdot \\ a_{m1} & a_{m2} & \cdots & a_{mn} \end{bmatrix}$$

The first subscript denotes the row; the second subscript denotes the column; thus a_{ij} is located in the ith row and jth column; $[a]$ is a shorthand way of representing the matrix, after it has been specified.

Square Matrix has the same number of rows and columns, i.e., $m = n$:

$$\begin{bmatrix} a_{11} & a_{12} & a_{13} \\ a_{21} & a_{22} & a_{23} \\ a_{31} & a_{32} & a_{33} \end{bmatrix}$$

is a 3×3 square matrix.

Row Matrix has 1 row and n columns ($m = 1$):

$$[a_1 \quad a_2 \quad a_3 \quad \cdots \quad a_n]$$

Column Matrix has m rows and 1 column ($n = 1$):

$$\begin{bmatrix} a_1 \\ a_2 \\ \cdot \\ \cdot \\ \cdot \\ a_m \end{bmatrix}$$

REPRESENTING A VECTOR BY MATRIX NOTATION

A vector $\bar{a} = a_x \bar{i} + a_y \bar{j} + a_z \bar{k}$ can be represented by arranging the coefficients a_x, a_y, a_z in a row or column matrix:

$$\bar{a} = \begin{bmatrix} a_x \\ a_y \\ a_z \end{bmatrix}$$

or

$$\bar{a} = [a_x \quad a_y \quad a_z]$$

by understanding that the entries taken in order are in the $\bar{i}, \bar{j}, \bar{k}$ directions, respectively.

BASIC MATRIX OPERATIONS

Addition and Subtraction applies only to matrices of the same order $m \times n$.

For $[a] + [b] = [c]$, add corresponding entries of $[a]$ and $[b]$ to form corresponding entry in $[c]$, i.e.,

$$c_{ij} = a_{ij} + b_{ij}$$

Example:

$$\begin{bmatrix} 3 & 2 & 1 \\ 4 & 5 & 6 \end{bmatrix} + \begin{bmatrix} 8 & 7 & 2 \\ 3 & 9 & 5 \end{bmatrix} = \begin{bmatrix} 11 & 9 & 3 \\ 7 & 14 & 11 \end{bmatrix}$$

For $[a] - [b] = [c]$,

$$c_{ij} = a_{ij} - b_{ij}$$

Example:

$$\begin{bmatrix} 3 & 2 & 1 \\ 4 & 5 & 6 \end{bmatrix} - \begin{bmatrix} 8 & 7 & 2 \\ 3 & 9 & 5 \end{bmatrix} = \begin{bmatrix} -5 & -5 & -1 \\ 1 & -4 & 1 \end{bmatrix}$$

Addition is (a) commutative:

$$a + b = b + a$$

(b) associative:

$$a + (b + c) = (a + b) + c$$

$$a + 0 = a$$

$$a + (-a) = 0$$

Multiplication of a Matrix:

(a) by a scalar number (k):

$$k[a] = [a]k = [b]$$

where $b_{ij} = ka_{ij}$; i.e., form $[b]$ by multiplying each entry of $[a]$ by the number k:

$$6\begin{bmatrix} 3 & 4 \\ 2 & 1 \end{bmatrix} = \begin{bmatrix} 18 & 24 \\ 12 & 6 \end{bmatrix}$$

(b) by another matrix, which is only possible if the two matrices are **conformable.** Two matrices are conformable only when the number of *columns* in the *first* equals the number of *rows* in the second.

Multiplication of two matrices follows a set procedure. For example,

$$[a] = \begin{bmatrix} a_{11} & a_{12} & a_{13} \\ a_{21} & a_{22} & a_{23} \end{bmatrix} \quad \text{and} \quad [b] = \begin{bmatrix} b_{11} & b_{12} \\ b_{21} & b_{22} \\ b_{31} & b_{32} \end{bmatrix}$$

are conformable and hence can be multiplied:

$$[c] = [a][b] = \begin{bmatrix} (a_{11}b_{11} + a_{12}b_{21} + a_{13}b_{31}) & (a_{11}b_{12} + a_{12}b_{22} + a_{13}b_{32}) \\ (a_{21}b_{11} + a_{22}b_{21} + a_{23}b_{31}) & (a_{21}b_{12} + a_{22}b_{22} + a_{23}b_{32}) \end{bmatrix}$$

Multiplication of two matrices is usually *not commutative.* That is, $[a][b]$ cannot be expressed $[b][a]$. In general, if $[a][b]$ is conformable, $[b][a]$ is not conformable. In the example above, $[b]$ is *premultiplied* by $[a]$, or $[a]$ is *postmultiplied* by $[b]$.

In general if $[a]$ and $[b]$ are of the orders $m \times n$ (*m* rows, *n* columns) and $n \times q$ (*n* rows, *q* columns) respectively, they are conformable in the sense $[a][b]$ and their product is a matrix of order $m \times q$ (*m* rows, *q* columns).

Multiplication of matrices (*a, b,* and *c* below are matrices) is:

(a) associative:

$$abc = a(bc) = (ab)c$$

(b) distributive:

$$a(b + c) = ab + ac$$

$$(a + b)c = ac + bc$$

(c) noncommutative in general (exceptions exist):

$$ab \neq ba$$

$$abc \neq bac \neq cab$$

For matrix multiplications, the order in which the matrices are written is vitally important, and must be maintained.

Equality of Matrices: Two matrices $[a]$ and $[b]$ are equal if $a_{ij} = b_{ij}$, that is, if the entries of b are identical with those of a, taken in the same position in the matrices.

Differentiation of a Matrix:

If $\bar{x} = [x_1 \quad x_2 \quad x_3 \quad \ldots \quad x_n]$

$$\frac{d\bar{x}}{dt} = \frac{d}{dt}[x_1 \quad x_2 \quad \ldots \quad x_n] = \left[\frac{dx_1}{dt} \quad \frac{dx_2}{dt} \quad \ldots \quad \frac{dx_n}{dt}\right]$$

or, expressed as a column matrix,

$$\frac{d\bar{x}}{dt} = \frac{d}{dt}\begin{bmatrix} x_1 \\ x_2 \\ \cdot \\ \cdot \\ \cdot \\ x_n \end{bmatrix} = \begin{bmatrix} \dfrac{dx_1}{dt} \\ \dfrac{dx_2}{dt} \\ \cdot \\ \cdot \\ \cdot \\ \dfrac{dx_n}{dt} \end{bmatrix}$$

Index

A

Actual value, 2
Analog computing, 129
  components, 134
  function generation, 132
  initial values, 141
  magnitude scaling, 144
  mathematical requirements, 130
  sign inversion, 132
  simulation, 146
Analogies, 38
Angles of departure and arrival, 261, 263
Angular criterion, root locus, 247, 249, 264
Asymptotic approximations, frequency response, 173–176

B

Basic physical laws, 18

Block diagrams, 60
  examples in formation and reduction of, 66
  manipulation of, 65
  reduction of, 62
Bode diagram, 172
  of first-order system, 174
  of numerator factors, 180
  of multiple factors, 183
  of open loop transfer functions, 231
  of second-order systems, 178
  of zero factors, 182
Breakaway and breakin, root locus, 258
Breakpoint, Bode diagram, 183

C

Capacitance, 25
Centroid, of root locus, 252–255
Characteristic equation, 91

Characteristic equation (*Cont.*):
  of feedback system, 209
  roots of, 92, 197
Classical solution of system equations, 90
Classification of differential equations, 406
Closed loop system, 2
Compensation, 307
  effects of, 335
  examples using frequency response, 340
  examples using root locus, 353
  feedback, 358
  parallel, 308
  selection of parameters, 338
  series, 308
  summary of, 358
  using frequency response techniques, 332
  using root locus techniques, 346
Compensators:
  frequency response characteristics of, 334
  lag, first-order, 329
  lead, first-order, 329
  lead-lag, second-order, 329
  pole-zero characteristics of, 351
  summary of, 333
Complementary solutions, 91, 106
Complex numbers, 155, 411
Compound controller actions, 310
Conditional stability, 206
Conduction, 27
Conformability, of matrices, 388
Conformal plotting, 216
Continuous automatic control, 2, 4
Contours:
  of constant magnitude ratio, 289, 293, 296
  of constant phase, 289, 293, 296
Controlled variable, 2
Controller action, 309
  derivative, 314
  integral, 310, 312
  proportional, 309, 311, 321
  proportional plus derivative, 310, 317, 323,

Controller action (*Cont.*):
  proportional plus integral, 310, 317, 324
  proportional plus integral and derivative, 310, 318, 324
  realization of, 311
  summary of, 326
Corner frequency, 180

D

Damped natural frequency, 108, 124, 350
Damping ratio, 111, 163, 350
Dashpot, 22
Dead zone, 367
Decibel, 172
  conversion table, 416
Decrement, linear, logarithmic, 371
Degree of stability, 226
Derivative action, 310, 314
Describing function, 372
Desired value, 2, 43
Differential equations:
  classification of, 11, 407
  formation of, 40
  solution of, 90, 113, 129
Discontinuous automatic control, 3
Disturbances, 7
Dominant poles and zeros, 349

E

Electrical laws, 24
Engineering system, 40
Engine speed governor, 15, 325
Error, 2
  actuation, 3
  frequency response, 178
  steady-state, 99
Experimental frequency response analysis, 187

F

Faraday's law of capacitance, 25
Feedback, 2
  compensation, 358
  gain constant, 212

Feedback (*Cont.*):
  transfer function, 208
First-order system:
  frequency response, 152, 174
  response to ramp input, 97
  response to sine input, 99
  response to step input, 95
  transfer functions, 45–52
Flapper nozzle, 37
Fluid pressure relationships, 28
Fluid restrictions, 30
Follow-up systems, 6
Forward gain constant, 212
Forward transfer function, 208
Frequency response, 102, 150
  Bode diagram, 172
  experimental, 187
  first-order systems, 152
  nondimensional plots, 154
  numerator factors, 165, 180
  polar plots, 153
  from root locus, 279
  second-order system, 158, 178, 296
  summary, 192
  zero factors, 169, 182

G

Gain constant:
  feedback, 212
  forward, 212
  margin, 227, 233
  open loop, 212
  system, 44
Gain margin, 227, 233, 301
Gears, 23

H

Harmonic oscillation, 370
Homogeneous equation, 91, 407
Hysteresis, 367

I

Improving system performance, 305
Inductance, 25
Initial conditions, 141

Input, 4, 7, 8, 43
  ramp 8, 43
  sine 8, 43
  step 8, 43
  vector, 385
Integral action, 310, 312
Interpreting experimental frequency
    response data, 188
Inverse Nyquist plot, 293

J

Jump resonance, 371

K

Kirchhoff's laws, 26

L

Lag:
  action, 328
  phase, 152, 328
  steady-state, 99
Laminar flow, 31
Laplace transformation, 76, 113
  functions of time, 114
  inverse, 121
  table of transforms, 116
Lead action, 328
Levers, 23
Limit cycling, 369
Linear analysis, 11, 363
Linear decrement, 371
Linear flow valves, 35
Linearization, 12
Linear spring, 20, 363
Logarithmic decrement, 371
Logarithmic plots, 172

M

Magnitude:
  criterion, root locus, 247, 249, 264
  ratio, frequency response, 154, 155
  ratio, open loop, 213
  scaling, 144
Margin:
  gain, 227, 233, 301
  phase, 227, 233, 301

Mathematical model, 41
Matrices, matrix operations, 419
Mechanical laws, 18

N

Natural frequency, 108, 111, 124, 350
Newton's law, 7, 19
Nichols:
  chart, 298
  plot, 295
Nonlinear:
  analysis, 362
  analysis techniques, 371
  behavior patterns, 369
  systems, 362
Nonlinearities, 365
  classification of, 368
Normalized closed loop system, 210
Numerator factors, 165
Nyquist criterion, 207
  Bode plot, 231
  definition, 212
  Nichols plot, 299
  origin of, 216
  polar plot, 214
  summary of application, 222

O

On-off control, 3, 367
Open loop:
  definition of, 208, 210
  gain constant, 212, 242, 244
  poles and zeros, 346
  sensitivity, 244
  system, 2
  transfer function, 207, 241, 286
Operators D and s, 118
Operator $j\omega$, 157
Ordinary differential equations, 407
Output, 4
  equation, 391
  vector, 386

P

Partial fractions, 122
Particular solution, 91

Phase, 152
  lag 152, 328
  lead, 166, 328
  margin, 227, 233, 301
  plane, 374, 383
  plane trajectory, 375
  portrait, 375
Phasor, 155
Pneumatic:
  controller, 320
  servomechanism, 82
Poles and zeros:
  dominant, 349
  of a function, 243
  open loop, 346
Potentiometer, 138
Proportional control action, 309, 311

Q

Quadratic time constant, 111

R

Ramp input, 8, 90
Regulator, 4
Regulator system, 6
Resistance, 24
Resonance, resonant frequency, 163
Response, 4, 43, 89, 94
  analog computer method, 129, 132
  classical method, 90
  Laplace transform method, 118
  first-order systems, 95
  second-order systems, 104, 123
  high-order systems, 127
Root locus:
  comments on, 265
  criteria for plotting, 246
  examples, 267
  method, 237
  nature of, 238
  rules for sketching, 250
  summary, 280
  summary of rules, 264
  use of Spirule, 277
Routh:
  array, 201
  criterion, 201, 202

S

Sampled data systems, 367
Saturation, 367
Second-order systems, response, 104, 123
Sensitivity, open loop, 244
Series compensation, 308
Servomechanism, 6
Signal flow diagrams, 393
Simulation, 146
Sine input, 8, 90
Solution of equations:
  analog computer, 129, 132
  classical, 90
  Laplace transforms, 118
  summary, 147
Spirule, 277
Spring, 20
  bellows, 36
  diaphragms, 36
Stability, 92
  of components and systems, 195
  degree of, 226
  effect of gain, 228
  Nyquist criterion, 207
  from open loop plots, 214, 231, 299
  Routh criterion, 202
  summary of, 234
  from time response, 197
State:
  equations, 386, 388
  model, 386, 392
  path or trajectory, 383
  space, 374
  variable analysis, 377

State (*Cont.*):
  variables, 375, 378
  vector, 375, 383
Steady-state error, 99
Steady-state term, 94
Step input, 8, 90
System:
  equation, 90
  response, 15, 89, 118

T

Thermal relationships, 26
Three-term controller action, 310, 318
Threshold, 367
Time constant, 44
Time scaling, 145
Transfer function, 9, 14, 40, 41
Transient term, 94
Turbulent flow, 31

U

Undamped natural frequency, 108, 111, 124, 350
Unity feedback, 208

V

Vector-matrix relationships, 378
Viscous friction, 21

Z

Zero:
  factors in transfer functions, 169
  of a function, 243
  open loop, 247, 346